J. & L. LOBMEYR

Zwischen Tradition und Innovation
Between Tradition and Innovation

Gläser aus der MAK-Sammlung
Glassware from the MAK Collection

19. Jahrhundert 19th century

GW00992072

MAK Studies 6

Diese Publikation erschien anlässlich eines Forschungsprojekts, das durch die Unterstützung des FWF (Fonds zur Förderung der wissenschaftlichen Forschung) ermöglicht und von Ulrike Scholda erarbeitet wurde. This catalogue was published as part of a research project conducted by Ulrike Scholda and supported by the Austrian Science Fund – FWF.

Besonderer Dank gilt Waltraud Neuwirth, die diesen Forschungs-auftrag als Projektleiterin begleitet hat. Special thanks to Waltraud Neuwirth who supervised this research project as project manager.

MAK

Stubenring 5, A-1010 Wien
Tel. (+43-1) 711 36-0
Fax (+43-1) 713 10 26
E-Mail: office@MAK.at
www.MAK.at

MAK Center for Art and Architecture, Los Angeles

Schindler House
835 North Kings Road
West Hollywood, CA 90069, USA
Tel. (+1-323) 651 1510
Fax (+1-323) 651 2340

Mackey Apartments
1137 South Cochran Avenue
Los Angeles, CA 90019, USA
Tel. (+1-323) 323 651 1510

E-Mail: office@MAKcenter.org
www.MAKcenter.org

Herausgeber Editor: Peter Noever
Redaktion Editing: Ulrike Scholda
Lektorat (dt.) Copy-editing (Ger.): Birgit Trinker
Übersetzung Translation: Michael Strand
Grafische Gestaltung Graphic design: Maria-Anna Friedl
Schrift Typeface: Bembo
Papier Paper: Nopacoat Prestige
Druck Printed by: Aumüller, Regensburg
Bindung Binding: Conzella, Pfarrkirchen

Umschlagabb. Cover ill. MAK, Inv.-Nr. inv. no. Gl 3343 (Kat.-Nr. cat. no. 35)

© Texte bei den Autoren Essays by the authors

© Photos: MAK/Georg Mayer; LOBMEYR ARCHIV, Wien/Georg Mayer
(S. pp. 6, 13, 20, 21, 69 links left, 71 links left, 75 links left, 80 rechts unten right bottom, 95 links left, 96 rechts right, 114 rechts right, 118 rechts right, 138 unten bottom)
Erzbischöfliches Dom- und Diözesanmuseum, Wien (S. p. 106);
Österreichische Nationalbibliothek, Wien, Bildarchiv (S. p. 19)

© 2006 MAK, Wien, und Prestel Verlag,
München · Berlin · London · New York

Erschienen bei Published by
Prestel Verlag
Königinstraße 9, D-80539 München
Tel. (+49-89) 38 17 09-0
Fax (+49-89) 38 17 09-35
E-Mail: info@prestel.de
www.prestel.de

Prestel Publishing Ltd.
4, Bloomsbury Place
London WC1A 2QA
Tel. (+44-20) 7323-5004
Fax (+44-20) 20 7636-8004

Prestel Publishing
900 Broadway. Suite 603
New York, N.Y. 10003
Tel. (+1-212) 995-2720
Fax (+1-212) 995-2733

www.prestel.com

Printed in Germany on acid-free paper

ISBN 3-7913-3601-0
ISBN 978-3-7913-3601-5

J. & L. LOBMEYR

Zwischen Tradition und Innovation
Between Tradition and Innovation

Gläser aus der MAK-Sammlung
Glassware from the MAK Collection

19. Jahrhundert 19th century

Herausgegeben von Edited by Peter Noever

Mit Textbeiträgen von With contributions by Ulrike Scholda

MAK

PRESTEL
MÜNCHEN · BERLIN · LONDON · NEW YORK

Inhalt Contents

Krug (Detail), Kat.-Nr. 13b
Pitcher (detail), cat. no. 13b

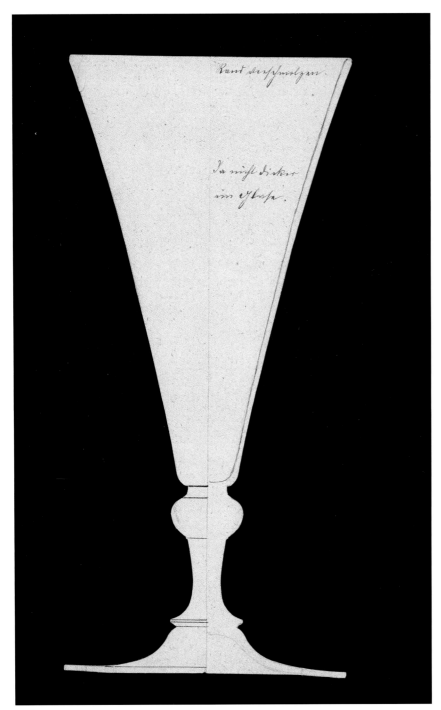

Stängelglas (Papierschnitt), Kat.-Nr. 45 (FAW)
Stem glass (papercut), cat. no. 45 (CAV)

Peter Noever

Lobmeyr & MAK
Innovation und Produktion Innovation and Production

Bereits in der ersten Hälfte des 19. Jahrhunderts pflegt man im Hause Lobmeyr elegante Entwürfe mit innovativen Herstellungs- und Glasbearbeitungstechniken zu verbinden. Das industriehistorisch klassische böhmische Terrain der Glasindustrie liefert zwar die Vorbilder, diese werden jedoch zum Teil schon frei interpretiert; Erzeugnisse von Lobmeyr bestechen durch Stilsicherheit wie auch durch höchste Qualität. Weltweit von Erfolg gekrönte Ausstellungsbeteiligungen sowie intensive Kontaktpflege mit internationalen Geschäftspartnern machen das Unternehmen in seiner Sparte zu einem der führenden in der Habsburgermonarchie, wie Aufträge etwa für die Beleuchtung des Palastes des ägyptischen Vizekönigs, des Palazzo Reale in Venedig und der Residenzen Ludwigs II. von Bayern (München, Herrenchiemsee) sowie die als Hochzeitsgabe für Kronprinz Rudolf gedachten Prunkgefäße eindrucksvoll zeigen.

Was ist aber nun das Geheimnis dieses exzeptionellen Geschäftserfolgs?

Zum einen die augenfällig raffinierte Ästhetik der in intensiver Zusammenarbeit mit Künstlern (Theophil von Hansen, Josef Storck, Friedrich von Schmidt) entstandenen Entwürfe, zum anderen die Hinwendung zu hochwertiger Produktion; last, but not least ist es Ludwig Lobmeyr selbst, der die intensive Kooperation zwischen Künstlern und Unternehmerschaft als für die Etablierung einer Produktkultur notwendig erkennt und seinen unternehmerischen Entscheidungen zu Grunde legt. Zudem gelingt Lobmeyr als erstem bürgerlichem Unternehmer das Bravourstück, ins österreichische Herrenhaus einzuziehen und somit seinen Überzeugungen auch auf politischer Ebene Gehör zu verschaffen. Zahlreiche Ehrungen und Medaillen geben Kunde vom Erfolg des Unternehmers und der Marke.

From the first half of the 19th century, the Lobmeyr glassware company combined elegant design with innovative manufacturing and glass refining technologies. The models were provided by the Bohemian glass industry, a classical terrain of industrial history, but were creatively reinterpreted. Lobmeyr products are distinguished by sureness of style and highest quality. Successful participation in exhibitions worldwide and intensive international business contacts made the enterprise an industry-leader in the Habsburg monarchy; impressive evidence of this are prestigious orders placed with the company, as, e. g., for the lighting of the palace of the Viceroy of Egypt, for the Venice Palazzo Reale, for two residences of King Ludwig II of Bavaria (Munich, Herrenchiemsee) as well as for the grand glass vessels dedicated as wedding gifts to the Austrian Crown Prince Rudolf.

What, then, was the secret of this exceptional business success?

For one thing, it was the obvious sophisticated aesthetic of designs produced in intense collaboration with artists (Theophil von Hansen, Josef Storck, Friedrich von Schmidt); for another, it was the turn toward high-quality production; and finally, it was the person of Ludwig Lobmeyr himself, who realized the benefits of intense cooperation between art and business in establishing a product culture and made this insight the basis of his entrepreneurial decisions. Moreover, Lobmeyr was the first bourgeois entrepreneur who received the honor of being appointed to a seat in the House of Lords (Herrenhaus), the first chamber of the Imperial Diet (Reichsrat), and thus also had a political forum to articulate his convictions. Numerous honors and medals witness the success of the brand and the man.

Ganz im obigen Sinn sind demnach die Bemühungen um einen engen Kontakt mit dem „k. k. Österreichischen Museum für Kunst und Industrie" (heute MAK) zu sehen. Diese Institution, unser Museum, hat sich die Geschmacksbildung bei den Produzenten wie auch den Konsumenten durch lebendige Verknüpfung von Lehre und Praxis, Kunst und Handwerk sowie Produktion und Reproduktion zum Ziel gesetzt. Lobmeyr nützt das Museum als Laboratorium seiner künstlerischen Produktion und die Vorbildsammlungen als Quelle kreativen Schaffens; im Gegenzug versetzt er das Museum durch großzügige Schenkungen in die Lage, auch in seinem Interesse forschend zu arbeiten. Demgemäß stehen das MAK und J. & L. Lobmeyr in einem Verhältnis exemplarischer Zusammenarbeit.

Der Erfolg dieser Partnerschaft liegt vor allem in ihrer Permanenz begründet. Deutlich zeigt sich, dass als Voraussetzung für ein beiderseitiges sinnvolles Agieren Investitionen in eine langfristige Kooperation vonnöten sind, die ihre Wirkung nicht allein in der unmittelbaren Zukunft entfalten. Ganz im Gegensatz zum Heute baut diese Partnerschaft auf stetem Erfahrungsaustausch und Wissenstransfer auf; nicht die kurzfristigen, sofort konsumierbaren Gegenleistungen des jeweiligen Partners stehen im Vordergrund, es gilt vielmehr, langfristigen Nutzen aus dem Potenzial einer kritischen Auseinandersetzung zwischen Gewerbetreibenden und Kunstvermittelnden zu ziehen.

Mit dem vorliegenden Bestandskatalog nimmt das MAK als Ort der Kunst seine selbstauferlegte gesellschaftliche Verantwortung für wissenschaftliche Dokumentation wahr. Die darin gewährte Gesamtschau der Sammlung von Lobmeyr-Gläsern des 19. Jahrhunderts soll auch Zeugnis von dieser generationenüberdauernden, befruchtenden Verbindung zwischen Kunst und Produkt ablegen. Zu Beginn des 21. Jahrhunderts ist bei Lobmeyr der Entwurf „IM GRIFF. Alles für den Hauswein" in Serie gegangen, ein zeitgenössischer Beitrag zu dieser besonderen Kooperation.

It is against this background that the interest in keeping close contact with the "Imperial Royal Museum of Art and Industry" (today the MAK) must be seen. The objective of the institution, our museum, was informing good taste in both producers and consumers by establishing a vital relationship between theory and practice, art and craft, production and reproduction. Lobmeyr used the museum as laboratory of his artistic production and drew on the museum's model collection as a source of creative inspiration collection; in return, he made generous donations to the institution to promote the museum's research work, which again was in his interest. The cooperation between the MAK and J. & L. Lobmeyr can be truly described as exemplary.

The success of this cooperation was mainly based on permanence. It clearly demonstrates that a necessary prerequisite of meaningful reciprocal activity is investment in a long-term cooperation that reaches out beyond the immediate future. Unlike what is usual today, this partnership was built on continuous exchange of experience and transfer of knowledge; it focused not on short-term easily realizable profits drawn from the partner, but used critical discussion between business and art as a potential for long-term mutual benefit.

With the catalogue of holdings presented here, the MAK as a place of art once more lives up to its self-assigned social responsibility for research and documentation. The survey of 19th century Lobmeyr glassware offered in this catalogue also bears witness of a generation-long fruitful relationship between art and merchandise. In the early 21st century, Lobmeyr went into series production with the design "IM GRIFF. Alles für den Hauswein," a wine tumbler with a thumb dent for sure grip and the most recent contemporary contribution to this special cooperation.

„Art arabe. Enluminures de manuscrits. Rosaces", in: A. Racinet: L'ornement polychrome, Paris 1869–1872, Bd. III (MAK, Inv.-Nr. K.I. 19377)

"Art arabe. Enluminures de manuscrits. Rosaces", in: A. Racinet: L'ornement polychrome, Paris 1869–1872, vol. III (MAK, inv. no. K.I.19377)

Einführung Introduction

Ulrike Scholda

Mit dem Satz „Man suchte die Kunstgewerbetreibenden heranzuziehen, ich sank von selber hin […]"[1] definierte Ludwig Lobmeyr (1829–1917) in seiner Autobiografie Ende des 19. Jahrhunderts sein Verhältnis zum Österreichischen Museum für Kunst und Industrie (ÖMKI, heute MAK) in Wien. Von der Gründung des Museums 1864 an hatte er regen Kontakt zu den dortigen Kunstwissenschaftlern, ab 1868 auch zu den in der neu gegründeten Kunstgewerbeschule tätigen Künstlern. Er nützte die Sammlungen und Einrichtungen des Museums und übte verschiedene Ämter aus; damit entsprach er der Gründungsidee des Zusammenwirkens von Gewerbetreibenden und Museum.

Die Firma J. & L. Lobmeyr reformierte in der zweiten Hälfte des 19. Jahrhunderts die böhmische Glasindustrie und nahm als Glasverleger eine führende Stellung in der Glasproduktion der gesamten österreichischen Monarchie ein. Bei den Lobmeyr-Gläsern aus dem 19. Jahrhundert in den Sammlungen des MAK handelt es sich einerseits um Schenkungen der Firma direkt nach der Produktion, andererseits um Ankäufe im Rahmen von Ausstellungen. Weitere Gläser stammen aus dem Nachlass Ludwig Lobmeyrs (1917).

Zur näheren Bestimmung und wissenschaftlichen Einordnung der Lobmeyr-Gläser kann auf vielfältige Quellen zurückgegriffen werden. Das wohl umfassendste Material befindet sich im Firmenarchiv in Wien, das allerdings im Wesentlichen noch unbearbeitet und ungeordnet ist. Dort finden sich Tausende von Zeichnungen, Papierschnitte der Formen genauso wie Dekorentwürfe. Die Papierschnitte und anderen Entwurfszeichnungen sind oft datiert und signiert; zusätzlich kann die ausführende Glashütte vermerkt sein.

"They sought to draw the arts and crafts, I sank all by myself […]"[1] – this is how Ludwig Lobmeyr (1829–1917) defined his relationship to the Imperial Royal Austrian Museum of Art and Industry (AMAI, today's MAK) in his autobiography at the end of the 19th century. From the founding day of the museum in 1864, he was in close contact with the art scholars there, and from 1868, also with the artists working at the new-established Industrial Arts School. He used the collections and museum facilities and held several posts in the institution, quite in conformity with the founding idea of the cooperation of museum and industry.

In the second half of the 19th century, the company of J. & L. Lobmeyr initiated a reform of the Bohemian glass industry and as an outsourcing glassware manufacturer was an industry leader in the entire Austrian monarchy. The MAK holdings of 19th century Lobmeyr glassware on the one hand are comprised of samples donated to the museum directly after production, and on the other, of objects purchased at exhibitions. Other glasses come from the estate of Ludwig Lobmeyr (1917).

Numerous sources are available for the dating and classification of the Lobmeyr glassware. The most comprehensive material is in the company archives in Vienna which, however, to date is mostly unsorted and unresearched. The archives include thousands of drawings, papercuts of forms and decoration designs. The papercuts and other design drawings are frequently dated and signed; in addition the producing glassworks are often indicated.

Firmenmarke J. & L. Lobmeyr, Schale aus „Glimmerglas" (Detail), Kat.-Nr. 33a
Brand J. & L. Lobmeyr, "glimmer glass" bowl (detail), cat. no. 33a

Die wichtigsten Gruppen stellen die (durchnummerierten) Trink- und Dessert-Service (siehe S. 52) und die verschiedenen Serien dar. Letztere umfassen eine variable Zusammenstellung von Objekten, die in einer bestimmten Technik und in durchgängigem Dekor ausgeführt sind, etwa Aufsätze, Schalen, Dosen oder Kännchen.

Daneben ist das Material nach unterschiedlichen Kriterien geordnet, nach Gefäßtypen (Krüge, Flakons, Sturzflaschen etc.), aber auch nach Einzelobjekten. Auch ein Lusterarchiv ist vorhanden. Des Weiteren finden sich Geschäftsbücher (Auftragsbücher), so genannte Strazza-Bücher (sie verzeichnen die täglichen Ausgänge), Entwurfsbücher, Bücher zu Bestellungen bei Glashütten, Veredlern usw., Rechnungsbücher, Fotos und Fotoplatten, Bildmaterial, Kataloge, Dokumente, Urkunden, Gipsabgüsse, Bücher und vieles mehr.

Ein weiterer Teil des Firmenarchivs befindet sich im Kunstgewerbemuseum Prag. Er wurde im Februar 1945 kurz vor Kriegsende vom damaligen Firmenchef Stefan Rath gemeinsam mit etwa 500 „Mustergläsern" von Wien nach Steinschönau (Kamenický Šenov) in Nordböhmen gebracht, wo Rath einen Werkstättenbetrieb führte. 1948 wurde der Betrieb von der Tschechoslowakei verstaatlicht, wodurch auch die dort befindlichen Archivalien in Staatsbesitz gelangten. Im Rahmen des Forschungsprojekts konnte aber dieses Material, das in rund 30 Kartons zum Großteil Papierschnitte des 19. und 20. Jahrhunderts umfasst, gesichtet und einbezogen werden.

Im Wiener Geschäft der heute noch bestehenden Firma J. & L. Lobmeyr in der Kärntner Straße befindet sich ein eigenes Firmenmuseum, das mehrere hundert Objekte des 19. und 20. Jahrhunderts bewahrt. Sie können als Vergleichsbeispiele herangezogen werden.

Ergänzend zu den Archivmaterialien sind die so genannten Werkzeichnungen zu nennen, die von der Firma 1883 und 1892 in insgesamt 18 Bänden dem ÖMKI ge-

The most important groups are the (numbered) drinking and dessert services (see p. 52) and the different series. The latter are comprised of a variable ensemble of objects produced in a certain technique and with identical decoration, such as centerpieces, bowls, boxes, or jugs.

Moreover, the material is ordered by different criteria such as type (jugs, flacon, bottles etc.), but also by individual objects. There is also an archives of chandeliers. In addition, there are ledger books (order books), so-called "strazza books" (records of daily outgoings), design books, books of orders placed with glassworks, refiners etc., accounts books, photos and photo plates, picture materials, catalogues, documents, certificates, plaster casts, books, and many more.

Another part of the company archives is in the Prague Arts and Crafts Museum. It was taken, together with some 500 "sample glasses" to Steinschönau (Kamenický Šenov) in Northern Bohemia in February 1945, shortly before the end of the war, by Stefan Rath, then head of the company who ran workshops there. In 1948, the enterprise was nationalized by Czechoslovakia which entailed that the archives came into state possession. In the research project, this material which mainly comprises about 30 boxes of papercuts from the 19th and 20th century could also be viewed and included.

In the Vienna shop of J. & L. Lobmeyr in Kärntnerstraße, which still exists today, several hundred objects from the 19th and 20th century have been preserved which can be used for comparison.

In addition to the materials in the archives, the so-called working drawings must be mentioned, of which 18 volumes were donated to the AMAI by the company in

schenkt wurden. Auf den rund 1000 Blättern finden sich weitere Hinweise zu Datierungen, Entwerfern usw. (siehe S. 24, 25). Zusätzliche Ergänzungen waren durch die Inventarbücher und Archivunterlagen im MAK möglich.

Ein weiterer Schwerpunkt wurde bei den Recherchen auf die einschlägige Literatur des 19. Jahrhunderts gelegt. Dabei handelt es sich um Ausstellungsberichte und -kataloge, teilweise schon illustriert, weitere zeitgenössische Publikationen und Zeitschriften. In Zusammenhang mit dem Museum sind dabei vor allem die „Mittheilungen des k. k. Österreichischen Museums für Kunst und Industrie" zu nennen, die über alle Vorgänge rund um Museum und Kunstgewerbeschule detaillierte Berichte brachten. Personelle Angelegenheiten wurden genauso erfasst wie Termine, Vorträge und neu ausgestellte Gegenstände; es finden sich Ausstellungsberichte und wissenschaftliche Abhandlungen. Die „Mittheilungen" wurden systematisch durchgearbeitet, und alle Angaben zu Lobmeyr wurden in eine Lobmeyr-Literaturdatenbank eingegeben, ebenso wie die sonstige Literatur zum Thema Lobmeyr aus dem 19. und 20. Jahrhundert. Eine Auswahl davon wurde in das Literaturverzeichnis dieses Kataloges und, wo relevant, bei den einzelnen Objekten aufgenommen.

Einen wesentlichen Beitrag zum Verständnis der Firma J. & L. Lobmeyr liefert die Autobiografie Ludwig Lobmeyrs, die dieser Ende des 19. Jahrhunderts verfasste; vor einigen Jahren wurde sie transkribiert und publiziert.[2] Sie gewährt Einblick in das persönliche und geschäftliche Leben Lobmeyrs vor einem kulturhistorischen Hintergrund – und vervollständigt das Bild der in der zeitgenössischen Literatur immer wieder erwähnten Persönlichkeit Ludwig Lobmeyrs, die zum Erfolg der Firma J. & . L. Lobmeyr in der zweiten Hälfte des 19. Jahrhunderts so wesentlich beigetragen hat. Er war an der Schnittstelle zwischen Entwurf und Ausführung tätig und überwachte beide Bereiche: „[…] nicht nur durch

1883 and 1892. The about 1000 drawings contain further information on dating, designers etc. (see p. 24, 25). Further additional information could be gathered from inventory books and archive materials kept at the MAK.

Another research focus was on relevant 19th century literature. This included exhibition reports and catalogues, some of them with illustrations, and other contemporary publications and journals. In connection with the museum, the "Mittheilungen des k. k. Österreichischen Museums für Kunst und Industrie" ["Notes of the Imperial Royal Austrian Museum of Art and Industry"] must be mentioned in this context, which brought detailed reports of all events pertaining to the museum and the Industrial Arts School. Personnel matters were recorded here as well as event schedules, lectures and new exhibits; there are exhibition reviews and research articles. The "Mittheilungen" were systematically worked through, and all information pertaining to Lobmeyr was entered in a Lobmeyr literature database, as well as other literature on Lobmeyr from the 19th and 20th century. A selection was included in the bibliography of this catalogue or in the individual object descriptions.

One essential contribution to an understanding of the company of J. & L. Lobmeyr is provided by the autobiography of Ludwig Lobmeyr which he wrote at the end of the 19th century; some years ago, it was transcribed and published.[2] It provides an insight into Lobmeyrs personal and business life against the backdrop of cultural history – and complements the image of the personality of Ludwig Lobmeyr who finds recurrent mention in contemporary literature and who contributed so substantially to the success of J. & L. Lobmeyr in the latter half of the 19th century. He worked at the interface of design and manufacturing, supervising both areas: "[…] not infrequently I exerted

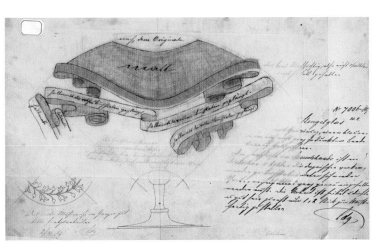

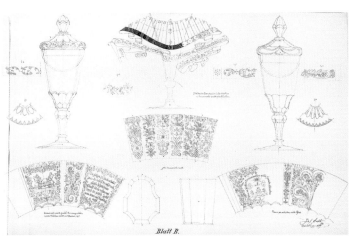

Stängelglas (Werkzeichnung), Kat.-Nr. 45 (FAW)
Stem glas (working drawing), cat. no. 45 (CAV)

„Gravirte Krystallgläser nach alten böhmischen Mustern", Blatt B, in: WZ, Bd. XII, S. 32
"Engraved crystal glasses after old Bohemian models", sheet B, in: WD, vol. XII, p. 32

das Auftraggeben allein, auch auf die Herstellung der Vorlagen habe ich nicht selten selbst wesentlichen Einfluß genommen. Es verbesserte sich allmälig mein Geschmack, dadurch wurden meine Erzeugnisse schöner, vornehmer, edler, um so mehr als ich bei jeder Wiederholung trachtete, dies oder jenes und wäre es auch nur eine Kleinigkeit, die mir nicht recht stimmte, die sonst kaum Jemand beachtete, zu ändern. Mein Schwager Kralik war mir dabei ein treuer, freudig hingebender Mitarbeiter, nach ihm folgte sein Sohn Karl, anfangs spröde, doch bald williger meinen Weisungen; die Glasbläser, Schleifer, Maler und Graveure waren gewiß sehr anstellig und aufmerksam, sie anerkannten, daß sie gut thun, sich leiten zu lassen, sie bedurften aber auch der bestimmten Führung; irgend selbständig war doch keiner von Allen."[3] Auch dem Künstler Theophil von Hansen erklärte Ludwig Lobmeyr, „dies und jenes in seinen Entwürfen sei technisch kaum ausführbar. Er ließ sich dies sagen und arbeitete die Zeichnungen um, hatte ich [L. Lobmeyr] noch Bedenken vorzubringen, so ging er, ohne ungeduldig zu werden, auch das drittemal an die Verbesserung, fielen denn auch die Gegenstände so aus, daß er seine Freude daran hatte."[4]

Der Entstehungsprozess eines Glases lässt sich durch das umfassend erhaltene Material in groben Zügen nachvollziehen: Der Entwurf, in den eigenen Werkstätten zum Teil von Ludwig Lobmeyr bzw. unter seiner Anleitung oder von Künstlern hergestellt, wurde in einen Papierschnitt[5] umgesetzt. Dieser wurde – versehen mit

considerable influence, not only by commissioning work, but also on the making of the designs. My taste gradually improved, which made my products more beautiful, more elegant, more exquisite; all the more so since, with each repetition, I sought to change this or that, even if it was just a nicety that did not suit me and that nobody else bothered about. Kralik, my brother-in-law, was my faithful and gladly dedicated collaborator in this; he was succeeded by his son Karl, reluctant in the beginning, but soon more willing to follow my instructions; the glassblowers, cutters, painters and engravers certainly were skilful and attentive; they realized that they would do well to let themselves be guided; in fact, they needed determined direction; none of all them could really rely on himself."[3] Ludwig Lobmeyr also spelled out to the artist Theophil von Hansen that "this or that in his designs was hardly technically feasible. He accepted this and overworked the drawings; and if I [L. Lobmeyr] still had objections, he went about improving it a third time, so that the objects eventually came out in such a way as he, too, could be pleased with."[4]

The production process of a specific glass object can be roughly reconstructed from the comprehensive extant material: the design, made in the workshops of Ludwig Lobmeyr either by himself or under his direction, or by artists, was rendered as a papercut[5], which was then forwarded – with instructions about the type of glass

Angaben zur Art des Glases, zum Dekor usw. – an die jeweilige Glashütte geschickt. Die Weiterbearbeitung des dort entstandenen Rohglases erfolgte im Falle Lobmeyrs entweder in Werkstätten in der Nähe der meist für ihn produzierenden Glashütte Meyr's Neffen in Südböhmen oder in einer eigenen Raffinerie in Nordböhmen (siehe S. 18). Dazu schrieb Ludwig Lobmeyr: „Bereits zu Lebzeiten des Vaters errichteten wir in Blottendorf bei Haida in Böhmen [...] eine sogenannte Raffinnerie. Wir nahmen einen Verwalter auf, mietheten Magazinsräume zur Einlagerung unserer sogenannten Rohwaaren (d. h. der Waaren wie sie vom Glasbläser allein hergestellt werden, und) welche nach Bedarf an die Schleifer, Graveure, Vergolder und Maler der dortigen Umgebung, die nahezu ausnahmslos nur Hausarbeiter waren, ihr eigenes Häuschen mit Garten, allenfalls auch ein Stück Feld hatten, vertheilt und, wenn fertig, wieder an unseren Vertreter abgeliefert wurden."[6]

Auf den Entwurfszeichnungen und Papierschnitten findet sich meist eine Modellnummer (mit bis zu vier Ziffern) mit einer Jahreszahl und Angaben zu einer Glashütte (bei Meyr's Neffen abgekürzt MNA). Dadurch kann die Ausführung eines Entwurfs in den dazugehörigen Bestellungsbüchern verifiziert werden. Dies bezieht sich natürlich nur auf die erste Ausführung des Objekts. Weitere Herstellungstermine müssen nicht immer auf dem Papierschnitt vermerkt sein und sind anhand der Bestellungsbücher nur in Einzelfällen rekonstruierbar. Vor allem bei Serien oder Trink-Servicen konnte eine Form unzählige Male hergestellt werden. Auch wurde ein und dieselbe Form für verschiedenen Dekor in unterschiedlichen Jahren verwendet. Daher ist, auch wenn das Entwurfsdatum eines Objekts bekannt ist, die Ausführung nur mit „ab (Entwurfsjahr)" festzulegen, es sei denn, Informationen aus anderen Quellen (etwa das Ankaufsjahr) lassen weitere Schlüsse zu. Auch die ausführende Hütte ist nicht immer sicher zu bestimmen; in der zweiten Hälfte des 19. Jahrhunderts handelte

or decoration required – to the glassworks. The refining of the raw glass produced there was done in workshops near the glassworks of Meyr's Neffen in South-Bohemia, where he had most work done, or in his own refinery in North-Bohemia (see p. 18). Ludwig Lobmeyr wrote about this: "In my father's lifetime already, we established a so-called refinery at Blottendorf near Haid in Bohemia. We took on a manager, rented warehouse space for storage of our so-called raw ware (that is, wares as they were produced by the glass blower) which, depending on what was needed, were distributed to cutters, engravers, gilders, and painters in the area, who were homeworkers almost without exception, having their own cottage and garden and, at most, a piece of field, and, if finished, were sent back to our representative."[6]

The design drawings and papercuts usually show a model number (up to four digits) plus the year and an indication of the glassworks (in the case of Meyr's Neffen abbreviated as MNA). Thus the production of a design can be verified in the respective order books. Of course, this only refers to the first-time production of the object. Other manufacturing dates are not always recorded on the papercuts and can be reconstructed from the order books in some cases only. Particularly in the case of drinking and dessert services, a form could be used countless times. Moreover, one and the same form could be used with different decorations in different years. Hence, even the design date is known, production can only be dated as "from (year of design)" unless further information can be gathered from other sources. The manufacturing glassworks cannot always be identified with certainty, either, though in the second half of the 19th century, it mainly was Meyr's Neffen who worked for Lobmeyr (see p. 18).

Firmenmarke J. & L. Lobmeyr, Deckeldose
(Detail), Kat.-Nr. 19b
Brand J. & L. Lobmeyr, lidded box (detail),
cat. no. 19b

es sich im Fall Lobmeyr jedoch vorwiegend um Meyr's Neffen (siehe S. 18).

Über die das Rohglas weiterverarbeitenden „Raffineure" weiß man bei Lobmeyr-Gläsern aus dieser Zeit selten Bescheid, nur Glasschneider wurden bei besonderen Stücken namentlich genannt (siehe etwa Kat.-Nr. 6, 15).

Nicht alle im MAK befindlichen Lobmeyr-Objekte tragen die um 1870 eingeführte Firmenmarke „JLL"; durch Quellennachweise konnten sie jedoch eindeutig Lobmeyr zugeschrieben und anhand der Quellen zu fast allen Objekten genaue Angaben gemacht werden, etwa zu Entwurfsdatum, Serienbezeichnung und Entwerfer. Bei den Serien, Trink-Servicen oder Einzelgegenständen wurden vorwiegend die im Archiv oder in den Werkzeichnungen genannten Bezeichnungen verwendet.

In diesen Bestandskatalog wurden alle in der Glassammlung des MAK befindlichen Objekte der Firma aus dem 19. Jahrhundert aufgenommen. Dem Katalogteil vorangestellt ist ein einleitender Text zur Bedeutung der Firma J. & L. Lobmeyr in Zusammenhang mit dem ÖMKI und der Reform der böhmischen Glasindustrie in der zweiten Hälfte des 19. Jahrhunderts im internationalen Kontext. Die einzelnen Objekte – soweit möglich, wurden sie Gruppen zugeordnet – sind in chronologischer Reihenfolge erfasst[7], um die Entwicklung der Firma, aber auch die Vielfalt ihrer Produkte zu zeigen.

Information about "refiners" who further processed the raw glass is rare in connection with Lobmeyr glass from that period; it was only in the case of special pieces that glass cutters were identified by name (see e.g. cat. nos. 6, 15).

Not all Lobmeyr objects in the MAK holdings bear the "JLL" brand that was introduced only in 1870; they could, however, be definitely ascribed to Lobmeyr through information from the sources available. These sources also made it possible to obtain precise information, such as design date, series' designation, and designer, about almost all objects. For the series, drinking services and individual objects, the designations used are those occurring in the archive or working drawings.

This catalogue of holdings contains all the company's objects from the 19th century in the MAK Glass Collection. The catalogue section is preceded by an introductory text about the significance of the company of J. & L. Lobmeyr in connection with the AMAI and the reform of the Bohemian glass industry in the second half of the 19th century in an international context. The individual objects – ordered in groups where possible – are listed chronologically[7], so as to facilitate a survey of the development of the company and the variety of their production.

1   Waltraud Neuwirth: Schöner als Bergkristall. Ludwig Lobmeyr.
    Glas Legende, Wien 1999, S. 230.
2   Ebd.
3   Ebd., S. 346.
4   Ebd., S. 225 f.
5   Dieser ist nicht zu verwechseln mit der Technik des
    Glasschnitts (Glasgravur).
6   Neuwirth, wie Anm. 1, S. 231.
7   Mit Ausnahme von Kat.-Nr. 50 und 51, die eine eigene
    Kategorie darstellen.

1   Waltraud Neuwirth: Schöner als Bergkristall. Ludwig Lobmeyr.
    Glas Legende, Vienna, 1999, p. 230.
2   ibid.
3   ibid., p. 346.
4   ibid., p. 225 f.
5   Not to be mistaken for the technique of glass cutting (engraving).
6   Neuwirth, same as no. 1, p. 231.
7   With the exception of cat. nos. 50 and 51, which represent a
    category of their own.

Ulrike Scholda

Zwischen Tradition und Innovation Between Tradition and Innovation

J. & L. Lobmeyr, das Österreichische Museum für Kunst und Industrie und die Entwicklung der böhmischen Glasindustrie J. & L. Lobmeyr, the Austrian Museum of Art and Industry, and the Development of the Bohemian Glass Industry

Die Anfänge

Die ersten Jahrzehnte der Firma Lobmeyr

Der aus Oberösterreich stammende Josef Lobmeyr (1792–1855) eröffnete um 1822/23 in Wien einen „Glaserladen" in der Weihburggasse und gründete damit die Firma Lobmeyr.[1] Anfangs verkaufte Josef Lobmeyr Produkte verschiedener Hersteller[2] und vertrat die wichtigsten böhmischen Glasraffinerien in Wien. So hatten auf der „1. Allgemeinen österreichischen Gewerbs-Produkten-Ausstellung" in Wien 1835 Joseph Lötz, Friedrich Egermann, F. Steigerwald und Johann Meyr als „bürgerlich[e] Glashändler in Wien" bei Lobmeyr ihr „Commissions-Lager".

Bald wurde Josef Lobmeyr aber auch zum Auftraggeber eigener Ware. Die im MAK befindlichen Werkzeichnungen von Objekten aus dem 19. Jahrhundert belegen, dass er etwa ab 1840 „eigene Muster" ausführen bzw. „nach eigenen Zeichnungen" arbeiten ließ. Neben verschiedensten Varianten von Biedermeiergläsern wurde schon bald die Produktion von Beleuchtungskörpern ein wichtiger Bereich. 1848 führte Lobmeyr für den Vizekönig von Ägypten einen großen Auftrag über Kron- und Wandleuchter aus. Ein weiterer Zweig umfasste schließlich auch die Herstellung von Spiegeln.

In den Jahren 1837 bis 1849 war Josef Lobmeyr Pächter einer Glasfabrik in Marienthal, westlich von Esseg (Osijek) in Slawonien (damals Königreich Ungarn). Dort wurde neben „gewöhnlichem" Hohl- und Tafelglas auch Kristall- und Farbenglas hergestellt. Außerdem widmete sich Lobmeyr dem gepressten Glas und hat „zu diesem Behufe nicht nur mehrere Reisen nach Frankreich

The Beginnings

The Early Decades of the Lobmeyr Company

Around 1822/23, Josef Lobmeyr (1792–1855), a native of Upper Austria, opened a "glassware store" in Vienna's Weihburggasse and thus set up the Lobmeyr company.[1] In the beginning, Josef Lobmeyr sold products of different manufacturers[2], representing the most important Bohemian glass factories in Vienna. So, for example, Joseph Lötz, Friedrich Egermann, F. Steigerwald and Johann Meyr exhibited at the "1st General Austrian Industry Products Exposition" as "bourgeois glassware merchants in Vienna" for whom Lobmeyr held "consignment stock".

Soon, however, Lobmeyr began to produce glassware under his own name, too. Working drawings of 19th century objects kept at the MAK show that, from about 1840, he had glassware produced in his "own designs" or "after own drawings". Aside from a variety of Biedermeier glassware, lamps soon became another important production segment. 1848, Lobmeyr executed a large order for chandeliers and wall candelabra placed by the Viceroy of Egypt. Another product line was the making of mirrors.

From 1837 to 1849, Josef Lobmeyr had a glass manufactory on lease at Marienthal west of Osijek in Slavonia (then part of the Kingdom of Hungary), where crystal and colored glass was produced aside from "ordinary" hollow glassware and plate glass. Moreover, Lobmeyr focused on pressed glass and "made several trips to France for this purpose, and also obtained

Pokal (Detail), Kat.-Nr. 19d
Goblet (detail), cat. no. 19d

gemacht, sondern sich auch Arbeiter von daher nebst einer bedeutenden Anzahl von messingenen Formen und den zu deren Gebrauche nöthigen Apparaten und Maschinen verschafft"[3]. Das gepresste Glas wurde zum Teil auch bemalt. Seine Waren galten als preiswert und wurden bis in die Türkei exportiert.

1841 errichtete Josef Lobmeyr eine Glasfabrik in Zwechewo (Zvečevo), ebenfalls in Slawonien, wo laut einer alten Geschäftskarte „alle Gattungen glatt geschliffene, fein brillantirte Cristall, und vergoldete Glasgegenstände, in allen bestehenden Farben, nach den neuesten Formen, und Dessins, so wie auch ordinäre weisse und grüne Hohlwaare, dessgleichen auch ordinäre und Lagertafeln" erzeugt wurden. Diese Fabrik betrieb Lobmeyr bis 1857, aber schon um 1850 bezog das Unternehmen den größten Teil des benötigten Glases von „Meyr's Neffen" in Südböhmen. Diese 1815 von Josef Meyr gegründete Firma besaß mehrere Glashütten. Nach dem Tod des kinderlosen Sohnes Johann Meyr 1841 führten die beiden Neffen Josef Taschek und Wilhelm Kralik (1807–1877) die Firma unter dem Namen „J. Meyr's Neffen" weiter.[4] Kralik hatte bis zu sieben Fabriken in Betrieb: Adolf, Eleonorenhain, Ernstbrunn, Franzensthal, Kaltenbach, Idathal und Louisenhütte. 1851 heiratete Wilhelm Kralik Louise, die Tochter von Josef Lobmeyr, was die Verbindung zwischen den Firmen natürlich stärkte. Gemeinsam mit Lobmeyr beteiligte er sich mit großem Erfolg an der Wiener Weltausstellung von 1873. Nach seinem Tod im Jahr 1877 wurde die Firma als „Wilhelm Kralik Söhne und Meyr's Neffe" weitergeführt.[5]

Auch die Weiterverarbeitung wie Schliff und Emailmalerei wurde zum Teil in den Meyr'schen Fabriken durchgeführt. Die weitere Veredlung, vor allem der Schnitt, erfolgte in Nordböhmen; in Blottendorf (Polevsko) bei Haida (Nový Bor) wurde unter Josef Lobmeyr eine Raffinerie errichtet. (Später bestanden unter dem Sohn Ludwig Lobmeyr eigene Werkstätten in der Gegend von Haida.)

workers from there, aside from a considerable number of brass molds as well as equipment and machinery needed for their use."[3] The pressed glass was partly decorated with painting. Lobmeyr's glassware was considered inexpensive and was exported as far as Turkey.

In 1841, Josef Lobmeyr set up a glass factory at Zvečevo, Slavonia, with production including, according to an old business card, „all kinds of polished, delicately brilliant-cut crystal and gilded glass objects, in all existing colors, after the latest forms and designs, as well as ordinary white and green hollow glassware, and besides, ordinary and staple plate glass." Lobmeyr operated this factory until 1857, although in 1850 already his company bought most of the glass needed from "Meyr's Neffen" ["Meyr's Nephews"] in South-Bohemia, a company that had been established by Josef Meyr in 1815 and owned a number of glassworks. After the death of Josef's childless son Johann Meyr in 1841, the business was continued by two nephews, Josef Taschek and Wilhelm Kralik (1807–1877), under the name of "J. Meyr's Neffen".[4] Kralik ran up to seven glass factories: Adolf, Eleonorenhain, Ernstbrunn, Franzensthal, Kaltenbach, Idathal, and Louisenhütte. In 1851, he married Josef Lobmeyr's daughter Louise, which of course strengthened relations between the two companies. Together with Lobmeyr, he participated with great success in the Vienna World's Fair of 1873. After his death in 1877, the company was continued under the name of "Wilhelm Kralik Söhne und Meyr's Neffe" ["Wilhelm Kralik Sons and Meyr's Nephew][5].

Some processing such as grinding and enamel painting was also done at the Meyr factories. The further processing, particularly the cutting, was then done in North-Bohemia, where Josef Lobmeyr had a glass refinery built at Blottendorf (Polevsko) near Haida (Nový Bor). (Later, under Josef's son Ludwig Lobmeyr, the company had its own refining workshops in the Nový Bor region).

Ludwig Lobmeyr
(Bildarchiv der ÖNB, Wien)
(Austrian National Library Photo Archives, Vienna)

Nach dem plötzlichen Tod Josef Lobmeyrs im Jahr 1855 übernahmen die Söhne Josef (1828–1864) und Ludwig (1829–1917) das Geschäft. Ab zirka 1860 wurde es unter dem bis heute gültigen Namen J. & L. Lobmeyr geführt.

J. & L. Lobmeyr stellte 1862 in London erstmals auf einer Weltausstellung aus und erhielt als Raffineur eine Medaille „für Vorzüglichkeit der Erzeugung von Krystallglas, Tafelgegenständen und Armleuchtern"[6]. Vor allem die Luster fanden Anklang. Die Firma besaß zu dieser Zeit keine eigene Glasfabrik mehr, ließ „wohl aber erkauftes Rohglas auf eigene Rechnung und nach eigenen Mustern von den Schleifern in Hayda und Umgebung raffiniren"[7] und exportierte einen Teil ihrer Waren.

„Zu den grössten und schönsten Sammlungen der österreichischen Abtheilung gehört unstreitig diejenige der Glaswaaren von J. und L. Lobmeyr in Wien. […] und trug nicht wenig bei zu dem rühmlichen Erfolge, welchen sich die Industrie des Kaiserstaats auf der Weltausstellung errang. Alle ausgestellten Gegenstände der Firma sind durchweg nach deren eigenen, selbstentworfenen Zeichnungen gearbeitet, die reichverzierten Glasservice, Candelaber- und Kronleuchterbestandteile sowie die anderen Glasartikel durch ihre Arbeiter in Böhmen (Deutschböhmen bei Hayda) geschliffen, gravirt, gemalt und vergoldet, die erforderlichen Bronzefassungen dagegen in Wien angefertigt. […] Tafel- und Desserttrinkgefässe mit feinen Gravirungen […] verdienen namentlich genannt zu werden, sowie es nicht unerwähnt bleiben soll, dass diese Gegenstände ungeachtet der äusserst gediegenen sorgfältigen Arbeit weitaus billiger im Preise sich stellen als ähnliche englische Erzeugnisse […]."[8]

After the sudden death of Ludwig Lobmeyr in 1855, his two sons Josef (1828–1864) and Ludwig (1829–1917) took over. From about 1860, the company went under the name of J. & L. Lobmeyr, which it has survived until today.

In 1862, J. & L. Lobmeyr for the first time took part in a World's Fair in London and, as a glass refiner, was awarded a gold medal "for excellence in the making of crystal glass, tableware, and candelabra."[6] The Lobmeyr chandeliers met with particular appreciation. At that time, the company did no longer operate its own glassworks, but had "purchased raw glass refined by cutters at and around Hayda for own account and to own designs"[7]; a part of the production was made for export.

"One of the largest and most beautiful assortments of the Austrian division doubtless was the one of glassware by J. und L. Lobmeyr in Vienna […] and it contributed not little to the splendid success won by the industry of the Empire at the World's Fair. All objects exhibited by the company are entirely made after own self-designed drawings, the richly decorated glass services, candelabra and chandelier parts as well as the other glass articles are cut, engraved, painted and gilded by its workers in Bohemia (German Bohemia near Hayda) while the necessary bronze sockets are made in Vienna. […] Table and dessert drinking vessels with delicate engravings […] deserve special mention, as it should not go unmentioned that, despite the very high quality and care in making, these objects are much cheaper in price than similar English products […]."[8]

Firma und Museum

Die Firma J. & L. Lobmeyr unter Ludwig Lobmeyr und die Gründung des Österreichischen Museums für Kunst und Industrie in Wien

In der Person Ludwig Lobmeyrs, der die Firma nach dem Tod seines Bruders Josef im Jahr 1864 allein weiterführen musste, verbanden sich künstlerisches Empfinden und Geschäftssinn. Es gelang ihm durch seine Firmenstrategie, in der zweiten Hälfte des 19. Jahrhunderts zum führenden Glasindustriellen der Monarchie aufzusteigen und sich auch international konkurrenzfähig zu präsentieren. Geschickt wusste er seine künstlerischen, geschäftlichen und persönlichen Eigenschaften, die Reformbestrebungen des Österreichischen Museums für Kunst und Industrie (ÖMKI, heute MAK) und die Fähigkeiten der Wiener Künstler zu verbinden. „Die Gründung des österr. ‚Museums für Kunst und Industrie‘ kam mir gerade rechtzeitig zu Hilfe. Denn damit stellte sich erst ein engerer Verkehr mit Kunstgelehrten und Künstlern ein."[9]

Schon auf der Weltausstellung in London 1862 war Lobmeyr mit Rudolf von Eitelberger in Kontakt gekommen, der damals die Gründung des ÖMKI vorbereitete[10] und mit dessen Eröffnung 1864 auch zum Direktor ernannt wurde. Ziel des Museums war die Förderung des Geschmacks sowohl von Entwerfern und Produzenten als auch von Konsumenten. Das ÖMKI und die 1868 ins Leben gerufene Kunstgewerbeschule erfüllten durch Bereitstellung von Anschauungsmaterial, Studium und Unterricht gemeinsam eine Vorbildfunktion in stilistischer wie technischer Hinsicht. Ludwig Lobmeyr stand von Anfang an in engem Kontakt mit Eitelberger und seinen Mitarbeitern, verwendete Museumsobjekte und die Vorbildersammlung als Anregung für Entwürfe und trug durch Schenkungen zur Erweiterung der Sammlungen bei. „Ich betrachtete mich nicht nur als Schüler aller jener Künstler und Kunstgelehrten, mit welchen ich in so regem Verkehre stand, sondern [ich] war es

Urkunde des ÖMKI für Ludwig Lobmeyr, 1874 (FAW)
Certificate of the AMAI for Ludwig Lobmeyr, 1874 (CAV)

Business and Museum

The J. & L. Lobmeyr company under Ludwig Lobmeyr and the founding of the Austrian Museum of Art and Industry

In the person of Ludwig Lobmeyr, who had to continue the business alone after the premature death of his brother, a sense of art combined with a sense of business. Through the strategy he pursued, he managed to rise to the position of the leading glass industrialist of the monarchy in the second half of the 19th century and a serious competitor in the international market. He showed great skill in aligning the reformatory efforts of the Austrian Museum of Art and Industry and the talents of Viennese artists with his artistic, business,

Widmungsblatt der Werkzeichnungen (FAW)
Dedication leaf of the working drawings (CAV)

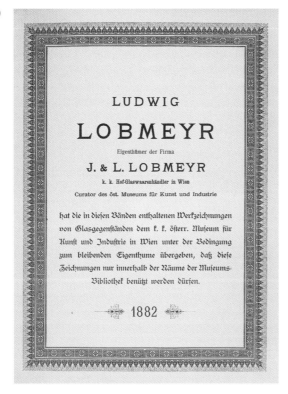

LUDWIG

LOBMEYR

Eigenthümer der Firma

J. & L. LOBMEYR

k. k. Hof-Glaswaarenhändler in Wien

Curator des öst. Museums für Kunst und Industrie

hat die in diesen Bänden enthaltenen Werkzeichnungen
von Glasgegenständen dem k. k. österr. Museum für
Kunst und Industrie in Wien unter der Bedingung
zum bleibenden Eigenthume übergeben, daß diese
Zeichnungen nur innerhalb der Räume der Museums-
Bibliothek benützt werden dürfen.

1882

[auch] thatsächlich."[11] Kontakte bestanden auch zu den Professoren der Kunstgewerbeschule. Von Anfang an stellte Lobmeyr seine neuen Arbeiten im Museum aus, immer wieder auch die Entwürfe für die Weltausstellungen.

Rudolf von Eitelberger veranstaltete so genannte Musealabende, zu denen er Künstler und Kunstindustrielle, darunter auch Ludwig Lobmeyr, einlud. Bei Lobmeyr fanden ab 1870 ähnliche Gesellschaften statt – für Persönlichkeiten des Museums, Künstler, Kunstindustrielle und andere, die dem Museum verbunden waren. Er zeigte bei dieser Gelegenheit seine neuesten Arbeiten, zu denen sich die Künstler dann äußern konnten.[12]

1869 war Ludwig Lobmeyr Gründungsmitglied und Kassier der Gesellschaft zur Förderung der Kunstgewerbeschule, 1874 wurde er „Curator" des Museums,

and personal capacities. "The founding of the Austr. 'Museum of Art and Industry' came to my help just in time. For it was only thus that closer relations with art scholars and artists developed."[9]

At the 1862 London World's Fair already, Lobmeyr had got in contact with Rudolf von Eitelberger who was then preparing the founding of the Austrian Museum of Art and Industry (AMAI)[10] and who was to be appointed its first director after the opening of the institution. The project objective was the promotion of good taste in designers and producers as well in consumers. The AMAI and the Industrials Arts School established 1868 assumed a model function in questions of style and technology by providing instructive and illustrative materials and through studies and education. From the very beginning, Ludwig Lobmeyr was in close contact with Eitelberger and his collaborators; he used the museum's exhibits and model collection as an inspiration for his own designs and contributed with donations to the expansion of the collections. "I did not only consider myself, but in fact was a pupil of all those artists and art scholars with whom I was in such active contact."[11] He also was in contact with professors at the Industrial Arts School. Early on, Lobmeyr exhibited his new creations at the museum, which regularly included his designs shown at the World Fairs.

Rudolf von Eitelberger held so-called museum soirees to which he invited artists and arts-and-crafts industrialists, among them Ludwig Lobmeyr. From 1870, similar gatherings for personalities from the museum, artists, industrialists, and others associated with the museum, took place in Lobmeyr's house. He used the occasion to present his latest creations and to invite opinions from the artists present.[12]

In 1869, Ludwig Lobmeyr was a founding member and the treasurer of the Society for the Promotion of the Industrial Arts School; in 1874, he became a "curator"

1876 Mitglied beim „Artistischen Aufsichtsrath" für die dem Handelsministerium unterstehenden Fachschulen, 1884 Mitglied des Wiener Kunstgewerbevereins. Er trat bei Ausstellungen immer wieder als Juror für den Bereich Glas auf und unterstützte das Museum bei der Durchführung von Ausstellungen.

Mit der ersten Weltausstellung in London 1851 begannen die internationalen Kunst- und Industrieausstellungen, die eine Zusammenschau von Technik und Kunst boten. Maschinelle Fertigungen, billige Kopien und der Missbrauch von Materialien boten bei der Ausstellung in London Anlass zur Kritik. Man sprach von fehlendem Geschmack und Stillosigkeit, Schlagworte, die das Kunstgewerbe in der zweiten Hälfte des 19. Jahrhunderts prägen sollten. Frankreich konnte 1851 vorerst die Führungsrolle in Fragen des Geschmacks und im Bereich des überlieferten handwerklichen Könnens übernehmen. Die anderen Länder erkannten das; vor allem in England, bald aber auch in Österreich setzten daraufhin Reformbewegungen ein. Auf den weiteren kunstgewerblichen Ausstellungen, auch unabhängig von den großen internationalen Kunst- und Industrieausstellungen, traten die kunstgewerblichen Sparten der verschiedenen Länder immer wieder in Wettstreit. Österreich erzielte durch die vom ÖMKI initiierte Reform schon Ende der sechziger Jahre erste Erfolge.

Durch den Besuch zahlreicher Ausstellungen im In- und Ausland war Ludwig Lobmeyr zum Kenner der internationalen Glasproduktion geworden. Sein Wissen über die Glasindustrie konnte er auch zu Papier bringen. So verfasste er gemeinsam mit Jakob von Falke[13] im Anschluss an die Wiener Weltausstellung 1873 einen „Ausstellungs-Bericht" über die Glasindustrie[14], wobei er den „commerziellen" und technischen Teil übernahm. Gleichzeitig veröffentlichte er gemeinsam mit Albert Ilg (historischer Teil) und Wendelin Boeheim (statistischer Teil) ein Werk über „Die Glasindustrie, ihre Geschichte, gegenwärtige Entwicklung und Statistik", das 1874 erschien.

of the museum, and in 1876 a member of the "Artistic Supervisory Board" for the technical colleges under the authority of the Ministry of Trade, and finally in 1884, a member of the Vienna Arts-and-Crafts Association. He recurrently acted as juror for glassware in exhibitions and supported the museum in organizing shows.

The first World's Fair held in London in 1851 marked the beginning of the international art and industry expositions which gave a survey of the art and technology of the day. Machine-based manufacturing, cheap copies, and misuse of materials gave reason to much criticism at the London exhibition. There was talk of a lack of taste and style; catchwords which prompted the arts-and-crafts movements of the latter half of the 19th century. In 1851, it was France which first took the lead in matters of taste and in the field of traditional craftsmanship. Other countries realized the need to catch up, which gave rise to reform movements, mainly in England, but soon also in Austria. The arts-and-crafts industries of the different countries competed against one another in numerous art-and-crafts exhibition that followed, also outside the circuit of large-scale international art and industry expositions. The AMAI-initiated reform earned Austria first successes in the 1860s already.

His numerous visits to exhibitions at home and abroad had made Ludwig Lobmeyr an expert in international glassware production. He also committed his knowledge of the glass industry to paper: so he published, together with Jacob von Falke[13], an "Exhibition Report" about the glass industry[14], in which he took over the "commercial" and technological sections, soon after the 1873 Vienna World's Fair. At the same time, he published, together with Albert Ilg (historical part) and Wendelin Boeheim (statistical part) a work about "The Glass Industry, Its History, Current Development and Statistics", which came out in Stuttgart 1874.

Die Lobmeyr-Gläser wurden ein wichtiger Bestandteil der Glassammlung des ÖMKI. Das erste Lobmeyr-Glas erwarb das Museum um 1870 (Inv.-Nr. Gl 929); es handelt sich um die Kopie eines Bergkristallgefäßes aus dem 16. Jahrhundert.

Immer wieder überließ Lobmeyr seine Gläser dem Museum als Schenkung – so nach der Wiener Weltausstellung einige Gläser des „Kaiser-Services", das in Zusammenarbeit mit dem Museum entstanden war. Fürst Liechtenstein widmete um 1880 einige Flaschen und Gläser von Trink-Servicen Lobmeyrs, die ansonsten nicht in der Sammlung vertreten sind.

Mehrere Glasobjekte aus dem 19. Jahrhundert, die sich in der Wohnung Ludwig Lobmeyrs befanden, wurden nach seinem Tod 1917 dem Museum vermacht. Rund 20 Gläser wurden vom Museum durch Ankauf, vorwiegend auf Ausstellungen, erworben. Bei über 30 Gläsern fehlen genaue Erwerbungsangaben; sie wurden erst um 1932 „nachträglich inventarisiert". Möglicherweise befanden sie sich aber schon im 19. Jahrhundert in den Museumssammlungen.

Nur wenige Einzelobjekte und ein umfassendes Trink-Service aus dem 19. Jahrhundert wurden erst in der zweiten Hälfte des 20. Jahrhunderts angekauft. Im 19. Jahrhundert waren nur einzelne Teile von Trink-Servicen erworben worden. Umfangreich ist auch die Sammlung von Lobmeyr-Gläsern, die im 20. Jahrhundert hergestellt wurden.

1879 und 1889 hatte Lobmeyr die Gelegenheit zu umfassenden Einzelausstellungen im ÖMKI. In den zeitgenössischen Presseberichten wurden diese Ausstellungen einmal mehr zum Anlass genommen, seine prägende Rolle als Erneuerer und Führer der österreichischen Glasindustrie zu betonen.

Ludwig Lobmeyr schenkte dem Museum auch Glasobjekte fremder Produktion oder vermittelte ihren Ankauf.

Lobmeyr glassware became an important part of the glassware collections held by the AMAI. The museum bought the first Lobmeyr glass around 1870; it was a copy of a 16th century rock-crystal vessel (inv.-no. Gl 929).

Lobmeyr repeatedly donated glasses to the museum – as, for example, after the Vienna World's Fair, a number of glasses from the "Imperial Service" which had been produced in cooperation with the museum. Around 1880, the Prince of Liechtenstein donated some bottles and glasses from Lobmeyr drinking services which otherwise are not represented in the collection.

Several 19th century glass objects from Lobmeyr's house were donated to the museum after his death in 1917. About 20 glasses were purchased by the museum, mainly at exhibitions. Acquisition information is missing for more than 30 glasses, which were "belatedly inventoried" around 1932, but may have been in the museum collections ever since the 19th century.

Only a few singular objects as well as a comprehensive 19th century drinking service were purchased as late as in the second half of the 20th century. In the 19th century, only parts of drinking services had been bought. The museum holdings also comprise a large collection of Lobmeyr glasses made in the 20th century.

In 1879 and 1889, Lobmeyr was given the opportunity to present large single exhibitions at the AMAI. In the contemporary press, these exhibitions were once more taken as an occasion to point to his pioneering role as an innovator and leader of the Austrian glass industry.

Ludwig Lobmeyr also donated to the museum glass objects of foreign production or helped to facilitate purchases. This included historical glasses such as rock-crystal vessels and numerous Bohemian glasses from the 17th and 18th century. In the early years of

Dazu gehörten historische Gläser wie Gefäße aus Bergkristall und zahlreiche böhmische Gläser des 17. und 18. Jahrhunderts. Schon in den Anfangsjahren des Museums erwarb er beispielsweise auf der „Kirchmeyerschen Auction" über 20 vorwiegend böhmische Gläser. 1875 überließ er dem Museum den Abguss eines antik römischen Glases, 1877 mehrere japanische Glasarbeiten, 1878 ein deutsches Rubinglas mit Montierung aus dem 18. Jahrhundert, ein venezianisches Glas aus dem 16. Jahrhundert und einen holländischen Becher aus dem 17. Jahrhundert, 1889 ein Glas aus einem Mumiengrab. Auch moderne Gläser aus England, Frankreich, Venedig oder Deutschland kamen durch Lobmeyrs Widmung in die Sammlung: 1881 erwarb er venezianische Gläser von Salviati und der Compagnia Venezia-Murano und Objekte der Rheinischen Glashütten in Köln-Ehrenfeld für das Museum, 1889 auf der Pariser Weltausstellung französische Gläser von Leveillé, Baccarat, Brocard, Sèvres und Gallé.

Ludwig Lobmeyr war sich der Bedeutung seiner Arbeiten als Vorbilder für die Glasindustrie sehr wohl bewusst. Aus diesem Grund überließ er 1883 dem Museum elf Bände mit Werkzeichnungen einer Auswahl von Gegenständen, die seit der Gründung der Firma ausgeführt worden waren, 1892 folgten weitere sieben Bände. Seine Absicht war, „damit namentlich unserer heimatlichen Glasindustrie förderlich sein zu können"[15].

Die 18 Bände mit rund 1000 Blättern boten einen Überblick über die Produktion der Firma seit ihrer Gründung und umfassten einfache Trink-Service genauso wie prunkvolle Tafelaufsätze in Originalgröße oder mit Maßangaben und mit Hinweisen auf Entwerfer, Datierungen u. a. Die Formen der Objekte sind als so genannte Schnitte dargestellt, der Dekor oft in Farbe. Die Zeichnungen dienen heute als wichtige Quellen bei der wissenschaftlichen Bearbeitung und Zuordnung der Lobmeyr-Gläser.

the museum already, he purchased more than 20 mainly Bohemian glasses for the museum at "Kirchmeyer's Auction". In 1875, he donated to the museum a cast of an antique Roman glass, in 1877 several Japanese glass objects, in 1878 an 18th century German ruby glass with silver mounting, a 16th century Venetian glass and a 17th century Dutch cup, and in 1889, a glass from a mummy's tomb. Modern glasses from England, France, Venice or Germany also got into the collection as donations by Lobmeyr: 1881, he purchased Venetian glasses by Salviati and the Compagnia Venezia-Murano and objects of the Rheinische Glashütten [Rhenisch Glassworks] in Cologne-Ehrenfeld for the museum, and 1889, at the Paris World's Fair, French glasses by Leveillé, Baccarat, Brocard, Sèvres, and Gallé.

Ludwig Lobmeyr was well aware of the significance of his works as models for the glass industry. For this reason, he donated to the museum eleven volumes of working drawings for a number of selected objects which had been produced since the establishing of the company, followed by seven additional volumes in 1892. His intention was "to be thus instrumental to our domestic glass industry."[15]

The 18 volumes of about 1000 drawings gave a survey of the production of the company ever since its foundation and comprised simple drinking services as well as ornate centerpieces in original scale or with measurements and indication of designers, dates etc. The shapes of the objects are represented as so-called sections, the decorations are frequently colorized. Today, the drawings are important sources for researching and categorizing Lobmeyr glassware.

„Flacons", in: WZ, Bd. X, S. 2
"Flacons", in: WD, vol. X, p. 2

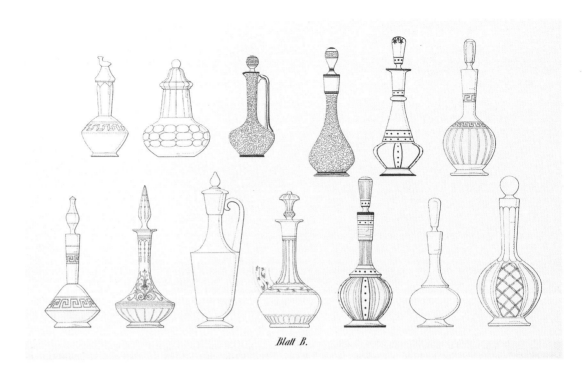

Blatt B.

Band I–III: Trink-Service

(Auswahl der Trink-Service Nr. 1–200)

Band IV–VI: Dessert-Service (Nr. 1–168)

Band VII: Trink-Gefässe

Band VIII: Trink-Gefässe etc.

Band IX: Zier-Gefässe

Band X: Krystall-Gefässe

Band XI: Blumen-Vasen

Band XII: Alte u. neue böhmische Gefässe

Band XIII: Verschiedenes

Band XIV: Trink-Service No. 173–200

Band XV: Gefässe in arabischem und indischem Style

Band XVI: Orientalische Gefässe

Band XVII: Neue Serien

Band XVIII: Kronleuchter, Arm- und Wandleuchter

Volume I–III: Drinking Services

(Selection from drinking services nos. 1–200)

Volume IV–VI: Dessert Service (nos. 1–168)

Volume VII: Drinking Vessels

Volume VIII: Drinking Vessels etc.

Volume IX: Decorative Vessels

Volume X: Crystal Vessels

Volume XI: Flower Vases

Volume XII: Old and New Bohemian Vessels

Volume XIII: Miscellaneous

Volume XIV: Drinking Service nos. 173–200

Volume XV: Vessels in Arabian and Indian Style

Volume XVI: Oriental Vessels

Volume XVII: New Series

Volume XVIII: Chandeliers, Candelabra, and Wall Lamps

Reform

Die böhmische Glasindustrie in der zweiten Hälfte des 19. Jahrhunderts

Die europäische Glasindustrie im 19. Jahrhundert war von einer vielfältigen Entwicklung und einem Wettstreit der verschiedenen Zentren geprägt.

1867 wurde vom führenden Kunstkritiker in Wien, Jakob von Falke, die Entwicklung der europäischen Glasindustrie im Laufe des 19. Jahrhunderts folgendermaßen beschrieben: „Es ist noch nicht lange her, dass die böhmische Glasindustrie die erste der Welt war und das geschliffene Glas Böhmens in allen Welttheilen den Markt beherrschte. […] Den ersten Stoss erhielt die böhmische Glasindustrie durch die Engländer. Sie brachten das bleihältige Glas oder das Flintglas in Mode, welches bei krystallinischer Schleifung in prismatischen Farben spielt, während gerade die Böhmen ihr Glas so farblos wie möglich, ähnlich dem echten Krystall, zu machen trachteten. Der neue Stoff empfahl sich durch seine unläugbaren Reize und es wurde dem böhmischen Glas ein grosser Theil seines commerciellen Gebietes entrissen. Den verlornen Boden wieder zu erobern, führten nun die Böhmen das gefärbte Krystallglas auf den Kampfplatz und verwendeten darauf ihre Kunst der Schleifung und Gravirung. Es gelang ihnen auch zum Theil, was sie wollten; wenigstens wurden diese Rubin- und Smaragdgläser u.s.w. ausserordentlich populär und aufs neue überschwemmte böhmisches Luxusglas den Erdboden. Unglücklicher Weise traf das gerade mit der höchsten Entartung des Geschmackes zusammen […] Da nun auch die Engländer keine formellen Reize zu bieten hatten, so kam es, dass bis auf die neueste Zeit das gesammte Krystallglas, farbig oder unfarbig, böhmisch oder englisch, von der abscheulichsten Plumpheit und Ungestalt der Formen so wie von gemeiner armseliger Ornamentation beherrscht war. Immerhin war diese Ornamentation wenigstens dem Material angemessen und

Reform

The Bohemian Glass Industry in the Second Half of the 19th Century

The European glass industry of the 19th century was characterized by diverse developments and a competition of rival centers.

1867, Vienna's leading art critic, Jakob von Falke, described the 19th century development of the European glass industry as follows: "Not long ago, the Bohemian glass industry was foremost in the world, and cut glass from Bohemia dominated the markets in all parts of the world. […] The first blow dealt to the Bohemian glass industry came from the English. They brought the lead or flint glass into fashion, which, if crystal-cut, was iridescent in prismatic colors, while the Bohemians particularly sought to make their glass as colorless as possible, similar to the real crystal. The new material caught on through its undeniable attractiveness, and so Bohemian glass was deprived of a large part of its commercial scope. To regain lost terrain, the Bohemians introduced colored crystal glass on the battle scene, bringing to bear their art of cutting and engraving. In part, they achieved what they were out for; at least, these ruby and emerald glasses etc. became extraordinarily popular, and once again the world was flooded with Bohemian glass. Unfortunately, this happened to coincide with an utmost degeneracy of taste […] As the English did not have anything to offer in terms of formal appeal, either, it so happened that, until most recently, crystal glass in its entirety, colored or colorless, Bohemian or English, was dominated by the most atrocious coarseness and unshapeliness of forms, as well as by cheap and poor ornamentation. It must be said, though, that this ornamentation at least was appropriate to the material and was based on its special characteristics. However, now the French came in, who actually had little say in the manufacturing of luxury

beruhte auf seinen Eigenthümlichkeiten. Nun kamen aber die Franzosen, welche eigentlich in der Fabrication des Luxusglases wenig mitzureden hatten, benützten den versunkenen ästhetischen Zustand und führten ihre Geschmacksweisen in die Verzierung des Glases ein. Ihrem Einflusse ist die Verzierung der Glasgefässe mit allen möglichen farbigen Malereien zuzuschreiben. Dazu musste das Glas erst in einen porzellanähnlichen opaken Zustand versetzt werden, wodurch man ihm seine Eigenthümlichkeit und seine Schönheit nahm. Jedenfalls ist dies also die unangemessenste Art künstlerischer Verzierung des Glases, und darum an sich geschmacklos, mag die Malerei auch noch so schön ausgeführt sein. Indessen wurde sie Mode, musste daher auch von den Böhmen neben dieser Weise angenommen werden und beherrschte leider so in den buntesten, verkehrtesten und widersinnigsten Arten, was zur Genüge bekannt, das Glas als Luxusgeräth."[16]

So erregte auf der ersten Weltausstellung 1851 in der österreichischen Glasabteilung vor allem das farbige Glas Aufsehen. Auch 1862 fand es noch mehr Anklang als das farblose Glas, das von schlechterer Qualität gewesen sein soll als das gewöhnlichste englische Glas. 1867 wurde das farbige böhmische Glas allerdings wegen schlechter Formen, überladener Malereien und porzellanartigen Eindrucks von Jakob von Falke schon heftig kritisiert: „[…] wenn dasselbe heute noch Bestand haben will, so muß es jedenfalls anders werden, als es ist. Selbst das Beste in dieser Art, was die österreichische Abteilung der Weltausstellung darbot, ist vor einer strengen Kritik verwerflich."[17] So konnten seiner Meinung nach die farbigen Vasen die Harmonie eines Raumes stören. Ebenso sprach er sich gegen Bemalung aus, die das Glas nicht mehr durchscheinend wirken lässt, oder gegen Überfangglas mit Schliff, „weil die Farben zu hart aufeinander stoßen und der Blick, anstatt der Hauptform zu folgen, nur die Linien des Ornaments betrachtet, welche die Form zerschneiden". Marmoriertes Glas bezeich-

glassware, and they took advantage of the sunken state of aesthetics to introduce their own tastes into glass ornamentation. It is to their influence that decoration of glass vessels with all sorts of colorful painting must be ascribed. For this purpose, the glass had to be brought into a porcelain-like opaque state, which meant depriving it of its special quality and beauty. In any case, it is the most inappropriate way of artistic glass decoration, and hence tasteless per se, however beautifully done the painting may be. Nevertheless, it came into vogue, and hence had to be adopted by the Bohemians as well, and thus has unfortunately come to prevail, as is sufficiently known, in glassware as a luxury article in the most garish, abstruse and senseless styles."[16]

At the first World's Fair of 1851, it thus was colored glass that drew most attention in the Austrian glassware department. 1862 again, it was more appreciated than the colorless glass, which was said to have been of poorer quality than the most common English glass. In 1867, however, the colored Bohemian glass was fiercely criticized by Jakob von Falke because of its ill-designed forms, florid painting, and porcelain-like appearance: "[…] if it wants to survive today, it will have to become different from what it is. Even the very best in its kind, as offered by the Austrian department at the World Fair, must seem rejectable to any strict critic."[17] Thus he found that the colored vases might disturb the harmony of a room. He also took a stance against painting which made the glass no longer look transparent, or against cut overlay glass, "because the color contrasts are too hard and the gaze, instead of following the overall contour, only takes in the lines of ornamentation that cut through the form." He called marbled glass a "false imitation." "All of these ornamentation styles strongly look like French novelty-chasing. Most important, without doubt, is the colored crystal glass which also provided the main characteristic of the Austrian-Bohemian exhibition in Paris. Unfortunately, though, it

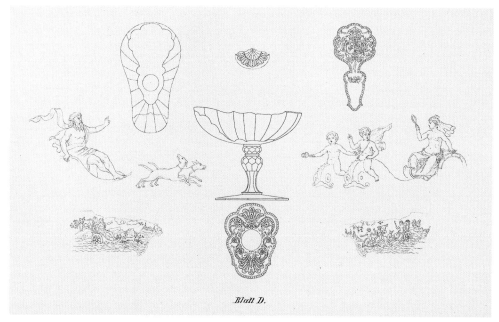

Blatt D.

172

Aus der Pariser Ausstellung.

nete er als „eine falsche Imitation". „Alle diese Orna-
mentationsweisen sehen aber stark nach der französischen Novitätenhascherei aus. Am wichtigsten ohne
Zweifel ist das gefärbte Krystallglas, das auch der öster-
reichisch-böhmischen Ausstellung in Paris den Haupt-
charakterzug gab. Aber gerade hierin trat leider auch der
roheste Geschmack zu Tage und machte den Anblick
des österreichischen Glases auf der Weltausstellung zum
größten Theil fast unerträglich. Soll dieser Industriezweig
künstlerisch Bedeutung erhalten, ja will er nur das Leben
fristen, so ist es ganz selbstverständlich, daß er im Sinne
der englischen Reform, was die Ornamente und die
Formen betrifft, umgewandelt werden muß."[18]

Die für notwendig befundenen Reformbestrebungen
des böhmischen Kristallglases richteten sich gegen das
undurchsichtige, farbige und bemalte Glas und propa-
gierten das farblose geschliffene oder geschnittene Glas,
wie es erfolgreich in England produziert wurde: „Wieder
waren es die Engländer, welche, diesen Zustand der Dinge erkennend, das Glas künstlerisch gewissermassen auf

was precisely here that the crudest taste made itself felt,
making the larger part of the Austrian glassware shown
at the World's Fair almost unbearable to look at. If this
industry is supposed to have any artistic significance, if,
in fact, it merely wants to survive, there can be no question that it will have to be transformed in the sense of
the English reform, as far as ornaments and shapes are
concerned."[18]

The reformatory efforts that were found necessary for
the Bohemian crystal-glassmaking industry were direct-
ed against opaque, colored, and painted glassware,
propagating instead colorless ground or cut glass as was
successfully produced in England: "Again, it was the
English who, realizing the state of affairs, artistically
reduced the glass to itself, so to speak […] basing the
aesthetic reform on the qualities of the glass, its refractivity, its clarity and transparency, and recognizing
that this should well go together with the shaping of
beautiful vessels. The models for these were the vessels
of the ancient Greek and the Renaissance period. The

Links: „Gefässe aus Krystallglas mit Figuren
und Ornamenten gravirt", Blatt D,
in: WZ, Bd. XII, S. 30
Left: "Vessels of crystal glass engraved with figures
and ornaments", sheet D, in: WD, vol. XII, p. 30

Rechts: Kanne und Trinkglas, Entwurf:
A. Rincklake, Ausführung: J. & L. Lobmeyr,
gezeigt auf der Pariser Weltausstellung 1867,
in: Gewerbehalle, 1867, S. 172
(MAK, Inv.-Nr. K.I. 380)
Right: Pitcher and drinking glass, design:
A. Rincklake, manufacturer: J. & L. Lobmeyr,
shown at the 1867 Paris World's Fair, in:
Gewerbehalle, 1867, p. 172 (MAK, inv. no. K.I. 380)

sich selbst zurückführten. [...] gründeten sie die ästhe-
tische Reform auf die Eigenschaften des Glases, auf seine Farbenbrechung, seine Klarheit und Durchsichtigkeit, und erkannten, dass sich damit schöne Gefässbildung
verbinden lassen müsse. Für diese waren die Vorbilder
in den Gefässen der Griechen und der Renaissance gegeben. Die Eigenschaft prismatischer Farbenbrechung
führte die Engländer dahin, crystallinische oder diaman-
tirte Schleifung der Oberflächen zum Princip zu erhe-
ben und den möglichsten Effect farbiger Lichter zu er-
zielen [...] Die Klarheit und Durchsichtigkeit des
Materials aber benützten sie in der Weise, wie man im
sechzehnten und siebenzehnten Jahrhundert den echten Krystall verziert hatte, sie umgaben die Gefässe näm-
lich mit den reizendsten Verzierungen ornamentaler oder
figürlicher Art, die entweder eingeschliffen oder einge-
ätzt waren [...]."[19]

Dasselbe wurde für das böhmische Glas gefordert – unter Einziehung der eigenen Tradition, wie es von Lobmeyr auch sofort erfolgreich umgesetzt wurde (siehe
Kat.-Nr. 1, 2, 5, 6). Jakob von Falke schrieb daher anlässlich der Weltausstellung 1867: „Lobmeyr hat die englische Reform wohl begriffen, hat den falschen
Triumphen des farbigen und bemalten Glases entsagt
und allen Nachdruck auf die künstlerische Gestaltung
und Verwerthung des klaren Krystallglases gelegt. [...]
Er hat allein die Ehre der böhmischen Glasindustrie ge-
rettet; [...] Wir wünschen eben, dass die Richtung, welche Lobmeyr mit solcher Entschiedenheit betreten hat
und worin er gegenwärtig in Oesterreich allein steht,
die allgemeine werde."[20] „Er [Lobmeyr] rettet die Ehre
vom Standpunkte des Geschmackes."[21]

Der deutsche Kunstkritiker Friedrich Pecht kritisierte
1867 die böhmische Glasindustrie, vor allem die Bemalung der Gläser und die fehlende künstlerische Seite,
hob aber Lobmeyr positiv hervor: „Nicht nur haben die
allereinfachsten Gebrauchsgegenstände, wie Trinkgläser
ec., die bewundernswürdige Reinheit und Klarheit des

Dessertaufsatz (Detail), Kat.-Nr. 21a
Dessert centerpiece (detail), cat. no. 21a

quality of prismatic refractivity lead the English to
making a principle of crystal or diamond cutting and
to achieve the utmost effect of colorful reflections [...]
They used the clarity and transparency of the material
in such a way as had been done in the sixteenth and
seventeenth century to decorate the real rock crystal,
namely by covering the vessels all around with the
loveliest decorations of an ornamental or figurative
kind, which were either cut or etched in [...]"[19]

The same was demanded for Bohemian glass – with
integration of the specific local tradition. This was
successfully implemented by Lobmeyr straightaway (see
cat. nos. 1, 2, 5, 6). Hence, on the occasion of the 1987
World's Fair, Jakob von Falke wrote: "Lobmeyr has well
understood the English reform, has renounced the false
triumphs of colored and painted glass and placed all
emphasis on the artistic design and the use of clear
crystal glass. [...] He alone has saved the honor of the
Bohemian glass industry; [...] It is to be wished that the
direction which was taken by Lobmeyr with such deter-
mination and which is at present being pursued by him
alone should be a general one."[20] "He [Lobmeyr] vindi-
cates honor from the point of view of taste."[21]

1867, the German art critic Friedrich Pecht also
criticized the Bohemian glass industry, notably the glass

Stoffs mit den böhmischen gemein, ja übertreffen sie oft noch darin, sondern sie zeigen auch eine Feinheit, einen Reiz der Form, der jenen meist abgeht."[22] Auch Falke meinte: „Alle Ueberlegenheit des Hauses Lobmeyr finden wir auch in seinem Tafelgeräth. Alle seine Krystalle sind weiß, das ist eine bemerkenswerthe Sache. Material und Arbeit sind von größter Reinheit."[23]

England verzichtete fast gänzlich auf farbiges Glas. Dieses wurde weiterhin vor allem in Frankreich und Böhmen hergestellt, trotz Reformbestrebungen der böhmischen Glasindustrie. Allerdings herrschte die Tendenz, farbiges Glas wieder durchscheinend herzustellen. Der Dekor sollte, der Form des Glases angepasst, nicht zu großflächig gewählt sein. Statt den gemäldeähnlichen Malereien wurde die „Anwendung des stylistischen Ornamentes"[24] gefordert. Lobmeyr griff dabei, wohl angeregt durch den Franzosen Brocard, die alte Technik der Bemalung mit Emailfarben wieder auf. „Das Material für die färbende Schicht wird kalt als feines Pulver mit dem Pinsel aufgetragen und nachträglich in Fluß gebracht, so daß der bereits vorhandene Glasgegenstand mit der färbenden Substanz imprägniert wird. Die aufzubrennenden Farben müssen sehr leicht schmelzbar sein, da anderen Falles die Form des Glases beim Einbrennen mit erweichen und geschädigt würde. Die aufzutragenden Substanzen sind bestimmte farblose Gemenge, die mit verschiedenen Metalloxyden gefärbt werden."[25] Die Farben konnten undurchsichtig oder auch transparent erscheinen. Dazu kam noch Golddekor: „Die Goldfarbe wird ebenso wie die übrigen Glasfarben auf dem zu decorirenden Glase aufgetragen, mit diesem in der Muffel eingebrannt [...]."[26]

Jakob von Falke erklärte anlässlich der Wiener Weltausstellung 1873 über das farbige bzw. farbig dekorierte Glas: „Nun muss es allerdings gänzlich anders werden, als es bisher in Böhmen geübt wurde und durch alle Lande als Geschmacksliebhaberei der ungebildeten Menge ging. [...] Suchen wir nach neuen Wegen und Beispielen von gefärbtem Glas, dessen Reize wir den Gefässen und

painting and the lack of artistic quality, but he, too, acknowledged Lobmeyr's achievements: "Not only do the simplest utensils, such as drinking glasses, have the same admirable purity and clarity of the material as those of Bohemian making, and in fact often even surpass them, but they also show a fineness, a charm of form that is lacking in the latter." [22] Falke, too, said: "All of Lobmeyr's superiority can also be found in his tableware. All of his crystalware is white, this is remarkable. The material and finishing are of the greatest purity."[23]

England almost entirely abandoned colored glass. This continued to be produced mainly in France and Bohemia, despite the reformatory efforts made in the Bohemian glass industry. There was, however, a tendency for transparent colored glass again. The decoration was supposed to be not too extensive and suited to the shape of the glass. Instead of picturesque painting, the call was for an "application of stylistic ornament"[24]. Inspired presumably by the Frenchman Brocard, Lobmeyr fell back on the old technique of enamel painting: "The material for the coloring layer is applied cold, with a brush, as a fine powder and then fluxed, so that the already existing glass object is impregnated with the coloring substance. The colors must be easily fusible, since otherwise the form of the glass will soften in the firing and become impaired. The substances applied are certain colorless mixtures which are colored with different metallic oxides."[25] The colors could be made to appear opaque or transparent. Then, gilding was added: "The gold color is applied to the glass to be decorated like the other glass colors and then fixed by firing in the muffle kiln [...]"[26]

On the occasion of the Vienna World's Fair of 1873, Jakob von Falke wrote about colored or color-decorated glass: "Now, however, things must become entirely different from what was hitherto practiced in Bohemia and spread to every place as the favored taste of the

Krug, Kat.-Nr. 33c
Pitcher, cat. no. 33c

Geräthen durchaus nicht entziehen möchten, so müssen wir uns wiederum in der Ausstellung von Lobmeyr umsehen, der auch hier als Führer erscheint und uns einen lehrreichen Vorgang vor Augen stellt […].“[27]

Lobmeyr war also auch an der Reform des farbigen Glases maßgeblich beteiligt und arbeitete ständig an Neuerungen: „Wir treffen ihn niemals auf Ausstellungen, ohne dass wir Versuche sehen, sein Reich zu erweitern oder alte verfehlte Manieren zu verbessern. Von diesem letzteren Gesichtspunkte aus ist eine Collection farbiger, transparenter Glasgeräthe in Blau, Roth und Grün zu beurtheilen. Viele werden sagen – und wir hören das oft –: ,Ich mag diese farbigen Gläser nicht, das lichte, farblose Krystallglas ist mir lieber …‘ In diesem Falle handelt es sich aber nicht um den Geschmack dieses oder jenes Individuums, sondern um einen Handelsgegenstand, der existirt und gekauft wird, und um ein Kunstmaterial, das sein Recht zur Existenz hat, weil es natürlich ist. Diese gefärbten, transparenten Gläser hatten ihren Weltmarkt und haben ihn noch. Allerdings sind sie im Begriffe, ihn zu verlieren, deshalb weil sie plump in ihren Formen, unschön in der Decoration, roh im Effecte geworden sind, zugleich aber der Geschmack des Publicums in Besserung und Verfeinerung begriffen ist. Die Aufgabe für den Fabrikanten stellt sich also einfach dahin, die Waare selbst zu verbessern und zu verfeinern, damit sie den erhöhten Anforderungen des Geschmacks entspricht. Und dies ist es, was Lobmeyr versucht hat. […] Dazu zeigt sich die erste Bedingung erfüllt, indem alle Formen der Vasen, Pocale u.s.w. gut und edel sind. Grelle Farbeneffecte sind in der Zusammenstellung vermieden; der Wechsel von Hell und Dunkel nur durch die Ausschleifung eines ,Ueberfanges‘ von derselben Farbe bewirkt. Wo eine zweite Farbe hinzugefügt worden, ist auch sie fein und transparent aufgetragen, so dass die Grundfarbe zusammenwirkt.“[28]

Neben transparentem Glas in verschiedenen Farben verwendete Lobmeyr schließlich auch wieder opakes und

uneducated mass […] If we look out for new ways and examples of colored glass, the charms of which we do certainly not seek to banish from vessels and utensils, we will again have to look around in the exhibition auf Lobmeyr who appears to be in the lead here, too, and puts an instructive process before our eyes […]”[27]

So, Lobmeyr also made a substantial contribution to the re-formation of colored glass and continually worked on further innovations: “We never meet him at exhibitions without seeing attempts to expand his realm or to improve old and misguided manners. The collection of colored transparent glass utensils in blue, red, and green must be judged from this point of view. Many will say – and this is something that we often hear –: ‘I do not like those colored glasses, I prefer the light, colorless crystal glass…’ In this case, however, the question is not about the taste of some individual or another, but about a commodity that exists and is bought, and about an art material that has a right to exist, because it is natural. These colored transparent glasses had, and still have, their world market. However, they are about to lose it, because they have become ungraceful in form, unsightly in decoration, crude in effect, while the taste of the public is going for improvement and refinement.
The task for the manufacturer therefore simply is improvement and refinement of the commodity so as to meet the heightened requirements of taste. And this is what Lobmeyr has attempted […] Furthermore, the prime condition is fulfilled in that all vases, goblets etc. are handsome and noble in shape. Garish color effects are avoided in combinations, the shading of light and dark is effected by cut-outs in a ‘casing’ of the same color only. Wherever a second color was added, it was applied delicately and transparently, too, so as to let the basic color blend in.”[28]

Apart from transparent glass in different colors, Lobmeyr finally came to use opaque and semi-opaque glass again, such as opal glass, which was produced in

halbopakes Glas wie das Opalglas, das in mehreren Pastelltönen erzeugt wurde (siehe Kat.-Nr. 24, 25). Vor allem in den siebziger Jahren experimentierte Lobmeyr auch mit verschiedenen Techniken; große Erfolge hatte er mit dem irisierenden Glas, weitere Neuerungen waren Craqueléglas (siehe Kat.-Nr. 34), Glimmerglas (siehe Kat.-Nr. 33) und Aluminiumdekoration (siehe Kat.-Nr. 37, 38, 44, 46).

several pastel tones (see cat. nos. 24, 25). It was mainly in the 1870s that Lobmeyr experimented with different techniques; his iridescent glass was particularly successful; other innovations were ice glass (see cat. no. 34), mica glass (see cat. no. 33), and aluminum decorations (see cat. nos. 37, 38, 44, 46).

Vorbilder
Die Suche nach einem Stil

Material, Form und Technik wurden in der zweiten Hälfte des 19. Jahrhunderts meistens mit einem entsprechenden Stil verbunden. Die Auseinandersetzung mit Schöpfungen der Vergangenheit als Vorbildern war dabei ein wesentlicher Aspekt. Schon vor Gründung des Kunstgewerbemuseums in Wien dienten die verschiedensten historischen Stile als Anregung. Bei den meisten Objekten der sechziger Jahre, die sich durch besondere Stilvielfalt auszeichnen, wurde der zitierte Stil auch angegeben, so waren auf der Weltausstellung 1867 von Lobmeyr Objekte „in griechischem Style", „in mittelalterlicher Art", „in altdeutschem Style" und „im Renaissance-Style" vertreten. Gleichzeitig wurden Objekte „in moderner Art" ohne historisches Vorbild gezeigt.

In den siebziger Jahren wurden von den Reformern als Vorbild für Glasgegenstände die geschliffenen und geschnittenen Kristallgefäße der Renaissance propagiert. Für das farbige Glas bzw. den farbigen Dekor wurde neben der Renaissanceornamentik außerdem das orientalische Prinzip der Flächendekoration aufgegriffen.

In den achtziger Jahren kam es zu einer etwas veränderten Sicht der Stilrezeption im Kunstgewerbe, was sich auch im Bereich Glas bemerkbar machte: „Geht nun der allgemeine Geschmack von den Mustern des 16. Jahrhunderts allmälig zu jenen jüngerer Zeiten über, so lässt sich dem eben nichts entgegensetzen, sondern nur die

Models
In Search of a Style

In the second half of the 19th century, material, form, and technique were usually informed by a specific period style. One essential aspect was confrontation with creations of the past to serve as models. Even before the founding of the Austrian Museum of Art and Industry, a variety of different historical styles was drawn on as sources of inspiration. In most objects from the 1860s, the decade distinguished by a particular diversity of styles, the style invoked was expressly indicated; at the 1867 World's Fair, for example, Lobmeyr showed objects "in Greek style", "in medieval manner", "in Old-German style", and "in Renaissance style". At the same time, the exhibition included objects "in a modern manner" which did not follow historical models.

In the 1870s, the reformers propagated the ground and cut vessels of the Renaissance period as models in glassmaking. Apart from Renaissance ornamentalism, the oriental principle of flat surface decoration was adopted for stained glass or colored decoration.

The 1880s ushered in a somewhat changed view of the reception of historical styles in arts and crafts, which also made itself felt in glassmaking: "If the general taste is now moving on from 16th century models to such of more recent periods, this is not something to oppose, but only to observe as a fact. The public as well as the

„Trink-Service, Krystallglas Blatt A No. 143.
No. 150. No. 157. mit griechischer
Gravirung in 3 Varianten. Nach Zeichnungen
des Oberbaur. R. v. Hansen 1872", in: WZ,
Bd. III, S. 14

"Drinking service, crystal glass sheet A no. 143.
no. 150. no. 157. with Greek engraving in three
variants. After drawings by Oberbaur. R. v.
Hansen 1872", in: WD, vol. III, p. 14

Tatsache beobachten. Publicum und Künstler betrachten sich mit Recht im Ganzen und Großen als so weit geschult, dass sie sich eine Bevormundung im Einzelnen nicht gerne wollen gefallen lassen. Franzosen und Engländer sind nun mit ihrem Geschmacke schon bei Louis XVI. und dem Empire angelangt, und es erscheint nur gesund und den thatsächlichen Verhältnissen entsprechend, wenn sich die Wiener Kunstindustrie den etwas schwereren, kräftigeren Vorbildern aus der Zeit Karls VI. und Maria Theresia's anschließt, in welcher unsere bedeutendsten Bauten mit ihren köstlich verzierten Innenräumen entstanden sind. [...] So waren noch die Wohnungen unserer Großeltern geschmückt, ehe der schlechte Geschmack hereinbrach [...] Da fügt sich auch Neues in diesem Style dem Vorhandenen an und erinnert an Ererbtes und Bekanntes, während man in jenen Renaissance-Zimmern doch meist nur das Gefühl hat, als ob man bei sich selbst zu Gast wäre. Dass eine solche

artists generally consider themselves educated enough, and rightly so, not to accept being paternalized in every detail any longer. The French and English have meanwhile arrived at Louis XVI and Empire in taste, and it seems only healthy and in keeping with given circumstances that the Viennese arts-and-crafts industry should follow the somewhat weightier and more robust models from the time of Karl VI and Maria Theresia in which our most important buildings with their splendidly decorated interiors have come to be built. [...] This is how our grandparents' houses were decorated before bad taste befell us [...] And here, new elements in that style add to the existing and are reminiscent of the inherited and familiar, while in those Renaissance rooms one always has a feeling of being but a guest in one's own home. That such a view of Baroque and Rococo forms is not just a personal opinion, but has gradually also gained ground with

Auffassung der Barock- und Rococo-Formen nicht etwa persönliche Meinung ist, sondern dass sie sich allmälig auch bei Fabrikanten Bahn gebrochen hat, die früher in puristischer Richtung führend waren, beweist die große und glänzende Ausstellung Ludwig Lobmeyr's. Alle die vielseitigen neuen Decorations-Methoden sind, mit Ausnahme der orientalisirenden, durchgehends von Mustern des 18. Jahrhunderts angeregt."[29]

Durch die wissenschaftliche Tätigkeit des Museums wurde die Wahl des jeweiligen historischen Stils auch begründet. Ziel war im Wesentlichen aber die Schöpfung eines eigenen zeitgemäßen Stiles durch Orientierung an entsprechenden Vorbildern. Jakob von Falke bringt es anlässlich einer Ausstellung Lobmeyrs im Museum auf den Punkt: „Freilich ist Alles, selbst was als die freieste Composition erscheint, mit einer gewissen Anlehnung an Vorhandenes geschaffen, und wer in diesen Dingen versirt ist, wird fast ausnahmslos ein Motiv entdecken, das wenigstens die Idee gegeben hat. Somit entbehren diese Schöpfungen jener vollen Originalität, welche die Werke griechischen oder gothischen Styles besitzen. Aber da eben eine gleiche Originalität heute nicht existirt, […] so war und ist der Weg, der hier von Lobmeyr mit eben so viel Einsicht wie Muth und Energie betreten worden, der einzig mögliche, der einzig richtige."[30] Über die aufwendigen Kristallgefäße Lobmeyrs meinte Falke schon 1875, dass sie als Luxusgeräte später einmal als Antiquitäten betrachtet würden, aber zur Zeit der Produktion „leiden sie nur an einem Fehler, der sonst in der Industrie als Vorzug gilt, an dem, neu zu sein"[31].

Lobmeyr konnte aus den reichen Beständen des Museums schöpfen: Als Vorbilder dienten ihm bzw. den für ihn entwerfenden Künstlern Objekte aus verschiedenen Materialien in den Sammlungen und die Vorbildersammlung in der Bibliothek. „Wie sehr mir außerdem dabei die Sammlungen des österr. Museums zugute kamen, kann ich nicht genug betonen. Die vorhande-

manufacturers shown in the great and brilliant exhibition of Ludwig Lobmeyr. Apart from those in oriental style, all the various different decorative methods have been inspired by 18th century designs."[29]

The research work done at the museum provided the basis for the choice of a historical style. The main objective, however, was the creation of an independent contemporary style by learning from historical models. Jakob von Falke brings it to the point on the occasion of a Lobmeyr exhibition shown at the museum: "Of course, everything here, even if it appears as the freest composition, was created with a view to suitable models, and who is well-versed in these things will almost always detect a motif which at least inspired the idea. Thus these creations lack that full originality which the works of Greek or Gothic making have. But as a same originality does not exist today, […] so the path pursued by Lobmeyr with as much insight as courage and energy was, and is, the only possible, the only right one."[30] In 1875 already, Falke said about Lobmeyr's lavish crystal objects that, as luxury pieces, they would one day be valued as antiques, but at the time of their making "they only have one deficiency, otherwise considered an asset in industry, namely, being new."[31]

Lobmeyr could draw on the rich holdings of the museum. He, or the artists designing for him, took objects from different materials in the collections and the model collection in the museum library as models for their own work. "I cannot emphasize enough how much I benefited from the collections of the Austrian Museum. The objects available there offered me much inspiration, and when I then came to the director, Hofrat Eitelberger, and asked him to lend me this or that model for a series of vessels I had to make, he not infrequently said: Well, we've got something much better here! Walked right to the library with me and – an

nen Gegenstände selbst boten mir viele Anregung und wenn ich dann zum Direktor, Hofrath Eitelberger kam und ihn bat, mir für eine Serie von Gefäßen welche auszuführen ich vorhatte, diese oder jene Vorlage zu leihen, sagte er nicht selten: Ei, da haben wir ja viel Geeigneteres! Ging gleich selbst mit in die Bibliothek und ließ mir, was ihm bei seinem außerordentlichen Gedächtnisse ein Leichtes war, eine Anzahl Blätter und Werke zeigen, unter denen ich frei wählen konnte, wobei er mir stets zur Seite blieb. Waren darunter Blätter, welche nur schwer wieder zu beschaffen gewesen wären oder gar Unika, so gerieth der Bibliothekar Dr. Schestag wohl in nicht geringe Aufregung, aber der Hofrath sagte, die Sammlungen seien in erster Linie da, das Kunstgewerbe zu entwickeln, nicht aber ängstlich den eigenen […] Bestand zu bewahren, und so konnte ich für auch die werthvollsten Vorlagen oder die heikelsten Gegenstände Wochen entnehmen. Es ist wohl selbstverständlich, dass ich sie den Arbeitern sorgfältig bis auf die Stelle, welche sie zu benützen hatten, mit fester Umhüllung oder selbst nur unter Glas und mit besonders sicherer Verpackung zusandte, so dass auch Alles unversehrt wieder zurückkam […]."[32]

Neben den anfangs verwendeten Objekten aus der Wiener Schatzkammer und böhmischen Glasgefäßen wurden im Laufe der Zeit je nach Stil auch Vorlagen in anderen Materialien gebraucht: so zum Beispiel das französische Sèvres-Porzellan[33], die französischen Henri-deux-Keramiken des 16. Jahrhunderts oder orientalische Keramiken und Metallarbeiten. Dekore und Formen wurden oft unabhängig voneinander übernommen.

Für figurale Darstellungen, graviert auf farblosem Kristallglas, wurden Malereien, zum Teil auch Deckenfresken, herangezogen[34], französische Malerei von der Renaissance bis zum Barock wurde in Emailmalerei umgesetzt, der Belvedere-Stuck in Gold auf farbigem Glas, für Miniaturenmalerei wurden große Pokale verwendet[35] etc.

easy thing for him with his extraordinary memory – had a number of drawings or works shown to me from which I could freely choose while he stayed by my side all the time. If this included drawings that would have been difficult to get again, or even unique specimens, the librarian, Dr. Schestag, was in no little excitement, but the Hofrat said that the collections were here in the first place to help develop the arts and crafts, and not to fearfully watch over one's own […] holdings, and so I was allowed to take out for weeks even the most valuable models or most delicate objects. It goes without saying that I forwarded them to the workers in solid wrapping, apart from the areas they had to use, or even under glass and in particularly safe packaging so that everything returned undamaged […]."[32]

Depending on the style, models in other materials were also drawn upon over time, apart from objects from the Vienna Treasury and Bohemian glassware, thus, for example, French Sèvres porcelain[33], French Henri deux ceramics from the 16th century, or oriental ceramics and metalwork. Ornaments and shapes were frequently taken over separately.

Paintings, sometimes also ceiling frescos, were used for figurative representations engraved on colorless crystal glass,[34] French paintings from the Renaissance to the Baroque were re-created in enamel painting, stucco from Belvedere Palace provided the model for gildings on stained glass; large goblets were used for miniature paintings[35], etc.

The varied use of models particularly shows in Lobmeyr's oriental-style glassware. The participation of oriental countries in the World's Fairs rekindled the European interest in the Orient. Ludwig Lobmeyr was presumably inspired by the oriental glass objects by French artist Joseph Brocard who had first presented copies of oriental glass utensils, mostly mosque lamps, bottle-like vessels or bowls, made in the lush technique

Die Vielfalt in der Verwendung von Vorbildern zeigt sich besonders gut an den orientalisierenden Gläsern Lobmeyrs. Durch die Teilnahme der orientalischen Länder an den Weltausstellungen wurde das Interesse für den Orient in Europa neu geweckt. Wahrscheinlich wurde Ludwig Lobmeyr von den orientalischen Glasobjekten des französischen Künstlers Brocard angeregt. Dieser hatte erstmals auf der Weltausstellung 1867 Kopien von orientalischen Glasgeräten, meist Moscheeampeln, flaschenartigen Gefäßen oder Schalen, in der aufwendigen Technik der Emailmalerei präsentiert. Lobmeyr blieb nicht beim Kopieren der wenigen erhaltenen orientalischen Gläser, sondern transformierte die orientalischen Formen, Dekore und Techniken in verschiedenen Materialien zu eigenständigen Serien. Dazu dienten ihm Objekte ebenso wie Ornamentstiche als Anregung. Ab 1869 erschien mit „L'ornement polychrome" von A. Racinet[36] ein Standardwerk zur Ornamentik, in das auch indische, persische, maurische und andere orientalische Dekore aufgenommen wurden. 1870–1877 gab der Franzose Prisse d'Avennes ein Werk über die arabische Kunst in Kairo heraus[37]; 1873 erschien ein umfassendes Werk über die orientalischen Keramiken des Londoner Kunstgewerbemuseums[38]. Zusätzlich wurden orientalische Objekte in verschiedensten Zeitschriften gezeigt, auf Ausstellungen präsentiert und auch vom ÖMKI angekauft.

Die ersten orientalisierenden Gefäße Lobmeyrs entstanden schon 1870: ein „Glasservice für Wasser, in indischem Stile"[39]. Auf der Eröffnungsausstellung des neuen Museumsgebäudes präsentierte Lobmeyr erstmals einen Spiegel im orientalischen Stil nach dem Entwurf von Prof. Josef Storck (1830–1902). 1872 folgten das Dessert-Service Nr. 30 „von dunkelgrünem Glase mit reicher Vergoldung in indischem Style" (Werkzeichnungen, Bd. V, S. 11–13) nach dem Entwurf von Josef Storck und „Vasen etc. aus weissem Beinglase mit persischer (flacher) Malerei" (Werkzeichnungen, Bd. XI, S. 30–33;

of enamel painting at the 1867 World's Fair. Lobmeyr did not content himself with copying of the few extant oriental glasses, but transformed the oriental shapes, designs, and techniques into independent series in different materials. He used objects and ornamental etchings as sources of inspiration. 1869, the first volume of "L'ornement polychrome" by A. Racinet[36] came out, a standard work on ornamentation which also included Indian, Persian, Moorish, and other oriental decorative designs. Between 1870 and 1877, the Frenchman Prisse d'Avennes edited a work about Arabian art in Cairo[37]; and in 1873, a comprehensive work on the oriental ceramics of the London arts-and-crafts museum was published.[38] In addition, oriental objects were featured in a number of journals and magazines, presented at exhibitions, and also purchased by the AMAI.

The earliest oriental-style vessels by Lobmeyr date back to 1870: a "glass service in Indian style."[39] At the opening exhibition of the new museum, Lobmeyr for the first time presented an oriental mirror to a design by Prof. Josef Storck (1830–1902). 1872, this was followed by the dessert service no. 30 "of dark green glass with rich decoration in Indian style" (Working Drawings, vol. V, pp. 11–13) to a design by Josef Storck and "Vases etc. of white bone glass with Persian (flat) painting" (Working Drawings, vol. XI, pp. 30–33) to a design by Prof. Valentin Teirich (1844–1876). At that time, the collection also included a "painted glass chandelier in oriental style"[40] with similar ornamentation by Teirich.

Both used ornaments from Racinet's collection; however, Teirich, did not only use Persian, but also Indian and Renaissance motifs. He explained this combination in terms of a vase: "The design and ornamentation of this vase use forms of the Renaissance, but gain the character of the oriental pieces through very vivid coloring."[41]

Furthermore, a wash bowl and pitcher set "with Moorish enamel painting", designed by Josef Salb, came

„Vasen etc. aus weissem Beinglase mit persischer (flacher) Malerei ornamentirt von Prof. Theirich. Blatt A", in: WZ, Bd. XI, S. 30
"Vases etc. of white bone glass with Persian (flat) painting, ornamented by Prof. Theirich. Sheet A", in: WD, vol. XI, p. 30

siehe Abb. S. 37) nach dem Entwurf von Prof. Valentin Teirich (1844–1876). Von Teirich gab es zu dieser Zeit auch schon einen „gemalte[n] Glasluster im orientalischen Style"[40] mit ähnlichen Ornamenten.

Beide benützten Ornamente, wie sie in Racinets Sammlung erfasst waren, Teirich verwendete allerdings nicht nur persische, sondern auch indische Ornamente und Renaissancemotive. Anhand einer Vase erklärte er diese Verbindung: „Die Zeichnung und Ornamentik dieser Vase bedient sich zwar der Formensprache der Renaissance, gewinnt jedoch durch eine sehr lebhafte Farbengebung ganz den Charakter der orientalischen Arbeiten."[41]

Weiters kamen 1872/73 nach einem Entwurf von Josef Salb eine Toilettegarnitur „mit maurischer Emailmalerei" und 1873 eine Serie „Vasen etc. mit orientalischen Emaildekorationen"[42] aus weißem Beinglas heraus, rubinrot überfangen, mit indischen Ornamenten in mehreren Farben.

Im Anschluss an die Weltausstellung wurde 1875 das Orientalische Museum in Wien unter der Leitung von Arthur von Scala eröffnet, um den Kontakt zwischen Österreich und dem Orient zu fördern.[43] Die 1886 in „Handelsmuseum" umbenannte Institution hatte den kulturellen und kommerziellen Austausch zum Ziel und baute auch eine eigene Sammlung auf. 1884 veranstaltete sie eine große „Orientalisch-Keramische Ausstellung" mit zahlreichen Objekten aus Privatsammlungen.

1876 fand im ÖMKI eine „historische Ausstellung des islamitischen Orientes, umfassend Darstellungen von Cultus- und Profanbauten", statt. In dieser wurden auch Zeichnungen, Originalornamentabdrücke und Fotos gezeigt, die unter anderem vom Architekten Franz Schmoranz (1845–1892) stammten. Schmoranz hatte zwischen 1868 und 1874 Sizilien, Ägypten, Palästina, Syrien, Kleinasien und Konstantinopel bereist und gemeinsam mit Johann Machytka die ägyptische Baugruppe

Vasen etc. aus weissem Beinglase mit persischer (flacher) Malerei ornamentirt von Prof. Theirich. Blatt A

out 1872/73, as well as, in 1873, a series of "vases etc. with oriental enamel decoration"[42] of white bone glass with ruby casing and Indian ornaments in several colors.

Following the World's Fair of 1875, the Oriental Museum was opened in Vienna under the direction of Arthur von Scala to promote contact between Austria and the Orient.[43] The institution, which was renamed into "Museum of Trade" in 1886, pursued the objective of cultural and commercial exchange and also built its own collection. 1884, it held a large "Oriental-Ceramic Exhibition" with numerous objects from private collections.

auf der Wiener Weltausstellung entworfen. Die beiden Architekten arbeiteten von Mitte der siebziger bis Mitte der achtziger Jahre gemeinsam an kunstgewerblichen und architektonischen Aufträgen.

Den Stellenwert, den der Orient auch im ÖMKI einnahm, dokumentiert das „Arabische Zimmer", das 1883 im ersten Stock des Museums eröffnet wurde.[44] Es war nach dem Entwurf von Franz Schmoranz und Johann Machytka einem arabischen Wohnraum nachempfunden. In diesem Zimmer mit Stuck-, Marmor- und Schnitzarbeiten, die von heimischen Kunsthandwerkern angefertigt wurden, waren auch mehrere orientalisierende Gläser von Lobmeyr ausgestellt.

Machytka und Schmoranz waren es auch, die für Lobmeyr in den Jahren 1876 bis 1878 eine beträchtliche Anzahl von Gefäßen „in arabischem Style" entwarfen. Die Formen, Ornamente und Inschriften des transparenten, meist gelben Glases mit Gold- und Emailmalerei gehen zum Teil auf konkrete Vorbilder zurück.

In der Folge entstanden noch einige Serien unter Mitarbeit verschiedener Künstler, etwa 1878 die persisch-rhodische Serie oder in den achtziger Jahren die indische und die spanisch-maurische Serie und eine weitere arabische Serie mit Ornamenten nach alten Mustern, allerdings mit transparenten Emailfarben. 1884 gab es eine türkische Serie „nach eigenen Zeichnungen".

In zwei Bänden der Werkzeichnungen ist eine große Zahl dieser Gläser aufgenommen, wobei die Begriffe „arabisch" und „orientalisch" sehr weit gefasst sind.

Bd. XV beinhaltet „Gefässe in arabischem Style" (siehe Kat.-Nr. 29), eine „Flasche aus grünlich weissem Glase mit Ornamenten und Jagdscenen in Schmelzemail und Gold. Arabisch XIII. Jahrhundert. Das Original in der k.k. Ambraser Sammlung" und „Gefässe in indischem Style" (siehe Kat.-Nr. 37).

1876, the AMAI showed a "Historical Exhibition of the Islamic Orient, comprising sacred and profane buildings," which also presented drawings, impressions of original ornaments, and photographs by, among others, the architect Franz Schmoranz (1845–1892). Schmoranz had travelled Sicily, Egypt, Palestine, Syria, Asia Minor, and Constantinople between 1868 and '74 and designed the Egyptian ensemble at the Vienna World's Fair. Between the mid-1870s and the mid-'80s, the two architects worked together on architectural and arts-and-crafts projects.

The significance that the Orient had in the AMAI is also evidenced in the "Arabian Room," which was opened on the first floor of the museum in 1883.[44] It was modeled, in a design by Franz Schmoranz and Johann Machytka, on an Arabic living room. In this room which was decorated with stucco, marble, and carving by domestic artisans, a number of oriental-style glasses by Lobmeyr were exhibited.

Machytka and Schmoranz had also designed a considerable number of vessels "in Arabian style" for Lobmeyr between 1876 and 1878. The forms, ornaments, and inscriptions of the transparent, mostly yellow glasses with gold and enamel painting go back to concrete models.

Subsequently, a number of other series were produced with the collaboration of different artists, as, for example, a Persian-Rhodian series in 1878 or, in the 1880s, the Indian and Spanish-Moorish series and another Arabian series with ornamentation after old designs, though in transparent enamel colors. In 1884, it was a Turkish series "after own drawings".

A large number of these glasses were included in two volumes of working drawings; the definitions of "Arabian" and "oriental" were very broadly used.

Vol. XV includes "vessels in Arabian style" (see cat. no. 29), a "bottle of greenish-tinted white glass with

Bd. XVI („Orientalische Gefässe") umfasst „Gefässe in persischem Style" (siehe Kat.-Nr. 31), die spanisch-maurische Serie (siehe Kat.-Nr. 30), die türkische Serie (siehe Kat.-Nr. 39), die „Serie im arabischen Styl aus Krystallglas mit transparenten Emailfarben u. eingravirten, vergoldeten Conturen" und die Alhambra-Serie (siehe Kat.-Nr. 43).

Interessant ist, dass Ludwig Lobmeyr über die Entstehung dieser orientalisierenden Gläser nichts in seiner Autobiografie schreibt, obwohl sie bis zum Anfang des 20. Jahrhunderts ein wichtiger Bereich seiner Glasproduktion waren. Parallel dazu wurden von Lobmeyr auch orientalische Glasgegenstände kopiert und bis zur Jahrhundertwende präsentiert. Noch auf der Pariser Weltausstellung 1900 wurden Gefäße nach altorientalischen Originalen gezeigt, deren Entwurf von Gustav Schmoranz, dem Bruder von Franz Schmoranz, stammte. Dieser war als Professor an der Prager Kunstgewerbeschule tätig und gab 1898 das Vorlagenwerk „Altorientalische Glas-Gefässe" heraus.

Kaum Einfluss auf Lobmeyr hatte die auf die Orientrezeption folgende Ostasienmode (China und Japan).

Künstler
Entwürfe für Lobmeyr

Ludwig Lobmeyr verfügte über die nötige künstlerische Begabung, um Entwürfe selbst anzufertigen. Doch nicht alle Entwurfszeichnungen, bei denen in den Werkzeichnungen „nach eigenen Zeichnungen" vermerkt ist, stammen von seiner Hand; viele sind sicherlich auch von seinen Zeichnern gemacht worden.

Ein innovativer Schritt Ludwig Lobmeyrs war zweifellos, dass er ab 1864 Künstler für Entwurfsarbeiten heranzog. So trat er zuerst mit dem dänischen Architekten Theophil von Hansen (1813–1891) in Kontakt, der nach einem mehrjährigen Aufenthalt in Griechenland seit

Becher, Kat.-Nr. 29c
Beaker, cat. no. 29c

ornamentation and hunting scenes fusible enamel and gold colors. Arabian 13th century. Original in the Imperial and Royal Collection at Ambras" and "vessels in Indian style" (see cat. no. 37).

Vol. XVI ("Oriental Vessels") comprises "vessels in Persian style" (see cat. no. 31), the Spanish-Moorish series (see cat. no. 30), the Turkish series (see cat. no. 39), the "Series in Arabian style of crystal glass with transparent enamel colors and engraved and gilded contouring," and the Alhambra series (see cat. no. 43).

It is interesting to note that Ludwig Lobmeyr does not say anything about the origins of these oriental style glasses in his autobiography, although they were an important segment of his glassware production until the early 20th century. Lobmeyr also copied and presented oriental glassware until about the turn of the century. Still at the Paris World's Fair of 1900, vessels after old-oriental models were exhibited which had been designed by Gustav Schmoranz, Franz Schmoranz's brother, who was a professor at the Prague Arts-and-Crafts School

1846 in Wien tätig war und zu einem der wichtigsten Architekten der Ringstraßenepoche wurde.

Hansen entwarf 1864 für Lobmeyr das Trink-Service Nr. 95 „mit griechischer Gravirung", wohl angeregt vom gravierten Kristallglas in England, wo die griechischen Motive und Formen für Glas propagiert wurden. Es entwickelte sich eine intensive Zusammenarbeit zwischen Lobmeyr und Hansen, über den Lobmeyr selbst meinte: „Er war die idealste Künstlernatur, welche ich je kennenlernte […]."[45] Hansen ließ sich für seine Arbeit meist nicht einmal entlohnen.[46]

Wie eng die Entwürfe des Künstlers und jene Lobmeyrs, in den Werkzeichnungen durch den Vermerk „nach eigenen Zeichnungen" ausgewiesen, zusammenhängen konnten, zeigt sich an den griechischen Servicen: Auf das Trink-Service Nr. 103, ein weiteres Service „mit griechischer Gravirung", nach einem Entwurf von

and in 1898 published a model book on "Old-Oriental Glass Vessels."

The East-Asian vogue (China and Japan) that followed the oriental reception hardly had an influence on Lobmeyr.

Artists
Designs for Lobmeyr

Ludwig Lobmeyr had the necessary artistic talent and produced designs by himself. But not all design drawings which are marked as being "after own drawings" in the working drawings are from his own hand; many of them were surely made by his draftsmen.

One innovative step taken by Lobmeyr doubtless was that he had designs done by artists after 1864. So he first got in contact with the Danish architect Theophil von

Links: „Trink-Service No. 103, Krystallglas Blatt A mit griechischer Gravirung. nach Zeichnung des Oberbaurathes R. v. Hansen 1866", in: WZ, Bd. II, S. 13
Left: „Drinking service no. 103, crystal glass sheet A with Greek engraving. After drawings by Oberbaurath R. v. Hansen 1866", in: WD, vol. II, p. 13

Rechts: Vase, Kat.-Nr. 30b
Right: Vase, cat. no. 30b

Gefäße für das Wiener Rathaus, Entwurf:
Friedrich von Schmidt, Ausführung:
J. & L. Lobmeyr, in: Gewerbehalle, 1874,
S. 122 (MAK, Inv.-Nr. K.I. 380)
Vessels for the Vienna City Hall, design: Friedrich
Schmidt, manufacturer: J. & L. Lobmeyr, in:
Gewerbehalle, 1874, p. 122 (MAK, inv. no. K.I. 380)

Hansen 1866 entstanden, folgte 1867 das Trink-Service
Nr. 108, „mit Mäander und Streifen gravirt nach eigenen Zeichnungen". Bis Mitte der siebziger Jahre entwarf Hansen zahlreiche Vasen, Tafelaufsätze sowie Trink-
und Dessert-Service mit griechischen Motiven bzw. „in
griechischem Style".[47] Noch 1872 entstanden die Trink-
Service „mit griechischer Gravirung in 3 Varianten"
(Nr. 143, 150, 157; siehe Abb. S. 33).

Ebenfalls in den sechziger Jahren begann eine fruchtba-
re Zusammenarbeit mit dem Maler August Eisenmenger
(1830–1907), einem der begabtesten Schüler des Aka-
demieprofessors Carl Rahl (1812–1865) und ab 1872
selbst Leiter einer Meisterklasse für Historienmalerei an
der Akademie der bildenden Künste in Wien. Theophil
von Hansen, der mit Rahl befreundet gewesen war, zog
nach Rahls Tod dessen Schüler für die malerische Ausstattung seiner Gebäude heran. Mit August Eisenmenger
arbeitete er außerdem bei seinen Entwürfen für Glas zusammen (siehe Kat.-Nr. 9, 15). So übernahm es Eisenmenger, in der Folge auch unabhängig von Theophil
von Hansen, bis in die neunziger Jahre, figurale Entwürfe
für Glasobjekte von Lobmeyr anzufertigen. Eisenmenger
orientierte sich dabei unter anderem an Entwürfen seines Lehrers Carl Rahl oder an antiken Vorlagen. Diese
konnten, mit Renaissanceornamenten kombiniert, in
farbloses Glas graviert werden oder auf farbigem Glas in
bunter Malerei aufgetragen werden. Es entstanden auch
Spiegel mit gemalten Figuren nach seinen Vorlagen.

Für die Weltausstellung in Paris 1867 sprach Lobmeyr
gezielt verschiedene Künstler an: „[…] wagte mich an
Hansen heran, der mich gleich liebenswürdig aufnahm
[…] Meine Ausstellung sollte eben vielseitig sein; ich
wendete mich also auch an Prof. Friedr. Schmidt, unseren ersten Gothiker, […] dann an den Architekten
J. Storck […] Verschiedenes und zwar nicht wenig, konnte ich ja selbst zeichnen, somit war Alles wohl vorge-
kehrt."[48]

Hansen (1813–1891) who, after a several-year stay in
Greece, had been working in Vienna since 1846 and was
to become one of the most important architects of
Ringstraße epoch in Vienna.

In 1864, Hansen designed the drinking service no. 95
"with Greek engraving" for Lobmeyr, presumably
inspired by engraved crystalware from England where
Greek forms and motifs were propagated. This lead to
an intense cooperation between Lobmeyr and Hansen,
about whom Lobmeyr once said: "He was the most
ideal natural artist I have ever met …"[45] In most cases,
Hansen even refused payment for his work.[46]

The close relationship between the designs by the artist
and those by Lobmeyr indicated in the working drawings as being "after own drawings" becomes evident in
the Greek services. The drinking service no. 103,
another service "with Greek engraving" made 1866 to a
design by Hansen, was followed in 1867 by the drinking
service no. 108 "engraved with meander and stripes,
after own drawings". Until the mid-1870s, Hansen
designed numerous vases, centerpieces, as well as drinking and dessert services with Greek motifs or "in Greek
style".[47] In 1872, a drinking service "after Greek
engravings in 3 variants" was produced (nos. 143, 150,
157; see ill. p. 33).

The 1860s also marked the beginning of a fruitful
cooperation with the painter August Eisenmenger
(1830–1907), one of the most talented pupils of the
academy professor Carl Rahl (1812–1865) and, from
1872, himself teacher of a master class of history painting at the Academy of Fine Arts in Vienna. After Rahl's
death, Theophil von Hansen, who had been a friend of
Rahl, hired his pupils for the painterly decoration of his
buildings. Moreover, he collaborated with Eisenmenger
for his glassware designs (see cat. nos. 9, 15). So Eisenmenger also took on figurative designs for Lobmeyr
glassware – later also independently of Hansen –, for

Hansen war für die allgemeine Anordnung der Ausstellung und den Entwurf der Tische verantwortlich. Weiters stammten die Glasentwürfe im griechischen Stil von Hansen und seinem Schüler Ernst Ziller. Für die Tafelaufsätze von Hansen, die als besondere Prunkstücke der Ausstellung galten, entwarf August Eisenmenger die Figuren. Die Objekte „in altdeutschem Style" bzw. im gotischen Stil (siehe Abb. S. 41) entwarfen der Architekt Friedrich von Schmidt, der an der Akademie unterrichtete und seit 1863 Dombaumeister von St. Stephan war, und sein Schüler August Rincklake. Spiegel „nach venezianischer Art" entstanden nach dem Entwurf des Architekten Prof. Josef Hieser. Die Leuchter im „Renaissance-Style" stammten von Josef Storck, der unter dem Architekten Eduard van der Nüll entscheidend an der Innenausstattung des Wiener Opernhauses mitarbeitete und Professor und Direktor an der Kunstgewerbeschule wurde.

Die Zusammenarbeit mit Künstlern wurde von Anfang an positiv und als wesentlicher Grund für den Erfolg Lobmeyrs gesehen: „Der Industrielle hat Künstler ersten Ranges herbeigerufen, und so wird denn sein Produkt zum echten Kunstwerk. Gesegnet ein solches Bündnis! Der wahre Künstler kennt und ehrt ein höheres Gesetz, als die Mode […]."[49] „Wohl wissend, dass die gewöhnlichen künstlerischen Kräfte, welche den Glasfabriken zu Gebote stehen, nicht ausreichen, hat er sich an die ersten der Wiener Architekten gewendet, von denen man wusste, dass sie mit Vergnügen für die Kleinkunst arbeiten und auch im Stande sind es zu thun."[50]

Ab Anfang der siebziger Jahre wurden vermehrt Lehrer der Kunstgewerbeschule herangezogen. Josef Storck, nun Professor der Fachschule für Architektur, entwarf weiterhin Leuchter, außerdem Spiegel und verschiedenste Glasgefäße. So war er auch am „Kaiser-Service" (siehe Kat.-Nr. 6) anlässlich der Eröffnung des Museumsgebäudes beteiligt. Von Storck und dem Architekten Teirich, der

which he followed designs by his teacher Carl Rahl or antique models. These wer sometimes combined with Renaissance elements, engraved in colorless glass or applied to stained glass as colorful painting. There were also mirrors produced with painted figures after his designs.

Lobmeyr deliberately sought contact with artists for the 1867 Paris World's Fair: "[…] approached Hansen, who kindly received me […] My exhibition was to be variegated; so I also turned to Prof. Friedr. Schmidt, our foremost Gothic man, […] and then to architect J. Storck […] There were various things which I could draw myself, actually quite a few, and so everything was well provided for."[48]

Hansen was responsible for the general exhibition layout and for the design of the tables. The glass designs in Greek style also came from Hansen and his pupil Ernst Ziller. The figures for Hansen's centerpieces, which were considered to be special highlights of the presentation, were designed by August Eisenmenger. Objects in "old-German style", or in Gothic style (see ill. p. 41), were designed by architect Friedrich Schmidt, who taught at the Academy and, since 1863, had been Cathedral Architect of St. Stephen's, and his pupil August Rincklake. Mirrors "in Venetian manner" were made to designs by architect Prof. Josef Hieser. The chandeliers in "Renaissance style" were designed by Josef Storck, who, under architect Eduard van der Nüll, significantly contributed to the interior decoration of Vienna Opera House and later become professor and director of the Industrial Arts School.

From the beginning, the collaboration with artists was considered one main reason for Lobmeyr's success: "The industrialist has called in first-rate artists, and so his product becomes a genuine work of art. Blessed be this alliance! The true artist knows and honors a higher law than fashion […]."[49] "Well aware that usual artistic

Schale mit Fuß, Kat.-Nr. 46c
Fotted Bowl ("Decorative Bowl"), cat. no. 46c

Vase, Kat.-Nr. 37b
Vase, cat. no. 37b

ab 1868 als Lehrer an der Kunstgewerbeschule tätig war, stammten neben renaissanceartigen Entwürfen auch die ersten Entwürfe im orientalischen bzw. indischen Stil.

Die Maler Ferdinand Laufberger (1829–1881) und Friedrich Sturm (1822–1898), beide Professoren in der Fachschule für Malerei, entwarfen neben Eisenmenger in den siebziger Jahren die figürlichen Darstellungen.

Immer wieder wurden für ein Objekt mehrere Künstler herangezogen, so bei gravierten Schalen um 1875 (siehe Kat.-Nr. 18), für die Josef Storck den ornamentalen Dekor entwarf, August Kühne (1845–1895), ehemaliger Schüler und ab 1877 Lehrer an der Kunstgewerbeschule, die Figuren im Zentrum.

Einige Künstler spezialisierten sich auf einen bestimmten Stil, wie Schmoranz und Machytka auf die orientalisierenden Dekore (siehe S. 37).

Ende der siebziger Jahre entstand wieder Kontakt zu neuen Künstlern: So wurden nun Entwürfe im Stil der Renaissance von Hermann Herdtle (1848–1926) umgesetzt, der seit 1876 eine Fachschule für Architektur leitete.

Vielseitig präsentierte sich ein ehemaliger Schüler (1875–1880) und Mitarbeiter im Atelier Herdtles, Moritz Knab, der in den achtziger Jahren eine indische Serie (siehe Kat.-Nr. 37), eine Serie mit rokokoartigem Dekor (siehe Kat.-Nr. 46), ein gotisches Trink-Service und renaissanceartigen Dekor für gravierte Gefäße in Zusammenarbeit mit August Eisenmenger und die Alhambra-Serie (siehe Kat.-Nr. 43) gemeinsam mit Franz Schmoranz entwarf. Knab war 1882 bis 1886 bei Lobmeyr als Zeichner angestellt und wurde später Direktor der Fachschulen in Nixdorf (Mikulášovice) und Gablonz (Jablonec).

Der Architekt Josef Salb (1845–1904) war von der Wiener Weltausstellung 1873 an als Entwerfer für Lobmeyr tätig, obwohl er ab 1876 als Professor an der Staatsgewerbeschule in Salzburg unterrichtete. Er lieferte bis in

talent available to the glass factories was not enough, he turned to the first of Viennese architects who were known to work with pleasure in craftwork and to have the capability for it."[50]

From the early 1870s, an increasing number of teachers of the Industrial Arts School were called in. Josef Storck, now professor at the School of Architecture, continued to design chandeliers as well as mirrors and different glass vessels. Thus he also contributed to the "Imperial Service" (see cat. no. 6) made on the occasion of the museum's opening. Storck and the architect Teirich also made the first designs in oriental and Indian style, aside from those echoing the Renaissance period. Aside from Eisenmenger, the painters Ferdinand Laufberger (1829–1881) and Friedrich Sturm (1822–1898), both of them professors at the School of Painting, also did designs for figurative representations in the 1870s.

Recurrently, several artists were engaged for one object, as for the engraved bowls around 1875 (see cat. no. 18), for which Josef Storck designed the ornamental decoration and August Kühne (1845–1895), a former pupil of the Industrial Arts School and, from 1877, a teacher at the institution, the figurines in the center.

Some artists specialized on a specific style, such as Schmoranz and Machytka on oriental-style decorations (see p. 37).

In the late 1870s, contacts with new artists were made. Designs in the style of the Renaissance were now made by Hermann Herdtle (1848–1926), since 1876 principal of a School of Architecture.

A highly versatile designer was Moritz Knab, a former pupil (1875–1880) and collaborator of Herdtle in his studio, who did the design for a series with Rococo-style decoration (see cat. no. 46), for a Gothic drinking services and Renaissance-style decorations for engraved vessels together with August Eisenmenger and, together with Franz Schmoranz, for the Alhambra series (see cat.

die achtziger Jahre sehr verschiedenartige Entwürfe: orientalische und indische ebenso wie Entwürfe im Renaissance- und Rokokostil (siehe Kat.-Nr. 32, 40). Er war auch für gläserne Huldigungsgeschenke an Kronprinz Rudolf anlässlich seiner Vermählung mit Prinzessin Stephanie 1881 verantwortlich.

In den neunziger Jahren wurden Künstler bei Entwürfen kaum mehr genannt, nur August Eisenmenger scheint bis gegen 1900 mit Zeichnungen für gravierte Glasteller auf.

Der „Regenerator"
Die Bedeutung Ludwig Lobmeyrs

Ludwig Lobmeyr war zweifellos die entscheidende Kraft bei der Reform der böhmischen Glasindustrie in der zweiten Hälfte des 19. Jahrhunderts. Der deutsche Kunstschriftsteller Friedrich Pecht meinte 1876 über ihn: „Er vertritt die große böhmische Industrie dieser Art fast ganz allein und mit um so mehr Recht, als er unzweifelhaft deren Regenerator ist, welcher sie aus totaler Versunkenheit wieder emporhob und zu Leistungen brachte, die durchaus originell, denen keiner Zeit und keines Landes nachstehen, den meisten überlegen sind. [...] Die eigenthümlichste Vereinigung des edelsten Idealismus mit größter Aufopferung für die Sache, mit der feinsten Menschenkenntnis und persönlicher Anspruchslosigkeit machen diesen seltenen Charakter unstreitig zu einem wahren Muster eines Unternehmers und Reformators. Um so mehr, als seine ganze Produktion durchaus auf seinem eigenen feinen Geschmack, seinem bedeutenden dekorativen Talent beruht."[51]

Als außergewöhnlich wurde auch die Vielfalt seiner Produktion gesehen: „Als besonders charakteristisch sei aber schließlich hervorgehoben, [...] wie Lobmeyr's industrielle Production, ungeachtet ihrer großartigen künstlerischen Entfaltung, doch in dem festen Boden des practischen Bedarfes wurzelt und für diesen neben den

no. 43). Knab was employed by Lobmeyr as a draftsman from 1882 to 1886 and later became director of the vocational schools of Nixdorf (Mikulášovice) and Gablonz (Jablonec nad Nisou).

The architect Josef Salb (1845–1904) worked as a designer for Lobmeyr after the 1873 Vienna World's Fair, although, from 1876, he held a professorship at State Crafts School in Salzburg. Until into the 1880s, he supplied a large variety of designs: oriental and Indian as well as Renaissance- and Rococo-style (see cat. nos. 32, 40). He was also responsible for the design of the tributary glassware gifts made to Austrian Crown Prince Rudolf on the occasion of his wedding with Princess Stephanie in 1881.

In the 1890s, design drawings rarely indicated the artists, with the exception of August Eisenmenger, who appears as designer of engraved glass plates until about 1900.

The "Regenerator"
The Significance of Ludwig Lobmeyr

Ludwig Lobmeyr doubtless was the decisive force in the reform of the Bohemian glass industry in the second half of the 19th century. In 1876, the German art critic wrote about him: "He represents the large Bohemian industry of this kind almost alone, and all the more rightly so, since he indubitably is its regenerator who lifted it from total depression and lead it to achievements which are all-out original, second to no time, nor country, superior to most. [...] The most idiosyncratic coalescence of the noblest idealism and utmost self-sacrifice for the cause, of the most intricate knowledge of human nature and personal unassumingness indisputably make this rare character a true paragon of an entrepreneur and reformer. All the more so, since his entire production is based on his own discriminating taste and his considerable decorative talent."[51]

Pokal mit Deckel, Kat.-Nr. 19a
Lidded Goblet, cat. no. 19a

reichsten und luxuriösesten Objecten auch die Gegenstände des gewöhnlichen Gebrauches liefert. Es beweisen dies die ausgestellten Trink-Services von der einfachsten Form und ohne die mindeste Verzierung, an denen sich aber trotzdem ein feiner Geschmack und eine disdinguirte Originalität in wohlthuender Weise bemerkbar machen. Es ist dies ein vollgiltiger Beweis der außerordentlichen Entwicklung, die ein Zweig der Kunst-Industrie durch die Thatkraft und Genialität eines einzelnen Mannes gewinnen kann."[52]

Jakob von Falke schrieb in seinen Lebenserinnerungen über Ludwig Lobmeyr: „Wenn Lobmeyr heute, vom künstlerischen Standpunkt aus betrachtet, als der erste Glasindustrielle der Welt dasteht, dem weder England, am wenigsten Frankreich einen gleichen an die Seite setzen könnte, so wird er selber gewiß nicht in Abrede stellen, wie viel er dem Museum und wie viel er, vielleicht noch in höherem Grade dem persönlichen und freundschaftlicheren Verkehre mit uns verdankt […] Und an diesen hunderten erlesener Gegenstände haben das Museum durch seine Vorbilder, Künstler und Kunstgelehrte durch ihre Kritik gewissermaßen mit gearbeitet. Ohne sie wäre es wohl nicht zu solcher Vollkommenheit gekommen, aber eben so wenig ohne die Intelligenz, den Geschmack, das Verständnis und das entschlossene, zu Opfern bereite Vorgehen Ludwig Lobmeyrs."[53]

Auch Ludwig Lobmeyr selbst sah seinen Erfolg in Zusammenhang mit dem ÖMKI und den Künstlern, aber ergänzte sehr selbstbewusst: „Dabei aber ward ich nicht nur deren aufmerksamer und gelehriger Schüler, sondern blieb – ich kann es ohne zu weitgehendes Selbstbewusstsein sagen – im Ganzen doch stets der Leiter, dem es gegeben war, die künstlerischen Kräfte für seine Zwecke zu verwerten, die Rathschläge der Kunstgelehrten zu benützen, meinen Schwager Kralik, den Fabrikanten, der die meisten meiner Schöpfungen auszuführen hatte, und andere Mitarbeiter in freudigem Eifer

The variety of his production was also considered to be exceptional: "A special characteristic to be emphasized here, [is] how Lobmeyr's industrial production, notwithstanding its magnificent artistic variegation, is rooted in the solid ground of practical need and, aside from the richest and most luxurious objects, also provides objects of common use. This becomes evident in the exhibited drinking services of the simplest form and without any decoration, in which nevertheless fine taste and distinguished originality become pleasantly apparent. This gives valid proof of the extraordinary development that one branch of the art industry can take through the energy and genius of a single man."[52]

In his memoirs, Jakob von Falke wrote about Lobmeyr: "If Lobmeyr today, from an artistic view, stands as the world's foremost glass industrialist unequalled by anybody that England, let alone France, could muster, he himself would surely not deny how much he owes to the museum and, perhaps even to a greater extent, to the personal contact and friendship with us […] And to these hundreds of exquisite objects, the museum has, in a way, contributed with its models, as have artists and art scholars with their criticism. Without them, such perfection would probably not have been attained, as it would not without the intelligence, taste, understanding, and determined self-sacrificing course that Lobmeyr took."[53]

Ludwig Lobmeyr himself saw his success as related to the AMAI and the artists, too, though he was self-confident enough to add: "In all this, I was not only their attentive and receptive pupil, but – as I can say without taking self-assurance too far – on the whole always remained the leader who was able to harness the artistic talent for his purposes, to make good use of the advice of art scholars, to keep up the spirited zeal in my brother-in-law Kralik, the manufacturer who had to execute most of my creations and other collaborators to put

zu erhalten, ihr bestes Können an die Arbeit zu setzen […] Dazu gehörte aber ferner auch der Kaufmann, die gute Leitung des Geschäftes, ein verbindlicher Verkehr mit der Kundschaft, Takt und Feingefühl nach allen Seiten."[54]

Auch bei einer Ausstellung im Museum 1896 wurde noch einmal betont, „welche Stütze das Museum in dieser Firma besitzt. Geschmack und Mode mag wechseln, auch Solidität der Techniken und der künstlerischen Ueberzeugungen da und dort in's Wanken kommen, Lobmeyr's Arbeiten werden dadurch nicht berührt; ihr künstlerischer Charakter in Formen und Decor, die Vollendung in der technischen Behandlung und Verwerthung des Materials bleibt sich stets gleich und erscheint doch in immer neuer Weise. Sich selbst und seiner künstlerischen Ueberzeugung treu zu bleiben, ist heute schwieriger denn je […]."[55]

Lobmeyr blieb dem Museum bis über die Jahrhundertwende hinaus verbunden. Seine Objekte waren auch auf den 1897 eingeführten „Winterausstellungen" vertreten und im Säulenhof war ständig eine Vitrine mit seinen Glasobjekten ausgestellt. Gegen Ende des 19. Jahrhunderts trat die Firma Lobmeyr allerdings in eine Phase ohne wesentliche Neuerungen ein. Erst als der Neffe Ludwig Lobmeyrs, Stefan Rath (1876−1960), 1902 Teilhaber der Firma J. & L. Lobmeyr wurde, kam es neben der Fortführung der traditionellen Formen und Dekore zu stilistischen Neuerungen.

their best skills into the work […] This furthermore included the commercialist, good business management, obligingness in customer relations, tact and sensibility on all sides."[54]

On the occasion of an exhibition in 1896, it was once more emphasized "how much of a pillar the museum has in this company. Taste and fashions may change, as the soundness of techniques and artistic convictions may begin to totter here and there. Lobmeyr's works, though, remain unaffected by all this, their artistic character in form and decoration, the perfection of technical treatment and use of material always remains the same and yet always appears new. Staying true to oneself on one's artistic conviction today is more difficult than ever […]."[55]

Lobmeyr remained affiliated with the museum beyond the turn of the century. His objects were regularly shown in the "Winter Exhibitions" which were introduced in 1897, and a showcase filled with his glass objects was on permanent display in the museum's Columned Hall. Toward the end of the 19th century, the Lobmeyr Company entered into a phase without substantial innovations. It was only after Ludwig Lobmeyr's nephew Stefan Rath (1876−1960) had become a partner in the company of J. & L. Lobmeyr that, aside from the continuation of traditional forms and decorations, a new impulse for stylistic innovation was given.

„Blumen Serie aus Krystallglas mit Gold und durchsichtigem Email, die Schlangen in opakem Email gemalt. Blatt A. 1888", in: WZ, Bd. XVII, S. 35

"Flower series of crystal glass with gold and transparent enamel, snakes painted in opaque enamel. Sheet A. 1888", in: WD, vol. XVII, p. 35

Blumen Serie aus Krystallglas mit Gold und durchsichtigem Email, die Schlangen in opakem Email gemalt. Blatt A. 1888.

1 Das erste erhaltene Geschäftsbuch beginnt im Februar 1823.
2 Josef Lobmeyr bezog am Anfang seine Waren von Blechinger in Böhmen, der gräfl. Bouquoy'schen Fabrik Silberberg, Pohl in Neuwalt sowie Meyr in Adolf und Eleonorenhain (Waltraud Neuwirth: Schöner als Bergkristall. Ludwig Lobmeyr. Glas Legende, Wien 1999, S. 164).
3 Bericht über die zweite allgemeine österreichische Gewerbs-Produkten-Ausstellung im Jahre 1839, Wien 1840, S. 37; zum Beispiel besuchte er um 1840 die Glasfabrik St. Louis in Frankreich, wo Pressglas hergestellt wurde.
4 Nach Tascheks Tod 1862 als „Meyr's Neffe".
5 In vielen zeitgenössischen Katalogen wurde die Firma weiterhin als „Meyr's Neffen" bezeichnet.
6 Österreichischer Bericht über die internationale Ausstellung in London 1862, herausgegeben unter der Leitung von Prof. Dr. Joseph Arenstein, Wien 1863, S. 661. Die 20 österreichischen Aussteller von Hohlglaswaren setzten sich zusammen aus sieben Glasfabrikanten, zwölf Glasraffineuren und einem Glasschneider.
7 Ebd., S. 658.
8 Illustrirter Katalog der Londoner Industrie-Ausstellung von 1862, Leipzig 1863, S. 161 f.
9 Neuwirth, wie Anm. 2, S. 345.
10 Ulrike Scholda: „Man suchte die Kunstgewerbetreibenden heranzuziehen, ich sank von selber hin ...". Ludwig Lobmeyr und das k. k. Österreichische Museum für Kunst und Industrie, in: Kunst und Industrie. Die Anfänge des Museums für angewandte Kunst in Wien, Ostfildern-Ruit 2000, S. 193–202.
11 Neuwirth, wie Anm. 2, S. 289.
12 Neuwirth, wie Anm. 2, S. 292.

1 The first extant account book starts in February 1823.
2 Josef Lobmeyr first purchased his glassware from Blechinger in Bohemia, from the glassworks of Count Bouquoy in Silberberg, from Pohl in Neuwalt as well as Meyr in Adolf and Eleonorenhain (Waltraud Neuwirth: Schöner als Bergkristall. Ludwig Lobmeyr. Glas Legende, Vienna 1999, p. 164).
3 Bericht über die zweite allgemeine österreichische Gewerbs-Produkten-Ausstellung im Jahre 1839, Vienna 1840, p. 37; so, e. g., he visited the glassworks at St. Louis in France, where pressed glass was made.
4 After Taschek's death in 1862 as "Meyr's Neffe" ["Meyr's Nephew"].
5 In many contemporary catalogues the company is still referred to as "Meyr's Neffen" ["Meyr's Nephews"].
6 Österreichischer Bericht über die internationale Ausstellung in London 1862, herausgegeben unter der Leitung von Prof. Dr. Joseph Arenstein, Vienna 1863, p. 661. The 20 Austrian exhibitors of hollow glassware included seven glass manufacturers, twelve glass refiners, and one glass cutter.
7 ibid., p. 658.
8 Illustrated Catalogue of the London Industry-Exposition of 1862, Leipzig 1863, p. 161 f.
9 Neuwirth, same as n. 2, p. 345.
10 Ulrike Scholda: "Man suchte die Kunstgewerbetreibenden heranzuziehen, ich sank von selber hin …". Ludwig Lobmeyr und das k. k. Österreichische Museum für Kunst und Industrie, in: Kunst und Industrie. Die Anfänge des Museums für angewandte Kunst in Wien, Ostfildern-Ruit 2000, pp. 193–202.
11 Neuwirth, same as n. 2, p. 289.

13 Jakob (auch Jacob) Falke (1825–1897), Erster Kustos und stellvertretender Direktor des ÖMKI, davor Bibliothekar des Fürsten Liechtenstein. 1873 in den Adelsstand erhoben.

14 Officieller Ausstellungs-Bericht, herausgegeben durch die General-
Direction der Weltausstellung 1873, Wien 1875. Falke verfasste den
Text über das venezianische, das englische und das böhmische Glas.

15 MAK-Archiv, 73/1883.

16 Jakob Falke: Das Glas auf der Pariser Weltausstellung, in: Mittheilungen
des k. k. österr. Museums für Kunst und Industrie, Bd. 2, Nr. 27,
15. Dez. 1867, S. 50 f.

17 Jacob Falke: Die Kunstindustrie der Gegenwart. Studien auf der Pariser
Weltausstellung im Jahre 1867, Leipzig 1868, S. 159.

18 Ebd., S. 161.

19 Falke, wie Anm. 16, S. 51 f.

20 Falke, wie Anm. 17, S. 155, 158 f.

21 Jacob Falke: Die künstlerisch-ästhetische Seite der auf der Ausstellung
vertretenen Industrie-Produkte, in: Bericht über die Welt-Ausstellung
zu Paris im Jahre 1867, herausgegeben durch das K. K. Österreichische
Central-Comité, Wien 1869, Bd. 1, Teil II, S. 109.

22 Friedrich Pecht: Kunst und Kunstindustrie auf der Weltausstellung von
1867, Leipzig 1867, S. 276 f.

23 Falke, wie Anm. 17, S. 157 (Falke zitiert aus einem Artikel des französischen Kunstkritikers und Kunstarchäologen Ferdinand de Lasteyrie
in „L'Opinion nationale".

24 Ludwig Lobmeyr, Albert Ilg, Wendelin Boeheim (Hrsg.): Die Glasindustrie, ihre Geschichte, gegenwärtige Entwicklung und Statistik,
Stuttgart 1874, S. 189.

25 Raimund Gerner: Die Glasfabrikation, Wien 1880, S. 297.

26 Ebd., S. 301.

27 Jacob Falke: Die Kunstindustrie auf der Wiener Weltausstellung 1873,
Wien 1873, S. 226 f.

28 Jacob Falke: Die Weihnachts-Ausstellung des Oesterr. Museums, in:
Mittheilungen des k. k. Oesterreich. Museums für Kunst und Industrie,
Bd. 6, Nr. 124, 1. Jan. 1876, S. 12.

29 Fr. Wickhoff: Die Weihnachtsausstellung im Oesterreichischen Museum,
in: Mittheilungen des k. k. Oesterreich. Museums für Kunst und
Industrie, Bd. 10, Nr. 220, 1. Jan. 1884, S. 7 ff.

30 Jakob von Falke: Glasausstellung im österreichischen Museum II., in:
Beilage zur Wiener Abendpost, Nr. 102, 3. Mai 1879, S. 1.

31 Falke, wie Anm. 28.

32 Neuwirth, wie Anm. 2, S. 289.

33 Leuchter, die das Porzellan imitierten, wurden von Lobmeyr schon
1862 in London ausgestellt; Gefäße nach den Bleu-du-Roi-Porzellanen
wurden 1871/72 auf der Ausstellung anlässlich der Eröffnung des
Museumsbaus gezeigt.

34 Außerdem wurden für einen Deckelpokal mit Teller (Gesamtentwurf
und Ornamente von Moritz Knab) zur Silberhochzeit von Mathilde
– Schwester Ludwig Lobmeyrs – und August Rath im Jahr 1889
Figuren in Umzeichnung von August Eisenmenger nach den Putti
des Wiener Opernhauses von C. Rahl in Glasschnitt umgesetzt
(siehe auch Kat.-Nr. 15).

35 So wurden für die „Minnesängerserie aus grünem Glas mit Emailmalerei nach Entwürfen von Dr. Rich. V. Kralik 1888" die Miniaturen
der Manesse'schen Liederhandschrift in der Pariser Nationalbibliothek
herangezogen, die 1887 von F. X. Kraus in Lichtdruck publiziert
worden waren. Richard Kralik war ein Neffe Ludwig Lobmeyrs.

36 A. Racinet: L'ornement polychrome. Cent planches en couleurs or et
argent, contenant environ 2000 motifs de tous les styles, art ancien et
asiatique, moyen-âge, renaissance, XVIIe et XVIIIe siècle. Livraison
I–X, Paris 1869–1872.

12 Neuwirth, same as n. 2, p. 292.

13 Jakob (Jacob) Falke (1825–1897), First Curator and Deputy Director
of AMAI, previously librarian of the Prince of Liechtenstein. Raised
to nobility in 1873.

14 Official Exhibition Report, edited by the Directorate General of the
1873 World's Fair, Vienna 1875. Falke wrote the text about Venetian,
English and Bohemian glass.

15 MAK Archives, 73/1883.

16 Jakob Falke: Das Glas auf der Pariser Weltausstellung, in:
Mittheilungen des k. k. österr. Museums für Kunst und Industrie,
vol. 2, no. 27, 15 Dec. 1867, pp. 50 f.

17 Jacob Falke: Die Kunstindustrie der Gegenwart. Studien auf der
Pariser Weltausstellung im Jahre 1867, Leipzig 1868, p. 159.

18 ibid., p. 161.

19 Falke, same as n. 16, pp. 51 f.

20 Falke, same as n. 17, pp. 155, 158 f.

21 Jacob Falke: Die künstlerisch-ästhetische Seite der auf der Ausstellung
vertretenen Industrie-Produkte, in: Bericht über die Welt-Ausstellung
zu Paris im Jahre 1867, herausgegeben durch das K. K.
Österreichische Central-Comité, Vienna 1869, vol. 1, sect. II, p. 109.

22 Friedrich Pecht: Kunst und Kunstindustrie auf der Weltausstellung
von 1867, Leipzig 1867, pp. 276 f.

23 Falke, same as n. 17, p. 157 (Falke quotes from an article by the
French art critic and archeologist Ferdinand de Lasteyrie in
„L'opinion nationale").

24 Ludwig Lobmeyr, Albert Ilg, Wendelin Boeheim (eds.): Die
Glasindustrie, ihre Geschichte, gegenwärtige Entwicklung und
Statistik, Stuttgart 1874, p. 189.

25 Raimund Gerner: Die Glasfabrikation, Vienna 1880, p. 297.

26 ibid., p. 301.

27 Jacob Falke: Die Kunstindustrie auf der Wiener Weltausstellung 1873,
Vienna 1873, pp. 226 f.

28 Jacob Falke: Die Weihnachts-Ausstellung des Oesterr. Museums,
in: Mittheilungen des k. k. Oesterreich. Museums für Kunst und
Industrie, vol 6, no. 124, 1 Jan. 1876, p. 12.

29 Fr. Wickhoff: Die Weihnachtsausstellung im Oesterreichischen
Museum, in: Mittheilungen des k. k. Oesterreich. Museums für Kunst
und Industrie, vol. 10, no. 220, 1 Jan. 1884, pp. 7 ff.

30 Jakob von Falke: Glasausstellung im österreichischen Museum II.,
in: Beilage zur Wiener Abendpost, no. 102, 3 May 1879, p. 1.

31 Falke, same as n. 28, p. 12.

32 Neuwirth, same as n. 2, p. 289

33 Chandeliers that imitated porcelain were exhibited by Lobmeyr 1862
in Londond already; vessels after the model of the Bleu-du-Roi
porcelains were shown 171/71 at the opening exhibition of the
museum.

34 In addition, contour-drawn figures by August Eisenmenger after the
putti of the Vienna Opera by C. Rahl were cut into a lidded goblet
with plate (design and ornamentation by Moritz Knab) for the silver
wedding of Lobmeyr's sister Mathilde and August Rath in 1889
(see also cat. no. 15).

35 So miniatures from the Manesse manuscript in the Paris National
Library which had been reproduced as collotype prints by F. X. Kraus
in 1887 wer used for the "Minnesinger series of green glass with
enamel painting to designs by Dr. Rich. V. Kralik 1888". Richard
Kralik was a nephew of Lobmeyr.

36 A. Racinet: L'ornement polychrome. Cent planches en couleurs or
et argent, contenant environ 2000 motifs de tous les styles, art ancien
et asiatique, moyen-âge, renaissance, XVIIe et XVIIIe siècle.
Livraison I–X, Paris 1869–1872.

37 Émile Prisse d'Avennes: L'art arabe d'après les monuments du Kaire depuis le VIIe siècle jusqu'à la fin du XVIIIe, Paris 1870 ff. (Texte 1877).

38 A Descriptive Catalogue of the Maiolica. Hispano-Moresco, Persian, Damascus and Rhodian Wares, in the South Kensington Museum, London 1873.

39 Mittheilungen des k. k. österr. Museums für Kunst und Industrie, Bd. 3, Nr. 55, 15. Apr. 1870, S. 138.

40 Blätter für Kunstgewerbe, Bd. 4, 1875, Taf. XXII.

41 Blätter für Kunstgewerbe, Bd. 3, 1874, S. 32; siehe auch Waltraud Neuwirth: Orientalisierende Gläser. J. & L. Lobmeyr, Wien 1981, S. 89 ff.

42 Werkzeichnungen, Bd. XI, S. 22 ff.

43 Johannes Wieninger: Er brachte viel Eigenartiges und Notwendiges mit. Arthur von Scala als Mittler zwischen Ost und West und die Grundlegung der Asiensammlungen des heutigen Museums für angewandte Kunst 1868–1909, in: Kunst und Industrie, wie Anm. 10, S. 164 ff.

44 Mary Patricia May Sekler: Le Corbusier und das Museum als eine Stätte des Lernens, in: Kunst und Industrie, wie Anm. 10, S. 252.

45 Neuwirth, wie Anm. 2, S. 287.

46 Neuwirth, wie Anm. 2, S. 286. Hansen wurde Anfang der siebziger Jahre auch mit der Einrichtung der Wohnung Ludwig Lobmeyrs in der Weihburggasse betraut (S. 338 f.).

47 Waltraud Neuwirth: Theophil von Hansen. Glas. Entwürfe für Lobmeyr, in: Antiquitäten-Zeitung, Nr. 4, 1981, S. 101–111, Nr. 5, 1981, S. 135–140.

48 Neuwirth, wie Anm. 2, S. 224 ff.

49 D. A. W. Ambros: Der Führer durch die kunstgewerbliche Ausstellung in Prag, Prag 1868, S. 3.

50 Falke, wie Anm. 17, S. 155.

51 Friedrich Pecht: Aus dem Münchner Glaspalast. Studien zur Orientierung in und außer demselben während der Kunst- und Kunstindustrie-Ausstellung des Jahres 1876, Stuttgart 1876, S. 150, 152 f.

52 Lobmeyr's Glas-Ausstellung im Museum, in: Die Presse, 6. Apr. 1879, S. 9.

53 Jacob von Falke: Lebenserinnerungen, Leipzig 1897, S. 209 f.

54 Neuwirth, wie Anm. 2, S. 345.

55 Die Weihnachts-Ausstellung des Wiener Kunstgewerbe-Vereines, in: Mittheilungen des k. k. Oesterreich. Museums für Kunst und Industrie, N. F. Bd. 6, Nr. 132, Dez. 1896, S. 241.

37 Émile Prisse d'Avennes: L'art arabe d'après les monuments du Kaire depuis le VIIe siécle jusqu'à la fin du XVIIIe, Paris 1870 ff. (Texts 1877).

38 A Descriptive Catalogue of the Maiolica. Hispano-Moresco, Persian, Damascus and Rhodian Wares, in the South Kensington Museum, London 1873.

39 Mittheilungen des k. k. österr. Museums für Kunst und Industrie, vol. 3, no. 55, 15 Apr. 1870, p. 138.

40 Blätter für Kunstgewerbe, vol. 4, 1875, plate XXII.

41 Blätter für Kunstgewerbe, vol. 3, 1874, p. 32; see also Waltraud Neuwirth: Orientalisierende Gläser. J. & L. Lobmeyr, Vienna 1981, pp. 89 ff.

42 Working Drawings, vol. XI, pp. 22 ff.

43 Johannes Wieninger: Er brachte viel Eigenartiges und Notwendiges mit. Arthur von Scala als Mittler zwischen Ost und West und die Grundlegung der Asiensammlungen des heutigen Museums für angewandte Kunst 1868–1909, in: Kunst und Industrie, same as n. 10, pp. 164 ff.

44 Mary Patricia May Sekler: Le Corbusier und das Museum als eine Stätte des Lernens, in: Kunst und Industrie, same as n. 10, p. 252.

45 Neuwirth, same as n. 2, 287.

46 Neuwirth, same as n. 2, p. 286. Hansen was also commissioned to do the interior decoration of Ludwig Lobmeyr's apartment in Weihburggasse (pp. 338 f.).

47 Waltraud Neuwirth: Theophil von Hansen. Glas. Entwürfe für Lobmeyr, in: Antiquitäten-Zeitung, no. 4, 1981, pp. 101–111, no. 5, 1981, pp. 135–140.

48 Neuwirth, same as n. 2, pp. 224 ff.

49 D. A. W. Ambros: Der Führer durch die kunstgewerbliche Ausstellung in Prag, Prague 1868, p. 3.

50 Falke, same as n 17, p. 155.

51 Friedrich Pecht: Aus dem Münchner Glaspalast. Studien zur Orientierung in und außer demselben während der Kunst- und Kunstindustrie-Ausstellung des Jahres 1876, Stuttgart 1876, pp. 150, 152 f.

52 Lobmeyr's Glas-Ausstellung im Museum, in: Die Presse, 6 Apr. 1879, p. 9.

53 Jacob von Falke: Lebenserinnerungen, Leipzig 1897, pp. 209 f.

54 Neuwirth, same as n. 2, 345.

55 Die Weihnachts-Ausstellung des Wiener Kunstgewerbe-Vereines, in: Mittheilungen des k. k. Oesterreich. Museums für Kunst und Industrie, N. Ser. vol. 6, no 132, Dec. 1896, p. 241.

Flasche, Trink-Service Nr. 126 (Detail), Kat.-Nr. 1d
Bottle, Drinking Service no. 126 (detail), cat. no. 1d

Abkürzungen		Abbreviations	
AJB	Anton Janke, Blottendorf	AJB	Anton Janke, Blottendorf
angek. v.	angekauft von	AMAI	Imperial-Royal Austrian Museum for Art
Ausf.	Ausführung		and Industry (today's MAK)
B	Breite	B	breadth
Bd.	Band	B	brand
bez.	bezeichnet	CAP	company archives Prague
D	Durchmesser	CAV	company archives Vienna
Entw.	Entwurf	D	diameter
FAP	Firmenarchiv Prag	des.	designated
FAW	Firmenarchiv Wien	DS	drinking service
fl.	Gulden	Dsg.	design
FM	Firmenmarke	H	height
H	Höhe	inv.	inventoried
inv.	inventarisiert	L	length
L	Länge	Lit.	literature
Lit.	Literatur	Mfr.	Manufacturer, manufactured
MNA	Meyr's Neffe(n), Adolf	MNA	Meyr's Neffe(n), Adolf
OMeA	Obersthofmeisteramt	p.	piece
ÖMKI	k. k. Österreichisches Museum für Kunst	pl.	plate
	und Industrie (heute MAK)	purch.	purchased
St.	Stück	subs.	subsequently
Taf.	Tafel	transl.	translated
TS	Trink-Service	vol.	vol
übers.	übersetzt	WD	working drawings
WZ	Werkzeichnungen		(MAK, inv. no. K.I. 7380)
	(MAK, Inv.-Nr. K.I. 7380)		

Trink-Service

Die Trink-Service stellten von Anfang an eine wichtige Produktgruppe der Firma Lobmeyr dar. In den 1883 und 1892 für das ÖMKI zusammengefassten Werkzeichnungen sind zahlreiche der von Lobmeyr herausgebrachten Trink-Service von der Gründung des Unternehmens in den zwanziger Jahren des 19. Jahrhunderts bis zum Trink-Service Nr. 200 im Jahre 1891 erfasst.

Während in den ersten Jahren viele Trink-Service nach fremden Mustern angefertigt wurden, waren es ab den sechziger Jahren immer mehr Service „nach eigenen Zeichnungen" oder nach Künstlerentwürfen.

In der ersten Hälfte des 19. Jahrhunderts wurden böhmische und englische, aber auch belgische und französische Muster genannt und um 1850 Muster „von Tacchi in Frankfurt" und „Steigerwald in München". In der zweiten Hälfte des 19. Jahrhunderts orientierte man sich zunächst an England mit seinen antikisierenden und an die Renaissance erinnernden Dekoren. So präsentierte Lobmeyr 1862 auf der Londoner Weltausstellung das Trink-Service Nr. 54 „mit Renaissance-Gravirung. theils nach alten Mustern um 1855". Bis in die siebziger Jahre folgten viele Service mit einer solchen Gravierung. Auch „bergkrystallartiges" geschliffenes Kristallglas war zu dieser Zeit bei Trink-Servicen beliebt. Es entstanden nach dem Entwurf des Architekten Theophil von Hansen 1864 das Trink-Service Nr. 95 „mit griechischer Gravirung" und in den darauf folgenden Jahren noch zahlreiche weitere Service in diesem Stil (siehe S. 41).

Zu einem Trink-Service gehörten in der Regel mehrere Stängelgläser für Wein, Champagner und Likör, Becher für Wasser und Bier, weiters Flaschen und Krüge.

Zahlreiche Adelige und prominente Persönlichkeiten gaben ihre Trink-Service bei Lobmeyr in Auftrag. Dazu wählten sie ein Trink-Service aus und ließen es mit ihrem persönlichen Monogramm versehen.

Drinking Services

Drinking services were an important production line for Lobmeyr from the beginning. The working drawings compiled for the AMAI in 1883 and 1892 include numerous of Lobmeyr's drinking services from the setting-up of the company in the 1820s to the drinking service no. 200 of 1891.

While many drinking services were produced after foreign patterns in the early years, there was a growing number of services "after own drawings" or to artists' designs that were produced from the 1860s.

In the first half of the 19th century, Bohemian and English, but also Belgian and French patterns were mentioned and around 1850 patterns "by Tacchi in Frankfurt" and "Steigerwald in Munich." In the second half of the 19th century, the models followed were English with its decorations in classical or Renaissance style. Thus, Lobmeyr presented the drinking service no. 54 "with Renaissance engraving, partly after old patterns around 1855" at the 1862 London World's fair. Many services with similar engraving followed until into the 1870s. "Rock-crystal-like" cut crystal glass was very popular for drinking services, too. 1864, the drinking service no. 95 "with Greek engraving" was produced to a design by Theophil von Hansen, and this was followed by numerous other services in this style in subsequent years (see p. 41).

A drinking service usually was comprised of a number of stem glasses for wine, champagne and liqueur, as well as beakers for water and beer and bottles and pitchers.

Numerous aristocrats and prominent personalities had their own drinking services made by Lobmeyr, which meant that they chose one specific service to which their personal monogram was applied.

On the whole, colored glass came to be rejected in the course of the arts-and-crafts reform of the AMAI for

Trinkgläser, Trink-Service Nr. 54,
in: WZ, Bd. I, S. 32
Glasses, Drinking Service no. 54,
in: WD, vol. I, p. 32

Farbiges Glas wurde im Rahmen der Kunstgewerbe-
reform des ÖMKI für Trink-Service im Wesentlichen
abgelehnt; Jakob von Falke meinte dazu 1883: „Das
weiße, farblose Krystallglas hat aber vor dem gefärbten
zunächst den Vorzug, dass es die Farbe der Flüssigkeit in
voller Klarheit zeigt und das Feuer des Weines ins Spiel
setzt, eine Eigenschaft, die der Trinker mit Recht wohl
zu schätzen weiß."[1] Nur am traditionellen grünen
Rheinweinglas hielt man fest: „theils weil [die Gläser]
historisch-künstlerische Spezialitäten sind, theils weil sie
gute, althistorische und originelle Formen haben, deren
Untergang unter der Schablone zu bedauern wäre.
Uebrigens steht die dunkelgrüne Farbe, obwohl sie die
des Weines nicht zur Wirkung kommen lässt, recht gut
auf der Tafel."[2]

Um 1845 kamen bei Lobmeyr die Dessert-Service auf,
die ab zirka 1860 im Dekor mit Trink-Servicen korres-
pondierten und die gleiche Nummerierung aufwiesen.

drinking services; Jakob von Falke wrote about it in
1883: "The white, colorless crystal glass mainly has one
advantage over the colored, that it shows the color of
the liquid in full clarity and brings out the fire of the
wine; a quality rightly appreciated by the drinker."[1]
Only the traditional green Rhine wine glass was
defended "partly because [the glasses] are a historical
artistic specialty; partly because they have good, history-
honored and original shapes the disappearance of which
behind a stock shape would be regrettable. Besides, the
dark green color, although it obscures the color of the
wine, appears nice on the table."[2]

Around 1845, Lobmeyr introduced dessert services,
which corresponded to the drinking services in
decoration and were given the same numbers.

1 Jacob von Falke: Die Kunst im Hause, 5. Aufl., Wien 1883, S. 361 ff.
2 Ebd., S. 362.

1 Jacob von Falke: Die Kunst im Hause, 5th impr., Vienna, 1883, pp. 361 ff.
2 ibid., p. 362.

1 „Trink-Service No. 54, Krystallglas mit Renaissance-Gravirung. theils nach alten Mustern um 1855"

Farbloses Glas mit Schliff und Schnitt

Obwohl das Trink-Service schon in den fünfziger Jahren entstand, gehörte es zu denen, die 1862 von Lobmeyr auf der Weltausstellung in London gezeigt wurden. Im Firmenarchiv sind die Entwurfszeichnungen im Wesentlichen zwischen 1852 und 1854 datiert und von Josef Lobmeyr signiert.

Mit der in den Werkzeichnungen genannten „Renaissance-Gravirung" ist wohl die Art des Glasschnittes gemeint, denn stilistisch geht der Dekor mehr auf böhmische Beispiele des 18. Jahrhunderts zurück.

WZ, Bd. I, S. 31–32 (siehe Abb. S. 53)

Lit.: Illustrirter Katalog der Londoner Industrie-Ausstellung von 1862, Abb. S. 162 (Serviceteile); Urbancová 1981, S. 76–77

1a

1a Stängelglas (Weinglas)

Ausf.: vor 1880
H 12,8 cm
Quellen: WZ, Bd. I, S. 32; FAP, Schnitt „MNA 311 25/4. 56"
Inv.-Nr. Gl 1465, Geschenk des Fürsten Liechtenstein, inv. Jan. 1880

1b Stängelglas (Rheinweinglas)

Ausf.: vor 1880
Grünes transparentes Glas mit Schliff und Schnitt
H 12,9 cm
Quellen: WZ, Bd. I, S. 32; FAP, Schnitt „MNA A 283([?]o.8) 4-58"
Inv.-Nr. Gl 1466, Geschenk des Fürsten Liechtenstein, inv. Jan. 1880

1c Stängelglas (Champagnerschale)

Ausf.: vor 1880
H 11,9 cm
Quellen: WZ, Bd. I, S. 32; FAP, Schnitt „MN 881, 1852", Schnitt „MNA & AJB 5929. 1876"
Inv.-Nr. Gl 1467, Geschenk des Fürsten Liechtenstein, inv. Jan. 1880

1 "Drinking Service no. 54, crystal glass with Renaissance engraving after old designs around 1855"

Colorless glass, ground and cut

Although this drinking service was already made in the 1850s, it was part of the assortment shown by Lobmeyr at the 1862 World's Fair in London. The design drawings in the company archives are basically dated between 1852 and 1854 and signed by Josef Lobmeyr. The "Renaissance engraving" mentioned in the working drawings presumably refers to the type of glass cutting, since, stylistically, the design rather derives from 18th century examples from Bohemia.

WD, vol. I, pp. 31–32 (see ill. p. 53)

Lit.: Illustrated Catalogue of the London Industry Exposition of 1862, ill. p. 162 (service parts); Urbancová 1981, pp. 76–77

1a Stem Glass (Wine Glass)

Mfr.: before 1880
H 12.8 cm
Sources: WD, vol. I, p. 32; CAP, section "MNA 311 25/4. 56"
Inv. no. Gl 1465, present of the Prince of Liechtenstein, inv. Jan. 1880

1b Stem Glass (Rhine Wine Glass)

Mfr.: before 1880
Green transparent glass, ground and cut
H 12.9 cm
Sources: WD, vol. I, p. 32; CAP, section "MNA A 283([?]o.8) 4-58"
Inv. no. Gl 1466, present of the Prince of Liechtenstein, inv. Jan. 1880

1c Stem Glass (Champagne Coupe)

Mfr.: before 1880
H 11.9 cm
Sources: WD, vol. I, p. 32; CAP, section "MN 881, 1852", section "MNA & AJB 5929. 1876"
Inv. no. Gl 1467, present of the Prince of Liechtenstein, inv. Jan. 1880

1b

1d Flasche

Ausf.: vor 1880

H 30 cm

Quellen: WZ, Bd. I, S. 31

Inv.-Nr. Dep. 94, Geschenk des Fürsten Liechtenstein,
inv. Jan. 1880

1d Bottle

Mfr.: before 1880

H 30 cm

Sources: WD, vol. I, p. 31

Inv. no. Dep. 94, present of the Prince of Liechtenstein,
inv. Jan. 1880

1c

1d

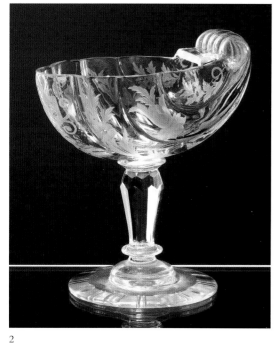

Stängelglas in Nautilusform, Böhmen,
um 1700 (MAK, Inv.-Nr. Gl 704)
Nautilus-Shaped Stem Glass, Bohemia,
around 1700 (MAK, inv. no. Gl 704)

2

2 Stängelglas in Nautilusform

Entw.: 1867
Farbloses Glas mit Schliff und Schnitt
H 11,8 cm, D 10,5 cm
Quellen: FAW, Bestellungsbuch MNA, 27. Aug. 1867, 8102,
„Champagnergläser Muschel II. Gr. weiß Ant. Janke";
FAP, bei Trink-Service Nr. 109, Schnitt „MNA 8102-1867/
AJB 195-1868"
Inv.-Nr. Gl 1468, Geschenk des Fürsten Liechtenstein,
inv. Jan. 1880

Kopien von böhmischen Gläsern wurden schon in den
Anfangsjahren des ÖMKI hergestellt. In diesem Fall
diente ein böhmisches Gefäß von zirka 1700 als Vorbild,
wie es sich seit 1870 in den Sammlungen des Museums
befand (Inv.-Nr. Gl 704, abgebildet von Jakob von Falke
1878 in der Zeitschrift „L'Art").
Der Schnitt dieses bei Meyr's Neffen ausgeführten Glases
erfolgte wahrscheinlich in der Gegend von Haida (Nový
Bor) in Nordböhmen über die Vermittlung von Anton
Janke, der die Firma dort vertrat.
Lit.: Urbancová 1981, S. 77

2 Nautilus-Shaped Stem Glass

Dsg.: 1867
Colorless class, ground and cut
H 11.8 cm, D 10.5 cm
Sources: CAV, order book MNA, 27 Aug. 1867, 8102,
"Champagnergläser Muschel II. Gr. weiß Ant. Janke";
CAP, with drinking service no. 109, section "MNA 8102-
1867/AJB 195-1868"
Inv. no. Gl 1468, present of the Prince of Liechtenstein,
inv. Jan. 1880

Replicas of Bohemian glasses were already made in the
early years of the AMAI. In this case, the model was a
Bohemian glass of about 1700, as had been in the
museum holdings since 1870 (inv. no. Gl 704, used 1878
as illustration by Jakob von Falke in "L'Art" journal).
This glass made by Meyr's Neffen was probably cut in
the Haida (Nový Bor) region in North-Bohemia by
mediation of Anton Janke, the local company
representative.
Lit.: Urbancová 1981, p. 7

3

Deckelpokal, Zeichnung von Valentin Teirich,
Wien, 1868 (MAK, Inv.-Nr. K.I. 1665)
Lidded Goblet, drawing by Valentin Teirich,
Vienna, 1868 (MAK, inv. no. K.I. 1665)

3   Pokal mit Deckel („nach einem Bergkrystall-Becher aus der kaiserl. Schatzkammer")

Ausf.: Meyr's Neffen, Adolf, 1868
Farbloses Glas mit Schliff
H 19,7 cm
Quellen: FAP, Schnitt „MNA 259-1868"
Inv.-Nr. Gl 929, inv. vor 1871

Das ÖMKI stellte nach der Gründung 1864 zunächst Objekte aus anderen Sammlungen aus. Das Vorbild für dieses Objekt, ein Deckelpokal aus Bergkristall, an Deckel und Fuß metallgefasst, befand sich in der Wiener Schatzkammer. Eine Zeichnung dieses Pokals wurde 1868 von Valentin Teirich angefertigt (Kunstblättersammlung des Museums, Inv.-Nr. K.I. 1665) und 1874 in den „Blättern für Kunstgewerbe" unter der Bezeichnung „Becher aus Bergkrystall in Gold gefaßt, 16. Jahrhundert" publiziert (Bd. 3, 1874, S. 8). Bei der Umsetzung in Glas durch Lobmeyr wurde die Montierung weggelassen.

1869 wurden vom Museum zwei Lobmeyr-Gläser „nach Mustern des 16. und 18. Jahrhunderts" angekauft („Mittheilungen", Nr. 45, 15. Juni 1869, S. 456), wahrscheinlich war eines davon der Pokal.

Valentin Teirich (1844–1876) war ab 1868 als Lehrer an der Kunstgewerbeschule tätig, unterrichtete zuerst „Perspektive, Schattenlehre und Projektionslehre", wurde 1870 Dozent an der Vorbereitungsschule und 1871 Professor dort. Ab 1872 gab er in enger Zusammenarbeit mit dem Museum und der Kunstgewerbeschule die Zeitschrift „Blätter für Kunstgewerbe" heraus. Angeregt durch seine Italienreisen publizierte er Vorlagenwerke zu Holz- und Marmorintarsien in Italien und Bronzen der italienischen Renaissance. Er reproduzierte nicht nur historische Objekte, sondern entwarf auch für verschiedene kunstgewerbliche Sparten. Seine Glasentwürfe für Lobmeyr waren meist von der Renaissance inspiriert (siehe Kat.-Nr. 8). Er gehörte aber auch zu den Ersten, die für Lobmeyr orientalische Entwürfe lieferten.

Lit.: Scholda 2000, S. 198

3   Lidded Goblet ("after a rock crystal beaker from the Imperial Treasury")

Mfr.: Meyr's Neffen, Adolf, 1868
Cut colorless glass
H 19.7 cm
Sources: CAP, section "MNA 259-1868"
Inv. no. Gl 929, inv. before 1871

After its foundation in 1864, the AMAI first showed objects from other collections. The model for this object, a lidded rock-crystal goblet, with metal mountings on the foot and lid, was in the Imperial Treasury in Vienna. A drawing of this goblet was made 1868 by Valentin Teirich (art prints and drawings collection of the museum, inv. no. K.I. 1665) and published 1874 in "Blätter für Kunstgewerbe" under the heading of "Beaker of rock crystal with gold mounting, 16th century" (vol. 3, 1874, p. 8). In Lobmeyr's re-creation, the mounting was left away.

1869, the museum purchased two Lobmeyr glasses "after models of the 16th and 18th century" ("Mittheilungen", no. 45, 15 June 1869, p. 456), one of them presumably was this goblet.

Valentin Teirich (1844–1876) was a teacher at the Industrial Arts School from 1868, where he taught "Perspective, Shading, and Projection", and became a lecturer in 1870 and in 1871 professor at the Preparatory School. From 1872, he edited the journal "Blätter für Kunstgewerbe" in close cooperation with the museum and the Industrial Arts School. Inspired by his trips to Italy, he published model books on wood and marble marquetries and bronzes from the Italian Renaissance. He did not only reproduce historical objects, but also made designs in different arts-and-crafts fields. His glass designs for Lobmeyr were mostly inspired by the Renaissance (see cat. no. 8). He also was among the first who provided oriental-style designs for Lobmeyr.

Lit.: Scholda 2000, p. 198

4 „Trink-Service No. 126, Krystallglas, im Vierpass eingeblasen mit feiner Renaissance-Gravirung. nach eigenen Zeichnungen 1870"

Entw.: Ernst Ziller (Dekor)
Farbloses Glas mit Schnitt

Der Architekt Ernst Ziller, ein Schüler Theophil von Hansens, hielt sich mehrmals in Athen auf. Ziller entwarf schon anlässlich der Weltausstellung in Paris 1867 für Lobmeyr Ampeln und Blumengefäße, kombiniert mit Holz oder Bronze. 1872 entwarf er die „Renaissancegravirung" für Pokale (WZ, Bd. VIII, S. 6). Er wurde von Ludwig Lobmeyr auch für Entwürfe anlässlich der Wiener Weltausstellung 1873 herangezogen.

Bei diesem Trink-Service wurde Ernst Ziller in den Werkzeichnungen zwar nicht genannt, allerdings beim dazugehörigen Dessert-Service als Entwerfer der Renaissanceornamente („Dessert-Service No. 126, Krystallglas mit muschelartig geformten Schalen n. eig. Zeichnungen u. reicher Renaissancegravirung. Nach Zeichnungen des Archit. Ziller 1872", Bd. VI, S. 9–11). Die Ornamente entsprechen stilistisch denen des Trink-Services Nr. 103 „mit griechischer Gravirung", das Hansen 1866 entwarf.

Das Trink- und Dessert-Service Nr. 126 wurde auch auf der Weltausstellung in Wien 1873 gezeigt, wo das Hamburger Museum für Kunst und Gewerbe eine Flasche daraus um 15 fl. erwarb.

WZ, Bd. II, S. 44–45
Lit.: Blätter für Kunstgewerbe, Bd. 1, 1872, Taf. 24; Lützow 1875, S. 368; Klesse 1996, S. 6–7

4a Flasche

H 34,9 cm
Quellen: WZ, Bd. II, S. 45; FAP, Schnitt einer Flasche (H 35,4 cm) dieses Services „MNA & AJB. 1986-1870"
Inv.-Nr. Gl 1463, Geschenk des Fürsten Liechtenstein, inv. Jan. 1880

4 "Drinking Service no. 126, crystal glass, mold-blown in the quatrefoil and with delicate Renaissance engraving after own drawings 1870"

Dsg.: Ernst Ziller (decoration)
Colorless cut glass

The architect Ernst Ziller, a pupil of Theophil von Hansen, made several study visits to Athens. Ziller designed hanging lamps and flower vessels, combined with wood and bronze, for Lobmeyr for the 1868 Paris World's Fair. 1872, he designed the "Renaissance engraving" for goblets (WD, vol. VIII, p. 6). He was also hired by Lobmeyr to do designs for the Vienna World's Fair of 1873.

Ziller's name ist not mentioned in the working drawings for this drinking service, but he is credited for the design of the Renaissance ornaments in the accompanying dessert service ("Dessert Service no. 126, crystal glass with shell-shaped bowls after own drawings and with rich Renaissance engraving. After a design by Arch. Ziller 1872", vol. VI, pp. 9–11). The ornaments are stylistically similar to those of the drinking service no. 103 "with Greek engraving" designed 1866 by Hansen. The drinking and dessert service no. 126 was also exhibited at the Vienna World's Fair where the Hamburg Arts and Crafts Museum purchased a bottle from it for 15 Austro-Hungarian Gulden.

WD, vol. II, pp. 44–45
Lit.: Blätter für Kunstgewerbe, vol. 1, 1872, pl. 24; Lützow 1875, p. 368; Klesse 1996, pp. 6–7

4a Bottle

H 34.9 cm
Sources: WD, vol. II, p. 45; CAP, section of a bottle (H 35.4 cm) from this service "MNA & AJB. 1986-1870"
Inv. no. Gl 1463, donation from the Prince of Liechtenstein, inv. Jan. 1880

Teile des Trink-Services Nr. 126, in: Blätter für Kunstgewerbe, Bd. 1, 1872, Taf. 24 (MAK, Inv.-Nr. K.I. 3251)

Parts of Drinking Service no. 126, details, in: Blätter für Kunstgewerbe, vol. 1, 1872, pl. 24 (MAK, inv. no. K.I. 3251)

4a

5 „Trink-Service No. 127, Krystallglas dünn mit Renaissance-Gravirung u. rothem Faden im gewundenen Stengel. nach eigenen Zeichnungen 1870"

Farbloses Glas mit Schnitt (teilweise poliert), Rubinfaden im Stängel

Dieses Trink-Service verbindet eine freie Umsetzung von Renaissancemotiven mit einem im Stängel eingeschmolzenen roten Faden. Rubinfäden im Stängel finden sich bei böhmischen Gläsern um 1700, Fäden in verschiedenen anderen Farben in England vorwiegend in der zweiten Hälfte des 18. Jahrhunderts.

WZ, Bd. II, S. 46

5a Stängelglas (Champagnerschale)
Ausf.: Meyr's Neffen, Adolf, vor 1880
H 12,8 cm
Quellen: WZ, Bd. II, S. 46; FAP, Schnitt „MNA & AJB. 1999-1870 TS 127/20"
Inv.-Nr. Gl 1464, Geschenk des Fürsten Liechtenstein, inv. Jan. 1880

6 „Trink-Service No. 132, Krystallglas, Kaiser-Service im Allerhöchsten Auftrage angefertigt. Formen nach eigenen Zeichnungen, Gravirung gezeichnet von Reg. Rth. Storck 1870"

Entw.: Ludwig Lobmeyr, Josef Storck
Ausf.: Meyr's Neffen, Adolf; Peter Eisert, Haida (Schnitt)
Farbloses Glas mit Schnitt (matt und poliert)

Das so genannte „Kaiser-Service" (Trink- und Dessert-Service Nr. 132) wurde 1869 vom Kaiser in Auftrag gegeben und in Zusammenarbeit mit dem ÖMKI realisiert. Zur geplanten Eröffnung eines eigenen Museumsgebäudes widmete der Kaiser 1869 50.000 fl. zur Förderung der Kunstindustrie und gab beim Museum unter Einbeziehung der Kunstgewerbeschule Folgendes in Auftrag: „[…] eine Anzahl von Gebrauchsgegenständen für den Hof, an welchen diejenigen Kunstgewerbe, welche sich in Österreich besonderer Pflege erfreuen, ihre Leistungsfähigkeit erproben sollten. Es wurde ein Tisch-

5 "Drinking Service no. 127, crystal glass thin with Renaissance engraving and red thread in twisted stem. after own drawings 1870"

Colorless cut glass (partly polished), ruby thread in stem

This drinking service combines a free adaptation of Renaissance motifs with a red thread fused into the stem. Ruby threads in the stem can be found in Bohemian glasses around 1700, threads in other colors were used in England mainly in the second half of the 18th century.

WD, vol. II, p. 46

5a Stem Glass (Champagne Glass)
Mfr.: Meyr's Neffen, Adolf, before 1880
H 12.8 cm
Sources: WD, vol. II, p. 46; CAP, section "MNA & AJB. 1999-1870 TS 127/20"
Inv. no. Gl 1464, donation from the Prince of Liechtenstein, inv. Jan. 1880

6 "Drinking Service no. 132, crystal glass, Imperial Service Made to His Majesty's order. Forms after own drawings, engraving designed by Reg. Rth. Storck 1870"

Dsg.: Ludwig Lobmeyr, Josef Storck
Mfr.: Meyr's Neffen, Adolf; Peter Eisert, Haida (cutting)
Colorless cut glass (matte and polished)

The so-called "Imperial Service" (drinking and dessert service no. 132) was ordered by the Emperor in 1869 and made in cooperation with the AMAI. For the projected opening of the museum in 1869 the Emperor made a donation of 50,000 Gulden for the promotion of industrial arts and ordered the following from the museum, with the collaboration of the industrial arts school: "[…] a number of utensils for the Court, in which those art and crafts which enjoy particular cultivation in Austria can demonstrate their capabilities. The order included a tablecloth, a centerpiece, a

Krüge und Trinkgläser, Trink-Service Nr. 127, in: WZ, Bd. II, S. 46
Drinking Service no. 127, Pitchers and Glasses, in: WD, vol. II, p. 46

5a

Teile des Trink-Services Nr. 132, gezeigt auf der Wiener Weltausstellung 1873,
in: Blätter für Kunstgewerbe, Bd. 2, 1873, Taf. 35 (MAK, Inv.-Nr. K.I. 3251)
Drinking Service no. 132, details, presented at the 1873 Vienna Worls's Fair,
in: Blätter für Kunstgewerbe, vo. II, 1873, pl. 35 (MAK, inv. no. K.I. 3251)

Schale für Zucker, Bordeauxglas, Dessertweinglas, Dessertteller, in:
Trink- und Dessert-Service aus Krystallglas, Blatt 5 (MAK, Inv.-Nr.
K.I. 3914)
Sugar bowl, Bordeaux glass, dessert wine glass, dessert plate, in: Drinking
and dessert service of crystal glass, sheet 5 (MAK, inv. no. K.I. 3914)

tuch, ein Tafelaufsatz, ein Schmuckschrank, ferner ein Hintergrund für den Thronsessel, endlich ein Trink- und Dessertservice aus Glas verlangt" („Illustrierte Zeitung", Leipzig, Nr. 1577, 20. Sept. 1873, S. 216).

Das Trink-Service bestand aus Stängelgläsern, Bechern, Flaschen und Krügen. Bei den zum Service gehörenden Trinkgläsern handelte es sich um Bordeauxglas, Chablisglas, Sherryglas, „Tokayerglas", „Liqueurglas" und Rheinweinglas. Die Becher dienten als Bierglas, Wasserglas, Limonaden- bzw. Punschglas und Mundbecher. Das dazugehörige Dessert-Service setzte sich aus Zuckerdose, Salzfass, Senfbecher, Schüsseln, Schalen und mehreren Aufsätzen zusammen. Die emaillierten Silbermontierungen wurden, wie auch bei anderen Arbeiten Lobmeyrs aus dieser Zeit, von Hermann Ratzersdorfer angefertigt (siehe Kat.-Nr. 13, 15, 19, 20).

Ludwig Lobmeyr entwarf die Formen der Flaschen, Krüge und Gläser, Josef Storck jene der Aufsätze, der Zuckerdose, des Senfbechers usw. sowie den Dekor. Formen und Dekor orientierten sich an Bergkristallgefäßen des 16. und beginnenden 17. Jahrhunderts sowohl italienischen wie auch deutschen und böhmischen Ursprungs in der Kaiserlichen Schatzkammer. Diese Gefäße galten für Jakob von Falke, Kustos und stellvertretender Direktor des Museums, als besonders geeignete Vorbilder für das böhmische farblose Kristallglas. Die Gravierungen wurden auf „vollen Glanz" herausgeschliffen, das heißt, die durch das Schneiden matten Flächen wurden auspoliert, was das Ornament noch feiner erscheinen lässt und eine andere Lichtwirkung mit sich bringt. Der Glasschneider dieser außergewöhnlich aufwendigen Gravierarbeit wurde auch namentlich genannt. Das Service konnte in Teilen schon auf der Eröffnungsausstellung des Museums 1871/72 gezeigt werden. Komplett wurde es auf der Wiener Weltausstellung 1873 präsentiert. Auch auf weiteren Ausstellungen wie in München und Philadelphia 1876 und in Triest 1882 gehörte es zu den repräsentativen Objekten der österreichischen Kunstindustrie.

decorative cabinet, furthermore, one backdrop for the throne chair, and finally, a drinking and dessert service of glass" ("Illustrierte Zeitung", Leipzig, no. 1577, 20 Sept. 1873, p. 216).

The drinking service comprised stem glasses, tumblers, bottles, and pitchers. The drinking glasses included in the service were Bordeaux, Chablis, Sherry, Tokay, liqueur, and Rhine-wine glasses. The glasses were a beer glass, a water glass, a lemonade or punch glass, and a tumbler. The dessert service consisted of a sugar bowl, a salt cellar, a mustard bowl, different dishes and bowls and a number of decorative tabletop pieces. The enameled silver mountings were, like other Lobmeyr pieces from that period, made by Hermann Ratzersdorfer (see cat. nos. 13, 15, 19, 20).

Ludwig Lobmeyr designed the shapes of the bottles, pitchers, and glasses, Josef Storck those of the tabletop pieces, the sugar and mustard bowls etc., and the decoration. Forms and decoration followed Italian and Bohemian made rock crystal vessels of the 16th and early 17th century in the Imperial Treasury. The vessels were considered as particularly well-suited models for colorless Bohemian crystal glass by Jakob von Falke, curator and deputy museum director. The engravings were cut "to high gloss", which means that the areas matted by the cutting were high-polished, which makes the ornamentation appear even more delicate and creates different light effects. The glass-cutter of this exceptionally lavish engraving was credited by name. Parts of the service could be presented in the museum's opening exhibition in 1871/72. The complete service was presented at the 1873 Vienna World's Fair. It was also featured as one of the most representative objects of the Austrian arts and crafts industry at exhibitions in Munich and Philadelphia in 1876 and in Trieste in 1882.

6a

6b

6c

Das Service, das für sechs Personen ausgeführt wurde, war in der Hofburg in einer Vitrine vor dem Audienzzimmer des Kaisers aufgestellt und wurde nicht benutzt. Heute befindet es sich in der Hofsilber- und Tafelkammer, Hofburg, Wien. Eine Flasche und zwei Gläser überließ Lobmeyr dem Museum.

WZ, Bd. II, S. 52–55, Bd. VI, S. 12–18

Lit.: Fachmännische Berichte, S. 66, 69; Falke 1873, S. 223 ff.; Blätter für Kunstgewerbe, Bd. 1, 1872, S. 59, Bd. 2, 1873, Taf. 35, S. 46, Bd. 3, 1874, Taf. 11, 22, 25, Bd. 5, 1876, Taf. 11; Trink- und Dessert-Service aus Krystallglas; Wiener Weltausstellungs-Zeitung, II. Jg., Nr. 213, 29. Juli 1873, S. 3; Scholda 1991, Kat.-Nr. 40; Neuwirth 1999, S. 288–291

6a   Flasche

Ausf.: Meyr's Neffen, Adolf, um 1870
Farbloses Glas mit Schnitt (matt und poliert, teilweise vergoldet)
FM: auf der Unterseite geschnitten; Monogramm: „FIJ" (Franz Joseph I.)
H 32,4 cm
Quellen: WZ, Bd. II, S. 55; FAW, 2556 und 2557-1870, „nach Krystallgefäßen des XVI. u. XVII. Jahrhunderts"
Inv.-Nr. Gl 1118, Geschenk v. J. & L. Lobmeyr, inv. 9. Apr. 1874

6b   Stängelglas (Rheinweinglas)

Ausf.: Meyr's Neffen, Adolf, wohl 1870
Grünes transparentes Glas mit Schnitt (matt und poliert)
H 13,7 cm
Quellen: FAP, „Kaiser-Service, schmal halbgeschält mit hellpolierter Gravierung, ausgeführt für Kaiser Franz Joseph I, 1870", Schnitt „MNA 5918-1870"
Inv.-Nr. Gl 1119, Geschenk v. J. & L. Lobmeyr, inv. 9. Apr. 1874

6c   Becher mit Fuß und Henkel (Punschglas)

Ausf.: Meyr's Neffen, Adolf, wohl 1870
Farbloses Glas mit Schnitt (matt und poliert)
H 10,8 cm
Quellen: FAP, „Kaiser-Service, schmal halbgeschält mit hellpolierter Gravierung, ausgeführt für Kaiser Franz Joseph I, 1870", Schnitt „MNA 5915-1870"
Inv.-Nr. Gl 1121, Geschenk v. J. & L. Lobmeyr, inv. 9. Apr. 1874

The service for six people was exhibited in a showcase in front of the Emperor's audience room at Hofburg Palace and was not used. Today it is part of the holdings of the Imperial Silver Collection. Lobmeyr donated one bottle and two glasses to the museum.

WD, vol. II, pp. 52–55, vol. VI, pp. 12–18

Lit.: Fachmännische Berichte, pp. 66, 69; Falke 1873, pp. 223 ff.; Blätter für Kunstgewerbe, vol. 1, 1872, p. 59, vol. 2, 1873, pl. 35, p. 46, vol. 3, 1874, pl. 11, 22, 25, vol. 5, 1876, pl. 11; Crystal Drinking and Dessert Service; Wiener Weltausstellungs-Zeitung, vol. 2, no. 213, 29 July 1873, p. 3; Scholda 1991, cat. no. 40; Neuwirth 1999, pp. 288–291

6a   Bottle

Mfr.: Meyr's Neffen, Adolf, around 1870
Colorless cut glass (matte and polished, partly gilded)
B: cut into the bottom; monogram: "FIJ" (Franz Joseph I.)
H 32.4 cm
Sources: WK, vol. II, p. 55; CAV, 2556 und 2557-1870, "after crystal vessels from the 16th and 17th century"
Inv. no. Gl 1118, donation J. & L. Lobmeyr, inv 9 Apr. 1874

6b   Stem Glass (Rhine wine glass)

Mfr.: Meyr's Neffen, Adolf, pres. 1870
Green transparent cut glass (matte and polished)
H 13.7 cm
Sources: CAP, "Imperial Service, Kaiser-Service, surface-ground with high-polished engraving, made for Emperor Franz Joseph I, 1870", section "MNA 5918-1870"
Inv. no. Gl 1119, donation from J. & L. Lobmeyr, inv 9 Apr. 1874

6c   Beaker with Foot and Handle (Punch glass)

Mfr.: Meyr's Neffen, Adolf, pres. 1870
Colorless cut glass (matte and polished)
H 10.8 cm
Sources: CAP, "Imperial Service, Kaiser-Service, surface-ground with high-polished engraving, made for Emperor Franz Joseph I, 1870", section "MNA 5915-1870"
Inv. no. Gl 1121, donation from J. & L. Lobmeyr, inv 9 Apr. 1874

Eröffnungsausstellung des ÖMKI, Wien,
1871 (MAK, Inv.-Nr. K.I. 4257/1)
Opening exhibition of the ÖMKI, Vienna, 1871
(MAK, inv. no. K.I. 4257/1)

7 „Serie dunkelgrün mit mittelalterl. venezianischem Schuppendecor", ab 1870

Grünes transparentes Glas mit farbigem Dekor und Gold

Schon auf der Ausstellung anlässlich der Eröffnung des Museumsneubaus 1871/72 waren Gefäße in dieser venezianischen Art ausgestellt: „Verschiedene Glasgeräthe, dunkelblau und grün, nach altvenezianischen Mustern, mit Emailfarben gemalt, nach eigener Zeichnung" („Katalog der österreichischen Kunstgewerbe-Ausstellung", S. 47). Auch auf der Wiener Weltausstellung 1873 und der Weltausstellung in Philadelphia 1876 wurden sie gezeigt.

In den Werkzeichnungen (Bd.VIII, S. 15–19) findet sich eine ähnliche Serie: „Gegenstände aus dünnem Krystallglase, sowohl mit emaillirtem Flechtwerk und Goldverzirungen in altvenezianer Art, als auch mit gravirtem Flechtwerk und Sträusschen ausgeführt, nach eigenen Zeichnungen". Der in Venedig im 15./16. Jahrhundert beliebte Schuppen- und Punktdekor auf dunklem Glas diente hier als Vorlage. Unter anderem bot die Glassammlung des ÖMKI entsprechende Vorbilder. Neben dem Schuppendekor wurden als Motive auch Medaillons mit Blumen in gleicher Technik und Farbenkombination verwendet. Die umfangreiche Serie umfasste Krüge, Becher, Vasen, Flaschen, Schalen und sogar eine Bowlegarnitur. Ein vergleichbarer Krug wurde vom Berliner

7 "Series, dark green with medieval Venetian scale decoration", from 1870

Green transparent glass with colored decoration and gilding

Venetian-style glasses of this kind were first exhibited at the opening exhibition of the new-built museum in1871/72: "Different glass utensils, dark blue and green, after old Venetian designs, painted with enamel colors, after own drawings" ("Katalog der österreichischen Kunstgewerbe-Ausstellung", p. 47). They were also shown at the 1873 Vienna World's Fair and at the 1876 World's Fair in Philadelphia.

A similar series is found in the working drawings (vol.VIII, pp. 15–19): "objects of thin crystal glass, made both with enameled basketry and gold decorations in old Venetian style, and with engraved basketry and sprays, after own drawings." The models here were the scale and dot decorations on dark glass that were popular in Venice in the 15th and 16th century. Among other places, the models were available in the AMAI glass collections. Apart from the scale decoration, medallions with flowers were used as motifs with the same technique and color combinations. The comprehensive series comprised pitchers, beakers, vases, bottles, bowls, and even a punch bowl set. A similar pitcher was bought at the Vienna World's Fair for 15.10 Marks by the Berlin Arts and Crafts Museum. (inv. no. 73, 1301).

Kunstgewerbemuseum 1873 auf der Weltausstellung in Wien um 15,10 Mark erworben (Inv.-Nr. 73, 1301). Als Maler wurde in den zeitgenössischen Quellen Franz Schimpke (1821–1903) aus der Gegend um Haida (Nový Bor) in Nordböhmen genannt: „Krystallgefässe mit buntem Flechtwerk und Gold in alt Venezianer-Art, gezeichnet von Lobmeyr, gemalt von Franz Schimpke" („Welt-Ausstellung 1873 in Wien").

Lit.: Falke 1873, S. 227; Welt-Ausstellung 1873 in Wien, S. 302; Lützow 1875, Abb. S. 153 (vergleichbare Objekte); Smith 1876, Abb. S. 67, 216 (vergleichbare Objekte); Mundt 1973, Kat.-Nr. 158

Contemporary sources name Franz Schimpke (1821–1903) from the Haida region in North-Bohemia as glass painter: "Crystal vessels with colorful basketry and gold in old Venetian style, drawn by Lobmeyr, painted by Franz Schimpke" ("Welt-Ausstellung 1873 in Wien").

Lit.: Falke 1873, p. 227; Welt-Ausstellung 1873 in Wien, p. 302; Lützow 1875, ill. p. 153 (similar objects); Smith 1876, ill. pp. 67, 216 (similar objects); Mundt 1973, cat. no. 158

7a Krug

Ausf.: Meyr's Neffen, Adolf
H 24,1 cm
Quellen: FAP, Serie „Dunkelgrün mit Schuppendekor", vergleichbarer Krug (etwas kleiner) Schnitt „MNA 4865-1870"
Inv.-Nr. Gl 1446, Geschenk des Fürsten Liechtenstein, inv. Dez. 1879

7a Pitcher

Mfr.: Meyr's Neffen, Adolf
H 24.1 cm
Sources: CAP, series "Dark green with scale decoration", similar pitcher (slightly smaller) sectikon "MNA 4865-1870"
Inv. no. Gl 1446, donation from the Prince of Liechtenstein, inv. Dec. 1879

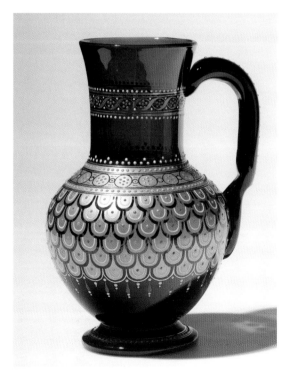

7a

8 „Gegenstände aus blauem Glase, eigene Formen, Ornamente in erhabenen weissen Email gemalt. Diese nach Entwürfen des Prof. Teirich, gezeichnet von Frl. Marie Ritter", ab 1872

Dunkelblaues transparentes Glas mit Dekor in Weiß und Gold

Auf der Wiener Weltausstellung 1873 wurde neben dieser Serie aus blauem Glas mit weißer Bemalung von Lobmeyr eine ähnliche Gruppe der Firma Reich gezeigt (siehe Abb. rechts unten), die genauso auf Anerkennung stieß: „Besser waren die schon erwähnten blauen Gefässe mit weißem Linienornament bei Reich & Comp. und J. & L. Lobmeyr" (Falke/Lobmeyr 1875, S. 22).

Die Firma Lobmeyr zog für den Entwurf der renaissanceartigen Ornamente den an der Kunstgewerbeschule als Lehrer tätigen Valentin Teirich (siehe Kat.-Nr. 3) heran. Marie Ritter, die seine Entwürfe umsetzte, war zu dieser Zeit Schülerin an der Kunstgewerbeschule.

WZ, Bd. IX, S. 1–5

8a Vase
Entw.: 1872
H 36,4 cm
Quellen: FAW, „Serie dunkelblau mit Goldrändern und weissem Emaildekor […]", Vase 211-72; FAP, vergleichbare Vasen Schnitt „MNA & Weltausst. 210 und 212-1872"
Inv.-Nr. Gl 1256, Geschenk des Kaisers, inv. 1875

8 "Objects of blue glass, forms to own designs, ornamentation painted in raised white enamel. Orn. to designs by Prof. Teirich, drawn by Miss Marie Ritter", from 1872

Dark blue transparent glass with white and gold decoration

Aside from this series of blue glass with white painting by Lobmeyr, a similar group by Reich & Comp. was shown at the 1873 Vienna World's Fair (see ill. bottom right) which also met with appreciation: "Better were the mentioned blue vessels with white linear ornamentation at Reich & Comp. and J. & L. Lobmeyr" (Falke/Lobmeyr 1875, p. 22).

Lobmeyr hired Valentin Teirich, a teacher at the Industrial Arts School, for the design of the Renaissance-style ornament. Marie Ritter, who executed his designs, was a student at the school at that time.

WD, vol. IX, pp. 1–5

8a Vase
Dsg.: 1872
H 36.4 cm
Sources: CAV, "Series dark blue with gold rims and white enamel decoration […]", Vase 211-72; CAP, similar vases section "MNA & Weltausst. 210 und 212-1872"
Inv. no. Gl 1256, donation from the Emperor, inv. 1875

8a

Vase, Firma Reich & Comp., um 1873 (MAK, Inv.-Nr. Gl 1055)
Vase, Reich & Comp., around 1873 (MAK, inv. no. Gl 1055)

Doppelhenkelvase dieser Serie,
in: WZ, Bd. XI, S. 39
Double-Handled Vase of this series,
in: WD, vol. XI, p. 39

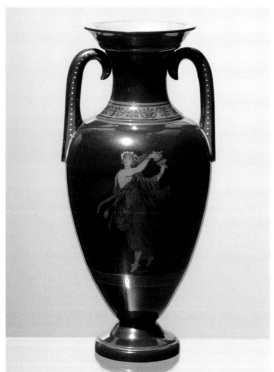

9a

9b

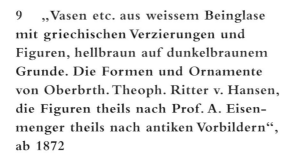

9 „Vasen etc. aus weissem Beinglase mit griechischen Verzierungen und Figuren, hellbraun auf dunkelbraunem Grunde. Die Formen und Ornamente von Oberbrth. Theoph. Ritter v. Hansen, die Figuren theils nach Prof. A. Eisenmenger theils nach antiken Vorbildern", ab 1872

Weißes opakes Glas (Beinglas) mit Bemalung in Braun und Weiß

Der dänische Architekt Theophil von Hansen war seit 1846 in Wien ansässig. Ab 1864 entwarf er Gläser für Lobmeyr, meist im griechischen Stil.

Die Glasgefäße dieser Serie aus braun bemaltem Beinglas sollten antike Tongefäße imitieren. Hansen waren die griechischen Vasen von seinem Aufenthalt in Athen in den Jahren 1838 bis 1846 zweifellos bekannt. Vorlagen für Form und Dekor fanden sich auch in Publikationen des Museums.

1866 wurde vom ÖMKI die Publikation „Umrisse Antiker Thongefässe. Zum Studium und zur Nachbildung für die Kunstindustrie sowie für Schulen" herausgegeben. Die Form der doppelhenkeligen Vasen der griechischen Serie im MAK entspricht den auf Taf. 20

9 "Vases etc. of white bone glass with Greek ornamentation and figures, light brown on dark brown ground. Figures and ornaments by Oberbrth. Theoph. Ritter v. Hansen, figures partly after Prof. A. Eisenmenger, partly after ancient models", from 1872

White opaque glass (bone glass) with brown and white painting

The Danish architect Theophil von Hansen lived in Vienna from 1846. From 1864, he designed glasses for Lobmeyr, mostly in Greek style.

The glass vessels of this series of brown-painted bone glass were supposed to imitate ancient clay vessels. Hansen doubtless knew Greek vases from his stay in Athens from 1839 to 1846. Models for forms and decorations were also to be found in the museum publications.

1866, the AMAI brought out a publication entitled "Contours of Ancient Clay Vessels. For Study and Imitation by the Arts Industry and for Schools". The shape of the double-handled vases of the Greek series corresponds to the amphorae shown in plate 20. 1867,

abgebildeten Amphoren. 1867 erschien eine Publikation über „Ornamente von antiken Thongefässen aus den Sammlungen des K. K. Museums F. K. U. I. und des K. K. Münz. u. Antikenk. gezeichnet von Rudolf Feldscharek im Auftrage des k. k. Museums".

Bei den vom Maler August Eisenmenger verwendeten Vorbildern für die figürlichen Darstellungen handelte es sich um antike Malereien, wie sie beispielsweise in der Publikation „Le pitture antiche d'Ercolano" (Neapel 1762) zu finden waren.

Zu dieser Serie, die auf der Wiener Weltausstellung 1873 gezeigt wurde, gehörten außer Vasen auch ein Aufsatz, eine Schale und eine Flasche. Jakob von Falke meinte anlässlich der Wiener Weltausstellung 1873: „Freilich möchten wir nicht alles von diesen Neuerungen billigen, wie uns z. B. die Nachahmungen antiker Thongefässe mit allen ihren Eigenthümlichkeiten, mit Form, Farbe und Zeichnung ganz verfehlt erscheinen, aber selbst bei denjenigen Gegenständen, die sich noch mit Gemälden schmücken, ist wenigstens eine bessere Form erreicht und die Malerei auf ein bescheideneres Mass zurückgeführt" (Falke 1873, S. 227). Auch Ludwig Lobmeyr selbst musste eingestehen: „Besseres in dieser Art wurde kaum je ausgeführt, aber es war doch verfehlt, Thongeschirr in Glas nachzuahmen; es fand auch keinen Anklang; das Opfer war nicht gering – mindestens habe ich eine Lehre daraus gezogen" (Neuwirth 1999, S. 345).

WZ, Bd. XI, S. 36–45
Lit.: Falke 1873, S. 227; Cohausen/Poschinger 1874, S. 469; Welt-Ausstellung 1873 in Wien, S. 302; Neuwirth 1981d, S. 138

a publication came out on "Ornaments of Ancient Clay Vessels from the Collections of the I. R. Museum o. A. a. I. and the I. R. Coins and Antiques Ch. drawn by Rudolf Feldscharek on behalf of the R. I. Museum."
The models that painter August Eisenmenger used for the figurations were ancient paintings as could be found for example in the publication "Le pitture antiche d'Ercolano" (Naples 1762).

This series which was shown at the 1873 Vienna World's Fair included, apart from vases, a centerpiece, a bowl, and a bottle. Jakob von Falke wrote on the occasion of the World's Fair: "Of course, we cannot approve of everything of these innovations, as, for example, the imitations of ancient clay vessels with all their peculiar characteristics, with forms, colors and drawings appear utterly mislead, but even in those objects which are still decorated with paintings a better form has been achieved and the painting has been reduced to a more modest extent." (Falke 1873, p. 227). Ludwig Lobmeyr himself conceded: "Anything better in its kind was hardly ever achieved; still, it was mislead. Imitating clayware in glass did not find favor, either; it was no little sacrifice – at least I have learnt a lesson from it." (Neuwirth 1999, p. 345).

WD, vol. XI, pp. 36–45
Lit.: Falke 1873, p. 227; Cohausen/Poschinger 1874, p. 469; Welt-Ausstellung 1873 in Wien, p. 302; Neuwirth 1981d, p. 138

9a, b   Vasen mit zwei Henkeln

Entw. u. Ausf.: vor 1873
Bez.: auf der Unterseite „III/1. III/2." (Gl 2581), „VIII./1. VIII/2." (Gl 2582)
H 28,8 bzw. 28,6 cm
Quellen: WZ, Bd. XI, S. 45
Inv.-Nr. Gl 2582 (9a), Gl 2581 (9b),
Vermächtnis Ludwig Lobmeyr 1917, nachträglich inv.

Die Tänzerinnen auf den Vasen sind mit verschiedenen Attributen, einem flatternden Tuch bzw. einem Schlaginstrument, ausgestattet.

9a, b   Double-Handled Vases

Dsg. a. mfr.: before 1873
Marks: at the bottom "III/1. III/2." (Gl 2581), "VIII./1. VIII/2." (Gl 2582)
H 28.8 and 28.6 cm
Sources: WD, vol. XI, p. 45
Inv. no. Gl 2581, Gl 2582, Ludwig Lobmeyr Legacy 1917, subs. inv.

The dancers in the vases carry different paraphernalia, such as a fluttering shawl or a percussion instrument.

10 Aufsatz

Entw. u. Ausf.: wohl 1873
Farbloses Glas mit farbigem Dekor und Gold
H 26 cm, D 31,8 cm
Inv.-Nr. Gl 1129, Geschenk v. J. & L. Lobmeyr, inv. 23. Apr. 1874

Gefäße „im altdeutschen Style", meist aus grünlichem Glas und mit Emailmalerei (Wappen und floraler Dekor), wurden auf den Weltausstellungen 1862, 1867 und 1873 gezeigt. Der Aufsatz mit Tieren des heimischen Waldes und den renaissanceartigen Ranken in Emailmalerei passt stilistisch zu diesen Serien, etwa der „Serie gemeingrün mit Malerei in Deutscher Renaissance".

Im Wiener Firmenarchiv findet sich unter „Div. Serien" eine kolorierte Zeichnung dieses Aufsatzes, signiert „Franz Gerasch".

10 Centerpiece

Dsg. a. mfr.: pres. 1873
Colorless glass with colored decoration and gilding
H 26 cm, D 31.8 cm
Inv. no. Gl 1129, donation from J. & L. Lobmeyr, inv. 23 Apr. 1874

Vessels "in old German style", mostly of greenish glass and with enamel painting (coat-of-arms and floral decoration) were shown at the World's Fairs of 1862, 1867, and 1873. The centerpiece with domestic woodland animals and Renaissance-style tendrils in enamel painting suited in style with these series, such as the "Series in common green with painting in German Renaissance style."

In the Vienna Company Archives, there is, under the heading of "Div. Series", a colored drawing of this centerpiece, signed "Franz Gerasch."

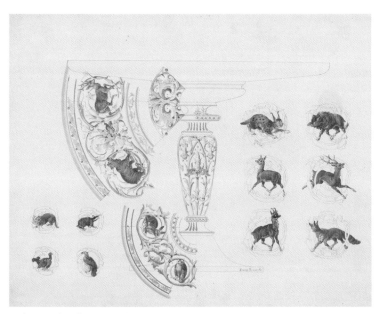

Aufsatz (Werkzeichnung, FAW)
Centerpiece (working drawing, CAV)

10

11 „Gegenstände innen hell, aussen dunkel überfangen mit durchschliffenen Hohlkehlen etc. und reicher Golddecoration. Nach eigenen Zeichnungen, Ornamente von Arch. Rehlender", um 1874

Farbloses Glas mit Überfang, Schliff (Hohlkehlen) und Dekor in Gold und Weiß

Die Gegenstände mit geschliffenem Überfang sind mit zarten Arabesken in Gold und Weiß bemalt. Zur Serie, die in verschiedenfarbigem Glas ausgeführt werden konnte, gehörten eine Doppelhenkelvase, ein Pokal, ein Krug, eine Deckeldose mit Teller, ein Becher mit Fuß, eine Flasche, ein Stängelglas, eine Schale mit Fuß, ein Aufsatz und Vasen. Form und Dekor des Aufsatzes sind im Firmenarchiv in der Serie „Krystall blau überfangen, durchschliffen mit Goldecor und Emailpunkten […]" von 1874 aufgenommen. Eine ähnliche Serie aus rosa Kristallglas mit maurischem Dekor in Gold, Weiß und Schwarz nach Zeichnungen von Josef Salb wurde auf der Weltausstellung 1873 präsentiert.
In ähnlicher Technik (siehe Kat.-Nr. 21) bzw. Dekor (siehe Kat.-Nr. 27) sind weitere Serien entstanden.
Der aus Deutschland stammende Georg Rehlender (geb. 1845 in Trebbin im Kreis Teltow/Brandenburg, gest. nach 1906) war Schüler der Berliner Bauakademie und wurde ab 1872 in Wien genannt. In den Jahren 1875 bis 1877 führte er gemeinsam mit Otto Girard ein „Atelier f. Architektur und Kunst-Industrie", danach war er offensichtlich wieder in Berlin tätig (Entwürfe von Innenausstattung und Grafik). In seinen Wiener Jahren entstanden viele Entwürfe für Lobmeyr, meistens Ornamente: für Serien aus Opalglas, die Serie „Aquamarin" mit orientalischen Ornamenten, für die persische Serie, für „Vasen etc. aus weissem Beinglase mit orientalischer flacher Malerei […]" u. a.
WZ, Bd. IX, S. 23–26

11 "Objects light inside, on the outside dark casing with carved fluting and rich gold decoration. After own drawings, ornamentation by Arch. Rehlender", around 1874

Colorless glass with casing, carved (fluting) and decoration in gold and white

The objects with cut casing are painted with delicate arabesques in gold and white. The series, which could be made in glass of different colors, includes a double-handled vase, a goblet, a pitcher, a lidded box with plate, a footed beaker, a bottle, a stem glass, a bowl, a tabletop piece, and vases. The form and decoration of the tabletop piece are recorded in the company archives in the 1874 series "crystal, blue casing, carved with gold decoration and enamel dots […]." A similar series of pink crystal glass with Moorish decoration in gold, white, and black after drawings by Josef Salb was presented at the 1873 World's Fair.
Series with decorations by Rehlender were made in similar technique (see cat. no. 21) and decoration (see cat. no. 27).
The Germany-born Georg Rehlender (b. 1845 in Trebbin in Teltow/Brandenburg, d. after 1906) was a student at the Berlin Academy of Architecture and appears as a Vienna resident after 1872. 1875–1877, he had a "Studio f. Architecture and Industrial Art" together with Otto Girard; after that, he apparently worked in Berlin again (interior decoration designs and graphic art). In his Viennese years, he produced many designs for Lobmeyr mostly ornaments for series of opal glass, for the "Aquamarine" series with oriental ornamentation, for the Persian series, for "Vases etc. of white bone glass with oriental flat painting […]" a. o.
WD, vol. IX, pp. 23–26

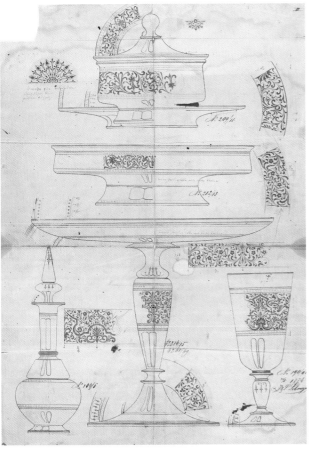

Werkzeichnungen zu dieser Serie (FAW)
Working drawings for this series (CAV)

11a

11a Aufsatz

Entw.: 1874
Farbloses Glas mit rotem Überfang, Schliff (Hohlkehlen)
und Dekor in Gold und Weiß
H 23,5 cm
Quellen: WZ, Bd. IX, S. 26; FAW, Zeichnung „Fruchtaufsatz
4268/69-74"
Inv.-Nr. Gl 1274, Geschenk v. J. & L. Lobmeyr, inv. 7. März 1876

11a Tabletop Piece

Dsg.: 1874
Colorless glass with red casing, carving (fluting)
and decoration in gold and white
H 23.5 cm
Sources: WD, vol. IX, p. 26; CAV, drawing "Fruchtaufsatz
4268/69-74"
Inv. no. Gl 1274, donation from J. & L. Lobmeyr,
inv. 7 March 1876

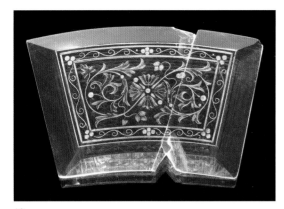

12

12 Plättchen

Entw. u. Ausf.: vor 1874
Farbloses Glas mit Schnitt (poliert)
L 9,4 cm, B 6 cm
Inv.-Nr. Gl 1122, Geschenk v. J. & L. Lobmeyr, inv. 9. Apr. 1874

Dieses viereckige Plättchen mit abfallend geschliffenen
Rändern war wohl für eine mit Montierung zusammen-
gesetzte Schale gedacht. Derartige Schalen waren in der
Renaissance aus Bergkristallplatten angefertigt worden
und wurden im Historismus entweder aus Bergkristall
oder Kristallglasteilen hergestellt.

12 Small Plate

Dsg. a. mfr.: before 1874
Colorless cut glass Schnitt (polished)
L 9.4 cm, B 6 cm
Inv. no. Gl 1122, donation from J. & L. Lobmeyr, inv. 9 Apr. 1874

This rectangular plate with chamfered edges was
intended as part of a bowl with mounting. Bowls of this
kind were made from rock crystals in the Renaissance
period and were produced from rock crstal oder crystal
parts in the era of Historicism.

„Teil eines Tellers aus Bergkrystall mit vergoldeter Fassung,
von Ratzersdorfer in Wien", in: Lützow 1875, S. 356
(MAK, Inv.-Nr. K.I. 3995)
"Detail of a rock–crystal plate with gilded mounting, by Ratzersdorfer
in Vienna", in: Lützow 1875, p. 356 (MAK, inv. no. K.I. 3995)

Theil eines Tellers aus Bergkryftall mit vergoldeter Faffung, von Ratzersdorfer in Wien.

13 Serie „Krüge etc. aus Krystallglas mit hellpolirter Renaissancegravirung nach eigenen Zeichnungen", um 1873

Farbloses Glas mit Schliff und Schnitt

Die Serie umfasste neben Krügen auch Stängelgläser und eine Flasche mit Henkel. Die Krüge konnten noch zusätzlich mit Silbermontierungen versehen sein. Die renaissanceartigen Gravierungen wie Füllhörner, Arabesken, Chimären usw. auf farblosem Kristallglas entsprachen den stilistischen Vorbildern, die zu dieser Zeit von den Theoretikern für das böhmische Kristallglas propagiert wurden. Während Ludwig Lobmeyr für Entwürfe ähnlicher Gefäße (siehe Kat.-Nr. 6) Künstler heranzog, ist diese Gruppe „nach eigenen Zeichnungen" entstanden.

WZ, Bd. VIII, S. 33–34

13 Serie "Pitchers etc. of crystal glas with highly polished Renaissance engraving after own drawings", around 1873

Colorless glass, ground and cut

Apart from pitchers, the series also included stem glasses and a bottle with handle. The pitchers sometimes had silver mountings. Renaissance-style engravings such as cornucopias, arabesques, chimeras etc. on colorless glass corresponded to the models propagated at that time by theoreticians for Bohemian crystal glass. While Lobmeyr hired artist for designs of similar vessels (see cat. no. 6), this series was made "after own drawings".

WD, vol. VIII, pp. 33–34

13b

13a

Schale, in: WZ, Bd. VIII, S. 34 (Ausschnitt)
Bowl, in: WD, vol. VIII, p. 34 (detail)

13a Schale

Entw. u. Ausf.: um 1873
Farbloses Glas mit Schliff und Schnitt
D 35,3 cm
Quellen: WZ, Bd. VIII, S. 34
Inv.-Nr. Gl 1090, angek. v. J. & L. Lobmeyr auf der Wiener
Weltausstellung um 300 fl., inv. 13. Febr. 1874

13b Krug mit Deckel

Entw. u. Ausf.: um 1873
Farbloses Glas mit Schliff und Schnitt (teilweise poliert),
Silbermontierung (Hermann Ratzersdorfer, Wien)
H 44,4 cm
Quellen: WZ, Bd. VIII, S. 34
Inv.-Nr. Gl. 1091, angek. v. J. & L. Lobmeyr auf der Wiener
Weltausstellung um 260 fl., inv. 13. Febr. 1874
Lit.: Lützow 1875, S. 372

13a Bowl

Dsg. a. mfr.: around 1873
Colorless glass, ground and cut
D 35.3 cm
Sources: WD, vol. VIII, p. 34
Inv. no. Gl 1090, purch. by J. & L. Lobmeyr at the Vienna
World's Fair for 300 Gulden, inv. 13 Febr. 1874

13b Pitcher with Lid

Dsg. a. mfr.: around 1873
Colorless glass, ground and cut (partly polished),
silver mounting (Hermann Ratzersdorfer, Vienna)
H 44.4 cm
Sources: WD, vol. VIII, p. 34
Inv. no. Gl. 1091, purch. by J. & L. Lobmeyr at the Vienna
World's Fair for 260 Gulden, inv. 13 Febr. 1874
Lit.: Lützow 1875, p. 372

Schale (Werkzeichnung, FAW)
Bowl (working drawing, CAV)

14

14 Schale

Entw.: Josef Storck, 1874
Ausf.: 1874
Farbloses Glas mit Schnitt (poliert)
L 29,7 cm, B 19,7 cm
Quellen: WZ, Bd. VIII, S. 35; FAW, Zeichnung „Nr. 5253 13. 4. 1874"
Inv.-Nr. Gl 1239, Geschenk v. J. & L. Lobmeyr, inv. 20. Jan. 1875

Diese Schale „mit hellpolirter Renaissancegravirung"
(stilisierte Pflanzen und Tiere) gehört zu einer Gruppe
von Arbeiten Lobmeyrs aus den siebziger Jahren, die das
Glas der Renaissance zum Vorbild haben (siehe Kat.-Nr.
6, 13, 19). Josef Storck hatte Anfang der siebziger Jahre
Bergkristallgefäße aus der Ambraser Sammlung und ita-
lienische Renaissancemotive aus dem 16. Jahrhundert
studiert und dokumentiert. Für mehrere runde und ovale Schalen mit figürlichen Darstellungen im Zentrum
entwarf Storck den Randdekor im Renaissancestil. Die
Figuren im Zentrum, die Götter (wie Tritonen, Aurora,
Merkur oder Flora) oder Allegorien, etwa der Lüfte, dar-
stellten, stammten von anderen Künstlern wie A. Kühne,
C. Niklas oder H. Bitterlich.

Lit.: Blätter für Kunstgewerbe, Bd. 5, 1876, Taf. 22;
Scholda 1991, Kat.-Nr. 46

14 Bowl

Dsg.: Josef Storck, 1874
Mfr.: 1874
Colorless glass, ground and cut (polished)
L 29.7 cm, B 19.7 cm
Sources: WD, vol. VIII, p. 35; CAV, Zeichnung "Nr. 5253 13. 4. 1874"
Inv. no. Gl 1239, donation from J. & L. Lobmeyr, inv. 20 Jan. 1875

This bowl with "highly polished Renaissance
engraving" (stylized plants and animals) belonged to a
group of pieces by Lobmeyr from the 1870s made to
the model of Renaissance glass (see cat. nos. 6, 13, 19).
In the early 1870s, Josef Storck had studied and
documented rock crystal vessels from the Ambras
collection and 16th century Italian Renaissance motifs.
Storck designed Renaissance-style decorations for
several round and oval bowls with figurative motifs in
the centers. The figures in the center which show
deities such as tritons, Aurora, Mercury, or Flora, or
allegories of, for example, the winds, were made by
other artists such as A. Kühne, C. Niklas, or H.
Bitterlich.

Lit.: Blätter für Kunstgewerbe, vol. 5, 1876, pl. 22;
Scholda 1991, cat. no. 46

15

„Die zwölf Monate. Deckenbild im Palais
Gutmann", in: Album der Gesellschaft für
vervielfältigende Kunst in Wien, 1875,
Blatt 25 (MAK, Inv.-Nr. K.I. 3450)
"The Twelve Months, ceiling frescoe in the Palais
Gutmann", in: Album der Gesellschaft für ver-
vielfältigende Kunst in Wien, 1875, pl. 25
(MAK, inv. No. K.I. 3450)

15 Aufsatz mit allegorischer Darstellung der zwölf Monate

Entw.: Theophil von Hansen, August Eisenmenger (Figuren), 1874
Ausf.: wohl Meyr's Neffen, Adolf, 1874; Carl Pietsch,
Steinschönau (Schnitt)
Farbloses Glas mit Schnitt, vergoldete Silbermontierung
mit Email (Hermann Ratzersdorfer, Wien)
FM: im Zentrum der Unterseite geschnitten
H 16,7 cm, D 34,1 cm
Inv.-Nr. Gl 1238, Geschenk v. J. & L. Lobmeyr, inv. 20. Jan. 1875

Diese Schale wurde nach der Weihnachtsausstellung 1874
dem Museum als Geschenk überlassen. Sie wurde wegen
der außergewöhnlichen Arbeit auch 1876 auf der Kunst-
und Kunstindustrie-Ausstellung in München gezeigt.
Die Figuren wurden an der Unterseite eingeschliffen,
sodass sie von oben „vermöge der Lichtwirkung in einem erhabenen Relief aufzuliegen scheinen […] Die
Modellirung ist so zart, sanft und lebendig zugleich, das
ganze Werk so sehr vollendet und bisher einzig, ein
wahres Cabinets- und Museumsstück […]" („Mittheilungen", Nr. 114, 1. März 1875, S. 311).

15 Centerpiece with allegory of the twelve months

Dsg.: Theophil von Hansen, August Eisenmenger (figures), 1874
Mfr.: pres. Meyr's Neffen, Adolf, 1874; Carl Pietsch,
Steinschönau (cutting)
Colorless cut glass, gilded silver mounting with enamel
(Hermann Ratzersdorfer, Vienna)
FM: cut in the bottom center
H 16.7 cm, D 34.1 cm
Inv. no. Gl 1238, donation from J. & L. Lobmeyr, inv 20 Jan. 1875

Following the 1874 Christmas exhibition, this bowl was
donated to the museum. Because of its exceptional
quality, it was also shown at the Munich Art and
Industrial Arts Exhibition of 1876.
The figures were cut into the bottom side so that,
viewed from above, they "appeared, due to the light
effect, as if standing out in relief […] The modeling is so
delicate, tender and lively at the same time, the whole
piece is of such perfection and uniqueness, a true
showpiece and museum piece […]" ("Mittheilungen",
no. 114, 1 March 1875, p. 311).

Für diesen außergewöhnlichen Glasschnitt ist der nord-böhmische Glasschneider Carl Pietsch (1828–1883) ver-antwortlich, der wiederholt für Lobmeyr gearbeitet hat (siehe Kat.-Nr. 18).

Die Figuren finden sich in gleicher Art und Anordnung auf einem runden Deckenfresko, das August Eisenmenger Anfang der siebziger Jahre für die Wohnung des Unter-nehmers Wilhelm Ritter von Gutmann in Wien (1, Beet-hovenplatz 3) ausgeführt hat. Die Umsetzung des farbi-gen Freskos in den kleinformatigeren monochromen Glasschnitt ist sehr gelungen.

Theophil von Hansen zog August Eisenmenger und an-dere Akademieprofessoren immer wieder für die figu-ralen Darstellungen seiner Glasentwürfe heran, etwa bei der griechischen Serie (Kat.-Nr. 9) oder bei den „Vasen aus weissem Beinglase mit Ornamenten und bunt ge-malten Figuren auf Goldgrund" („Die Formen und Ornamente nach Entwürfen des Oberbrth. Th. R. v. Hansen, die Figuren nach den Professoren A. Eisen-menger, Rahl u. a. m.", WZ, Bd. 11, S. 48–51).

Lit.: Mittheilungen, Nr. 114, 1. März 1875, S. 311 (Weihnachtsausstellung 1874); Spiegl 1980, S. 113, Abb. 127

The North-Bohemian glass cutter Carl Pietsch (1828–1883) who repeatedly worked for Lobmeyr (cf. cat. no. 18) was responsible for this extraordinary cutting technique.

The same type and array of figures is found in a round ceiling fresco made by August Eisenmenger for the apartment of the entrepreneur Wilhelm Ritter von Gutmann in Vienna (1, Beethovenplatz 3) in the early 1870s. The rendering of the colored fresco in a smaller monochrome glass cutting is very accomplished.

Theophil von Hansen repeatedly called in August Eisenmenger and other academy professors for figurative representations in his glass designs, as for example for his Greek series (cat. no. 9) or for the "vases of white bone glass with ornamentation and colored painted figures on gold ground" ("Forms and ornaments to designs by Oberbrth. Th. R. v. Hansen, figures after professors A. Eisenmenger, Rahl a. o.", WD, vol. 11, pp. 48–51).

Lit.: Mittheilungen, no. 114, 1 March 1875, p. 311 (Christmas exhibition 1874); Spiegl 1980, p. 113, ill. 127

16 Serie „Krystall mit gezahnten Hohlkehlen", ab 1874

Farbloses Glas mit Schliff

Das farblose Kristallglas wurde nur durch den Schliff or-namentiert. Der in Böhmen und England in der ersten Hälfte des 19. Jahrhunderts beliebte Steindelschliff ist bei dieser Serie auf die Kanten der Hohlkehlen redu-ziert.

Ein dazu passendes Trink- und Dessert-Service entstand 1875 „nach eigenen Zeichnungen" (WZ, Bd. III, S. 38–39, Bd. VI, S. 34–35) und umfasste Aufsätze, Schalen, Teller, Deckeldosen und sogar eine Bowlegarnitur.

16 Series "Crystal with toothed grooves", from 1874

Colorless cut glass

Colorless crystal glass was ornamented by cutting only. The brilliant cutting which was very popular in the first half of the 19th century is reduced to the edges of the grooves here.

A fitting drinking and dessert service was made 1875 "after own drawings" (WD, vol. III, pp. 38–39, vol. VI, pp. 34–35) and comprised centerpieces, bowls, plates, lidded boxes, and even a punch bowl set.

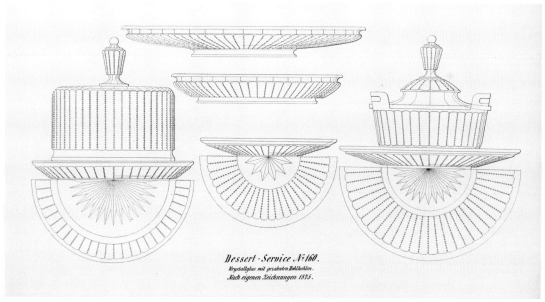

Teile des Dessert-Services Nr. 160, „aus Krystallglas mit gezahnten Hohlkehlen. Nach eigenen Zeichnungen 1875", in: WZ, Bd. VI, S. 35
Dessert Service no. 160, details, from "Crystal glass with toothed grooves. After own drawings 1875", in: WD, vol. VI, p. 35

16a Pokal mit Deckel

Entw.: 1874
Ausf.: Meyr's Neffen, Adolf, 1874
H 44,7 cm
Quellen: FAP, Schnitt „MNA 4907 1874 7/11"
Inv.-Nr. Gl 1240, angek. v. J. & L. Lobmeyr, inv. 20. Jan. 1875

16a Lidded Goblet

Dsg.: 1874
Mfr.: Meyr's Neffen, Adolf, 1874
H 44.7 cm
Sources: CAP, section "MNA 4907 1874 7/11"
Inv. no. Gl 1240, purch. by J. & L. Lobmeyr, inv. 20 Jan. 1875

17 „Gegenstände aus Krystallglas, außen glatt, mit eingeblasenen Hohlgängen. Nach eigenen Zeichnungen", ab 1876

Farbloses Glas mit eingeblasenen Hohlgängen

Für diese Technik der eingeblasenen Hohlgänge wurde die Hütte von Josef Eduard Schmid in Annathal (Annín) in Südböhmen herangezogen. Josef Eduard Schmid (1836–1910) war mit einer Tochter Wilhelm Kraliks verheiratet. Die Technik erinnert an venezianischen Fadendekor, und auch die Form mit dem balusterartigen Stiel und Flügeln scheint venezianische Formen aus dem 17. Jahrhundert aufzugreifen.

17 "Object of crystal glass, polished outside, with blown-in hollow columns. After own drawings", from 1876

Colorless glass with blown-in hollow columns

The technique of blowing hollow columns into the glass was done in the glassworks of Josef Eduard Schmid in Annathal in South-Bohemia. Josef Eduard Schmid (1836–1910) was married to a daughter of Wilhelm Kralik.
The technique is reminiscent of Venetian trailing, and the form with a baluster-like stem and wings also seems to fall back on 17th century Venetian forms.
In the working drawings a comprehensive series in this

16a

In den Werkzeichnungen ist eine umfangreiche Serie in dieser Technik erfasst: Vasen, Flaschen, Krüge, Becher, Aufsätze, Schale, Deckeldosen, Pokale, Stängelgläser, Kännchen u. a. Viele der Gefäße sitzen auf vier Beinen oder haben vier Henkel, teilweise auch Flügel, ähnlich wie der Pokal.

WZ, Bd. VIII, S. 20–25

technique is recorded: vases, bottles, pitchers, center-pieces, bowls, lidded boxes, goblets, stem glasses, jugs etc. Many of these vessels have four legs and some also have wings, similarly to the goblet.

WD, vol. VIII, pp. 20–25

17a Pokal mit Deckel

Entw.: 1876
H 46,1 cm
Quellen: WZ, Bd. VIII, S. 24; FAP, Schnitt „Schm. A. 2. 1876"
Inv.-Nr. Gl 2580, Vermächtnis Ludwig Lobmeyr 1917, nachträglich inv.

17a Lidded Goblet

Dsg.: 1876
H 46.1 cm
Sources: WD, vol. VIII, p. 24; CAP, section "Schm. A. 2. 1876"
Inv. no. Gl 2580, legacy Ludwig Lobmeyr 1917, subs. inv.

17a

Glasgefäße „mit eingeblasenen Hohlgängen",
in: WZ, Bd. VIII, S. 25
Glass objects with "blown-in hollow columns",
in: WD, vol. VIII, p. 25

18a

18b

18 Ovale Platten mit Figuren

Von mehreren Künstlern sind figürliche Darstellungen
für ovale Platten aus farblosem Glas mit renaissanceartigem Randdekor entworfen worden. Die von unten
geschnittenen Figuren im Zentrum stellen meist Tritonen, Meerjungfrauen oder andere mythologische Meeres-
wesen dar. Schalen in dieser Art wurden bis um die
Jahrhundertwende erzeugt.

18a Ovale Platte mit Triton

Entw.: August Kühne (Figur), Josef Storck (Dekor)
Ausf.: wohl Meyr's Neffen, Adolf, 1875; Carl Pietsch,
Steinschönau (Schnitt)
Farbloses Glas mit Schnitt (teilweise poliert)
FM: auf der Unterseite am Rand geschnitten
L 27,9 cm, B 20,4 cm
Quellen: WZ, Bd.VIII, S. 31 („Nach eig. Zeichnungen. Orna-
mente gezeichnet v. Regr. Prof. Storck. Figur nach Modell v. A.
Kühne"); FAP, Randornament „Gravirung Pitsch Glas MNA
5945.1875", „für männlichen und weiblichen Triton"
Inv.-Nr. Gl 1270, angek. auf der Weihnachtsausstellung 1875,
inv. 8. Jan. 1876
Lit.: Mittheilungen, Nr. 124, 1. Jan. 1876, S. 11 ff.; Blätter für
Kunstgewerbe, Bd. 8, 1879, Taf. 35; Schmidt 1925, S. 55, 103,
Taf. 9; Mundt 1973, Kat.-Nr. 204; Spiegl 1980, Abb. 129;
Scholda 1991, Kat.-Nr. 51

18b Ovale Platte mit Triton und Nereide

Entw.: August Eisenmenger (Figuren), Josef Storck (Dekor),
vor 1880
Ausf.: Carl Pietsch, Steinschönau (Schnitt), vor 1880
Farbloses Glas mit Schnitt
FM: auf der Unterseite am Rand geschnitten;
Signatur des Glasschneiders: „CP" oben in der Mitte

18 Oval Platters with Figures

Several artists designed figurative representations for
oval platters of colorless glass with Renaissance-style
rim decorations. The intaglio-cut figures mostly show
tritons, mermaids, or other mythological sea creatures.
Bowls of this type were produced until around the turn
of the century.

Vorlage zur Platte 18b (FAW)
Model for platter cat. no. 18b (CAV)

18a Oval Platter with Triton

Dsg.: August Kühne (figure), Josef Storck (decoration)
Mfr.: pres. Meyr's Neffen, Adolf, 1875; Carl Pietsch,
Steinschönau (cut)
Colorless cut glass (partly polished)
B: cut into the bottom rim
L 27.9 cm, B 20.4 cm
Sources: WD, vol.VIII, p. 31 ("After own drawings.
Ornaments drawn by Regr. Prof. Storck. Figure after model
by A. Kühne"); CAP, rim ornament "Engraving Pitsch Glass
MNA 5945.1875", "for male and female Triton"
Inv. no. Gl 1270, purch. at the 1875 Christmas exhibition,
inv. 8 Jan. 1876
Lit.: Mittheilungen, no. 124, 1 Jan. 1876, pp. 11 ff.; Blätter für
Kunstgewerbe, vol. 8, 1879, pl. 35; Schmidt 1925, p. 55, 103,
pl. 9; Mundt 1973, cat. no. 204; Spiegl 1980, ill. 129; Scholda
1991, cat. no. 51

18b Oval Platter with Triton and Nereid

Dsg.: August Eisenmenger (figures), Josef Storck (decoration),
before 1880
Mfr.: Carl Pietsch, Steinschönau (cut), before 1880
Colorless cut glass
B: cut into the bottom rim; cutter's signature "CP" top center
L 35.6 cm, B 26.9 cm

18c

„Krystallglasschale von J. & L. Lobmeyr", gezeigt auf der
Weihnachtsausstellung 1898, in: Blätter für Kunstgewerbe, Bd. 27,
1898, Taf. 2 (MAK, Inv.-Nr. K.I. 3251)
"Crystal glass bowl by J. & L. Lobmeyr", presented at the Christmas
exhibition 1898, in: Blätter für Kunstgewerbe, vol. 27, 1898, pl. 2
(MAK, inv. No. 3251)

L 35,6 cm, B 26,9 cm
Inv.-Nr. Gl 1517, angek. v. J. & L. Lobmeyr um 350 fl.,
inv. 2. März 1880
Lit.: Spiegl 1980, Abb. 131; Scholda 1991, Kat.-Nr. 52

Inv. no. Gl 1517, purch. by J. & L. Lobmeyr for 350 Gulden,
inv. 2 March 1880
Lit.: Spiegl 1980, ill. 131; Scholda 1991, cat. no. 52

18c Platte mit Seekentaurin (Kentaurotritonin)

Entw.: wohl August Eisenmenger (Figur), 4. Viertel d. 19. Jh.
Farbloses Glas mit Schnitt, Rand poliert
FM: an der Oberseite am Rand geschnitten
L 27,7 cm, B 21,5 cm
Quellen: FAW, Randornament 5945-75; 1889 führte Franz
Ullmann einen „Teller oval mit weibl. Triton (5945-75)" aus
Inv.-Nr. Gl 2747, nachträglich inv.
Lit.: Blätter für Kunstgewerbe, Bd. 27, 1898, Abb. Taf. 2
(Weihnachtsausstellung 1898); Glass by J. & L. Lobmeyr of
Vienna, Abb. S. 253; Scholda 1991, Kat.-Nr. 50

18c Platter with Female Sea Centaur (Female Centaur Triton)

Dsg.: pres. August Eisenmenger (figure), 4th quart. 19th cent.
Colorless cut glass, rim polished
B: cut into the topside rim
L 27.7 cm, B 21.5 cm
Sources: CAV, rim ornament 5945-75; 1889, Franz Ullmann
made a "plate, oval with fem. Triton (5945-75)"
Inv. no. Gl 2747, subs. inv.
Lit.: Blätter für Kunstgewerbe, vol. 27, 1898, ill. pl. 2
(Christmas exhibition 1898); Glass by J. & L. Lobmeyr of
Vienna, ill. p. 253; Scholda 1991, cat. no. 50

Der Randdekor geht auf einen Entwurf von 1875 zurück. Solche Teller und Schalen mit mythologischen Figuren im Zentrum wurden noch auf der Weihnachtsausstellung des Museums 1898 und der Pariser Weltausstellung 1900 präsentiert. 1898 wurde eine vergleichbare Schale mit demselben Randornament auf der Weihnachtsausstellung des Museums gezeigt (Abb. in den „Blättern für Kunstgewerbe", Bd. 27, 1898). Im Zentrum befindet sich ein Seekentaur. Die gleiche Schale mit Triton wurde auch 1900 auf der Pariser Weltausstellung präsentiert. In einem Katalog dazu wurde die Figur Prof. Eisenmenger zugeschrieben.

The rim decoration dates back to a design of 1875. Plates and bowls with mythological figures in the center were still presented at the museum's 1898 Christmas exhibition and the 1900 Paris World's Fair. 1898 a similar bowl with the same kind of rim ornament was shown at the museum's Christmas exhibition (ill. in "Blätter für Kunstgewerbe", vol. 27, 1898). In the center, there was a see centaur. The same bowl with a Triton was presented at the 1900 Paris World's Fair. In the exhibition catalogue, the figure was ascribed to August Eisenmenger.

19 Serie „Krystall mit umschnittenen Hohlkehlen 1876"

Farbloses Glas mit Schliff und Schnitt (poliert, teilweise matt)

Gefäße dieser Serie wurden gemeinsam mit der Prunkvase von Hermann Herdtle (siehe Kat.-Nr. 20) für Kronprinz Rudolf als Geschenk zu seiner Hochzeit 1881 angefertigt. Dafür wurden die Gläser noch in emaillierten Silbermontierungen (von Hermann Ratzersdorfer) gefasst. In dieser Art sind sie auch in die Werkzeichnungen aufgenommen worden: „Prunkgefässe aus Krystallglas mit ornamentaler Glanzgravirung und emaillierten Fassungen aus Edelmetall. Zur Huldigungsgabe der Österr. Handels- u. Gewerbekammer anlässlich der Vermählung Sr k. u. k. Hoheit des Kronprinzen 1881" (WZ, Bd. VIII, S. 37–48).

„Diese Prunkgefäße […] umfassen 45 Objekte (Pocale, Kannen, Becher, Blumengefäße etc.) und sind nach Art jener Prachtgefäße ausgeführt, die, eine Zierde der kaiserlichen Schatzkammer bildend, aus der Zeit des kunstsinnigen Kaiser Rudolf II. stammen […] Was die Ausf. der Gegenstände betrifft, so entwarf […] Lobmeyr die Zeichnungen zu den Pocalen, Kannen etc., deren ornamentale Ausschmückung Herr Professor Salb besorgte […]" („Mittheilungen", Nr. 183, 1. Dez. 1880, S. 233). Im Museum befindet sich ein Teil dieser Gefäße aus der ursprünglichen Serie von 1876 ohne Montierungen. Stilistisch schließt diese Gruppe an die gravierten Gläser des Kaiser-Services an (siehe Kat.-Nr. 6).

Lit.: Mittheilungen, Nr. 183, 1. Dez. 1880, S. 233; Mittheilungen, Nr. 190, 1. Juli 1881 (Beilage, S. 6); Huldigung der Oesterreichischen Handels- und Gewerbekammern; Gewerbehalle, Heft 1, 1886, Taf. 3

19a Pokal mit Deckel (siehe Abb. S. 45)
Entw.: 1876
Farbloses Glas mit Schliff und Schnitt (poliert, teilweise matt)
FM: auf der Unterseite am Rand geschnitten
H 18,7 cm
Quellen: WZ, Bd. VIII, S. 43; FAP, Schnitt „MNA 9436. 1876 III. Gr." Inv.-Nr. Gl 2740, nachträglich inv.

19 Series "Crystal with cut-around grooves 1876"

Colored glass, ground and cut (partly polished, partly matte)

The vessels of this series were made in 1881 together with the grand vase by Hermann Herdtle (see cat. no. 20) as a wedding present for Crown Prince Rudolf. The glasses were set in enameled silver mountings (by Hermann Ratzersdorfer). This is how they are recorded in the working drawings: "Grand vessels of crystal glass with polished ornamental engraving and enameled mountings of precious metal. A tributary gift from the Austr. Chamber of Trade and Commerce for the wedding of His Imperial and Royal Highness the Crown Prince in 1881" (WD, vol. VIII, pp. 37–48).

"These grand vessels […] comprise 45 objects (goblets, jugs, beakers, flower vessels etc.) and are made in the manner of those grand vessels which originate from the time of the art-interested Emperor Rudolf II. and are showpieces in the Imperial Treasury […] As far as the making of the objects is concerned, Lobmeyr made […] the design drawings for the goblets, jugs etc., the ornamental decoration of which was provided by Professor Salb […]" ("Mittheilungen", no. 183, 1 Dec. 1880, p. 233).

The museum holdings include one part of these vessels from the original series of 1876 without mountings. In style, this group follows the engraved glassware of the Imperial Service (see cat. no. 6).

Lit.: Mittheilungen, no. 183, 1 Dec. 1880, p. 233; Mittheilungen, no. 190, 1 July 1881 (supplement, p. 6); Huldigung der Oesterreichischen Handels- und Gewerbekammern; Gewerbehalle, issue 1, 1886, pl. 3

19a Lidded Goblet (see ill. p. 45)
Dsg.: 1876
Colorless ground and cut glass (polished, partly matte)
B: cut into the bottom rim
H 18.7 cm
Sources: WD, vol. VIII, p. 43; CAP, section "MNA 9436. 1876 III. Gr."; Inv. no. Gl 2740, subs. inv.

19b

19b (Unterteller Saucer)

Teile der Huldigungsgabe, in: Huldigung der Oester-
reichischen Handels- und Gewerbekammern, Taf. 6
(MAK, Inv.-Nr. K.I. 10268)
Parts of the tributary gift, in: "Huldigung der Oesterreichi-
schen Handels- und Gewerbekammern", pl. 6
(MAK, inv. no. K.I. 10268)

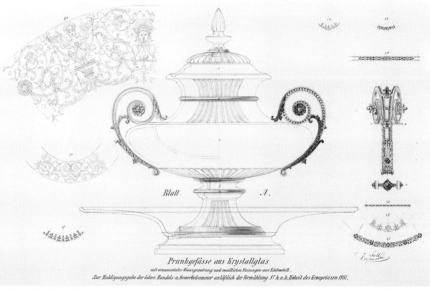

Deckelgefäß der Huldigungsgabe, in: WZ, Bd. VIII, S. 37
Lidded Goblet of the tributary gift, in: WD, vol. VIII, s. 37

19b Deckeldose mit Unterteller

Entw.: 1876
Farbloses Glas mit Schliff und Schnitt (poliert)
FM: auf der Unterseite am Rand geschnitten
H 13,7 cm, D (Teller) 20,2 cm
Quellen: WZ, Bd. VIII, S. 40; FAP, Schnitt „9428 Adolf […]
Büchsen m. Deckel & Teller kristall m. umschnittenen
Hohlkehlen 2 St. für Metallfassung […] 18.11.1876"
Inv.-Nr. Gl 2741, Gl 2743, nachträglich inv.

19c Pokal mit Deckel

Entw.: 1876
Farbloses Glas mit Schliff und Schnitt (poliert)
FM: auf der Unterseite am Rand geschnitten
H 17,4 cm
Quellen: WZ, Bd. VIII, S. 41; FAP, Schnitt „MNA 9438. 1876 III. Gr."
Inv.-Nr. Gl 2742, nachträglich inv.

19d Pokal

Entw.: 1876
Farbloses Glas mit Schliff und Schnitt (poliert, teilweise matt)
FM: auf der Unterseite am Rand geschnitten
H 25,1 cm
Quellen: WZ, Bd. VIII, S. 42; FAP, Schnitt „MNA 9439. 1876 IV. Gr."
Inv.-Nr. Gl 2746, nachträglich inv.

19b Lidded Box with Saucer

Dsg.: 1876
Colorless ground and cut glass (polished)
B: cut into the bottom rim
H 13.7 cm, D (plate) 20.2 cm
Sources: WD, vol. VIII, p. 40; CAP, section "9428 Adolf […]
Büchsen m. Deckel & Teller kristall m. umschnittenen
Hohlkehlen 2 St. für Metallfassung […] 18.11.1876"
Inv. no. Gl 2741, Gl 2743, subs. inv.

19c Lidded Goblet

Dsg.: 1876
Colorless ground and cut glass (polished)
B: cut into the bottom rim
H 17.4 cm
Sources: WD, vol. VIII, p. 41; CAP, section "MNA 9438. 1876 III. Gr."; Inv. no. Gl 2742, subs. inv.

19d Goblet

Dsg.: 1876
Colorless ground and cut glass (polished, partly matte)
B: cut into the bottom rim
H 25.1 cm
Sources: WD, vol. VIII, p. 42; CAP, section "MNA 9439. 1876 IV. Gr."; Inv. no. Gl 2746, subs. inv.

19c

20 Kanne („Prunkvase")

Entw.: Hermann Herdtle, 1877
Ausf.: Meyr's Neffen, Adolf, 1877; Peter Eisert, Haida (Schnitt)
Farbloses Glas mit Schliff und Schnitt (poliert), vergoldete Silbermontierung mit (transluzidem) Email (Hermann Ratzersdorfer, Wien)
H 41,5 cm
Quellen: WZ, Bd. VII, S. 48; FAW, Bestellungsbuch MNA, 9. März 1877, 152, „Vasen feinstes Krystallglas im Rohglase, die besten 2 St. davon auf das Allersorgfältigste bergkristallartig geschliffen m. klein umschnittenen Walzen, die glatten Flächen fein überschliffen. 3 thlg., Fälze Rimen und Zapfen polirt"; FAP, Serie 101, „kristall mit umschnittenen Hohlkehlen", Schnitt „MNA 152.1877/9/3"
Inv.-Nr. Gl 1402, angek. auf der Pariser Weltausstellung 1878, inv. Jan. 1879

Die Kanne – meist als Prunkvase bezeichnet – besteht aus zwei Teilen, die durch die Montierungen zusammengehalten werden.

20 Jug ("Grand Vase")

Dsg.: Hermann Herdtle, 1877
Mfr.: Meyr's Neffen, Adolf, 1877; Peter Eisert, Haida (cut)
Colorless ground and cut glass (polished), gilded silver mounting with translucent enameling (Hermann Ratzersdorfer, Vienna)
H 41.5 cm
Sources: WD, vol. VII, p. 48; CAV, order book MNA, 9 March 1877, 152, "Vasen feinstes Krystallglas im Rohglase, die besten 2 St. davon auf das Allersorgfältigste bergkristallartig geschliffen m. klein umschnittenen Walzen, die glatten Flächen fein überschliffen. 3 thlg., Fälze Rimen und Zapfen polirt"; CAP, Serie 101, "kristall mit umschnittenen Hohlkehlen", section "MNA 152.1877/9/3"
Inv. no. Gl 1402, purch. at the 1878 Paris World's Fair, inv. Jan. 1879

The jug – mostly referred to a grand vase – consists of two parts held together by the mountings.

19d

Kanne aus Achat, Mailand, 4. Viertel d. 16. Jh., Zeichnung von
Heinrich Kautsch, 1881, nach dem Original im Museo di
Capodimonte, Neapel (MAK, Inv.-Nr. K.I. 3977/14)
Jug of agate, Milan, last quarter of the 16th century, drawing by
Heinrich Kautsch, 1881, original in the Museo di Capodimonte,
Neapel (MAK, inv. no. K.I. 3977/14)

20

In die Werkzeichnungen wurde diese Kanne bei Gefäßen aufgenommen, die anlässlich der Hochzeit von Kronprinz Rudolf 1881 angefertigt wurden: „Prunkgefässe aus Krystallglas mit ornamentaler Glanzgravirung und emaillierten Fassungen aus Edelmetall. Zur Huldigungsgabe der Österr. Handels- u. Gewerbekammer anlässlich der Vermählung Sr k. u. k. Hoheit des Kronprinzen 1881. Blatt M. Entworfen u. gezeichnet von Prof. H. Herdtle. H. Herdtle fec: 1877."

Vorbilder für diese von Renaissancegefäßen inspirierte Kanne waren die böhmischen und italienischen Bergkristall- oder Halbedelsteingefäße vom Ende des 16. Jahrhunderts (siehe Abb. S. 85). Dekor und Schnitt entsprechen denen des Kaiser-Services von 1870 (siehe Kat.-Nr. 6).

Dieses Prunkgefäß wurde für die Pariser Weltausstellung 1878 erzeugt, wo es vom Museum erworben wurde. Für das Hochzeitsgeschenk wurde eine weitere solche Prunkvase angefertigt. Diese wurde 1882 auf der „Österreichisch-ungarischen industriellen und landwirthschaftlichen Ausstellung" in Triest gezeigt.

Lit.: Blätter für Kunstgewerbe, Bd. 8, 1879, S. 12, Taf. 13; Mittheilungen, Nr. 190, 1. Juli 1881 (Beilage, S. 6); Huldigung der Oesterreichischen Handels- und Gewerbekammern

In the working drawings, this jug was listed among the vessels made for the wedding of Crown Prince Rudolf in 1881: "Grand vessels of crystal glass with polished ornamental engraving and enameled mountings of precious metal. A tributary gift from the Austr. Chamber of Trade and Commerce for the wedding of His Imperial and Royal Highness the Crown Prince in 1881. Sheet M. Designed a. drawn by Prof. H. Herdtle. H. Herdtle fec: 1877."

The models for this jug inspired by Renaissance vessels were late 16th century Italian and Bohemian vessels of rock crystal or semi-precious stones. (see ill. p. 85). Decoration and cutting are similar to the Imperial Service of 1870 (see cat. no. 6).

This grand vase was made for the 1878 Paris World's Fair where it was bought by the museum. Another vase of this type was made as gift for the royal wedding. This was shown at the 1882 "Austro-Hungarian Industrial and Agricultural Exhibition" in Trieste.

Lit.: Blätter für Kunstgewerbe, vol. 8, 1879, p. 12, Taf. 13; Mittheilungen, Nr. 190, 1. July 1881 (suppl., p. 6); Huldigung der Oesterreichischen Handels- und Gewerbekammern

21 „Gegenstände hellgrün, rosa oder blau überfangen mit Hohlkehlen durchschliffen, mit Golddecoration und gelbgeätzten Ornamenten auf matten Grunde. Nach eigenen Zeichnungen. Ornam. theils v. Arch. Rehlender", ab 1875

Farbloses Glas mit farbigem Überfang, teilweise gelb geätzt, mit Schliff und Dekor in Weiß und Gold

Die Serie wurde in drei Farben ausgeführt und umfasste: Aufsätze, Vasen, Flaschen, Krüge, Flasche mit Becher, Teller, Becher mit Fuß, Pokal mit Deckel, Stängelgläser. Entsprechend den Reformbestrebungen in Hinblick auf das farbige Glas wurde auf die Transparenz des Glases

21 "Objects, light green, pink or blue casing, with cut-in grooves, with gold decoration and yellow etched ornaments on matte ground. After own drawings. Ornam. partly by Arch. Rehlender", from 1875

Colorless glass with colored casing, partly yellow etching, cut and with decoration in white or gold

The series was produced in three colors and comprised: centerpieces, vases, bottles, pitchers, bottle with tumbler, plate, beaker with foot, lidded goblet, stem glasses. In accordance with the reform efforts with regard to colored glass, much emphasis was placed on keeping the

21a

Objekte dieser Serie, gezeigt auf der Pariser
Weltausstellung 1878, in: Gewerbehalle,
1878, Taf. 65 (MAK, Inv.-Nr. K.I. 380)
Objects of this series, presented at the Wolrd's
Fair in Paris 1878, in: "Gewerbehalle", 1878,
pl. 65 (MAK, inv. no. K.I. 380)

21b

Wert gelegt, was in der zeitgenössischen Kritik auch positiv vermerkt wurde, so anlässlich der Weihnachtsausstellung 1875 im ÖMKI: „Grelle Farbeneffecte sind
in der Zusammenstellung u. s. w. vermieden; der Wechsel
von Hell und Dunkel nur durch die Ausschleifung
eines ‚Ueberfanges‘ von derselben Farbe bewirkt. Wo
eine zweite Farbe hinzugefügt worden, ist auch sie fein
und transparent aufgetragen, so dass sie mit der Grundfarbe zusammenwirkt" („Mittheilungen", Nr. 124,
1. Jan. 1876). Oder auch auf der Weltausstellung 1878 in
Paris: „[…] die eingeschliffenen Hohlkehlen erscheinen
also durchsichtig. Die Bandornamente sind auf mattem
Grunde mit Gold umsäumt und gelb geätzt, demnach
alle Flächen des Glases transparent" („Gewerbehalle",

glass transparent, which was appreciated by contemporary critics as on the occasion of the 1875 Christmas
exhibition at the AMAI: "Garish color effects are
avoided in combinations, the shading of light and dark
is effected by cut-outs in a 'casing' of the same color
only. Wherever a second color was added, it was applied
delicately and transparently, too, so as to let the basic
color blend in" ("Mittheilungen", no. 124, 1 Jan. 1876).
Or at the 1878 Paris World's Fair: "[…] the cut-in
grooves thus appear transparent. The ribbon ornaments
on matte ground are seamed with gold and etched in
yellow, so that all areas of the glass are transparent"
("Gewerbehalle", issue 9, 1878). The Hamburg Arts and
Crafts Museum bought a footed bowl from this series

Heft 9, 1878). Das Kunstgewerbemuseum Hamburg erwarb auf der Kunst- und Kunstindustrie-Ausstellung
1876 in München eine blaue Fußschale dieser Serie um
17 Mark.

Georg Rehlender entwarf in den siebziger Jahren zahlreiche Dekore für Lobmeyr'sche Gläser. In ähnlicher
Technik entstand 1874 eine Serie (Kat.-Nr. 11).

WZ, Bd. IX, S. 19–20
Lit.: Mittheilungen, Nr. 124, 1. Jan. 1876, S. 12 ff.
(Weihnachtsausstellung 1875); Gewerbehalle, Heft 9, 1878,
Taf. 65; Jedding 1977, Kat.-Nr. 343

21a Dessertaufsatz

Entw.: 1875
Ausf.: Meyr's Neffen, Adolf, 1875
Farbloses Glas mit grünem Überfang und Dekor
FM: auf der Unterseite gemalt
H 8,3 cm, D 27,2 cm
Quellen: WZ, Bd. IX, S. 19; FAW, „Dessertaufsatz N: 7112/14
28/III 1875 J. & L. Lobmeyr"
Inv.-Nr. Gl 1273, Geschenk v. J. & L. Lobmeyr, inv. 1. Juni 1876

21b Unterteller zu Sturzflasche

Entw.: 1875
Ausf.: Meyr's Neffen, Adolf, 1875
Farbloses Glas mit rotem Überfang und Dekor
D 20 cm
Quellen: WZ, Bd. IX, S. 20; FAW, 7126-28 C, „Teller zu
Sturzflasche"; FAP, Schnitt „MNA 7126-28 1875 C"
Inv.-Nr. Gl 1299, Geschenk v. J. & L. Lobmeyr, inv. 1. Juni 1876

22 „Vasen aus hell aquamarinblauem Glase, eigene Formen, mit orientalischen Gold und Emailornamenten, diese nach Zeichnung der Architekten Girard u. Rehlender", ab 1875/76

Blaues transparentes Glas mit Dekor in Gold, Rot, Weiß und Lila

Einzelne Gläser dieser Serie wurden schon 1875 in der
Stuttgarter Zeitschrift „Gewerbehalle" publiziert. Zu
„eigenen Formen" Lobmeyrs wurden die Ornamente
von den Architekten Otto Girard und Georg Rehlender
entworfen, die in den siebziger Jahren für Lobmeyr wiederholt ornamentale Entwürfe lieferten.

for 17 Marks at the 1876 Munich Art and Industrial
Arts Exhibition.

Georg Rehlender designed numerous decorations for
Lobmeyr in the 1870s. Another series in similar
technique was produced 1874 (cat. no. 11).

WD, vol. IX, pp. 19–20
Lit.: Mittheilungen, no. 124, 1. Jan 1876, pp. 12 ff. (1875
Christmas exhibition); Gewerbehalle, issue 9, 1878, pl. 65;
Jedding 1977, cat. no. 343

21a Dessert Centerpiece

Dsg.: 1875
Mfr.: Meyr's Neffen, Adolf, 1875
Colorless glass with casing and decoration
B: painted on the bottom side
H 8.3 cm, D 27.2 cm
Sources: WD, vol. IX, p. 19; CAV, "Dessert centerpiece N:
7112/14 28/III 1875 J. & L. Lobmeyr"
Inv. no. Gl 1273, donation from J. & L. Lobmeyr, inv. 1 June 1876

21b Saucer for Bottle

Dsg.: 1875
Mfr.: Meyr's Neffen, Adolf, 1875
Colorless glass with red casing and decoration
D 20 cm
Sources: WD, vol. IX, p. 20; CAV, 7126-28 C, "Teller zu
Sturzflasche"; CAP, papercut "MNA 7126-28 1875 C"
Inv. no. Gl 1299, donation from J. & L. Lobmeyr, inv. 1 June 1876

22 "Vases of light aquamarine-blue glass, self-designed forms, with gold and enamel ornamentation after a design by Architects Girard a. Rehlender", from 1875/76

Blue transparent glass with decoration in gold, red, white, purple

Some glasses from this series were published 1875 already
in the Stuttgart "Gewerbehalle" journal. The architects
Otto Girard and Georg Rehlender, who repeatedly
provided ornamental designs for Lobmeyr in the 1870s,
also provided the ornaments for Lobmeyr's "self-
designed" forms.

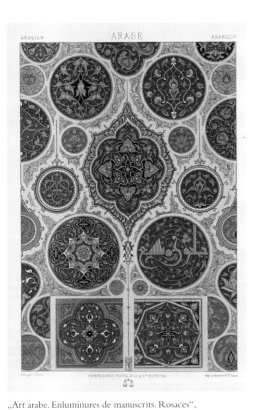

„Art arabe. Enluminures de manuscrits. Rosaces",
in: A. Racinet: L'ornement polychrome, Paris 1869–1872,
Bd. III (MAK, Inv.-Nr. K.I. 19377)
"Art arabe. Enluminures de manuscrits. Rosaces",
in: A. Racinet: L'ornement polychrome, Paris 1869–1872,
vol. III (MAK, inv. no. K.I. 19377)

22a   22b

Vasen dieser Serie, in: WZ, Bd. XI, S. 29
Vases of this series, in: WD, vol. XI, p. 29

Bei dieser frühen orientalisierenden Serie diente unter anderem Racinets Werk „L'ornement polychrome" von 1872 als Vorlage für die maurischen Dekorelemente (Taf. „Art arabe. Enluminures de manuscrits. Rosaces") (siehe Abb. S. 9, 89).

Auf den Entwurfszeichnungen im Firmenarchiv wurden genaue Vorgaben für die Malerei gemacht: „[…] möglichst bei allen Emailflächen an den Rändern den Glasgrund durchwirken lassen"; „[…] bitten wir thunlichst zu beachten, dass das Email nicht ganz an die Goldlinien anstößt da dadurch die Verzierung leichter wird und nicht wie aufgeklebt erscheint".

In den Werkzeichnungen wurden nur Vasen abgebildet, hergestellt wurden aber auch Krüge, Flakons, Becher, Tassen, Schalen, ein Aufsatz und ein „Liqueurglas". Die im Firmenarchiv erhaltenen Entwürfe sind meist mit 1876–1880 datiert.

WZ, Bd. XI, S. 27–29
Lit.: Neuwirth 1981c, S. 153–231; Fillitz 1996, Bd. 2, Kat.-Nr. 21.151

22a Flakon
Entw.: 1876
FM: auf der Unterseite gemalt
H 18 cm
Quellen: WZ, Bd. XI, S. 27 ff.; FAP, Serie 2, „Aquamarin mit Gold und Emaildekor", Schnitt „8259-1876 MNA"
Inv.-Nr. Gl 2572, aus dem ehem. Arabischen Zimmer, 1932 nachträglich inv.

22b Krug
Entw.: 1876
FM: auf der Unterseite gemalt
H 23, 9 cm
Quellen: WZ, Bd. XI, S. 27 ff.; FAP, Serie 2, „Aquamarin mit Gold und Emaildekor", Schnitt „8254-1876 MNA"
Inv.-Nr. Gl 2571, aus dem ehem. Arabischen Zimmer, 1932 nachträglich inv.

The models for the Moorish decoration elements of this early oriental-style series were taken from Racinet's "L'ornement polychrome" of 1872 (pl. "Art arabe. Enluminures de manuscrits. Rosaces") (see ill. pp. 9, 89). The design drawings in the company archives contain detailed instructions for the painting work: "[…] if possible let the glass shine through on all edges of the enameled areas;" "[…] we ask you to take care not to make the enamel border directly on the gold lining as this makes the decoration appear lighter and not like stuck-on."

The working drawings comprise vases only; however, production also included only pitchers, flacons, beakers, cups, bowls, a centerpiece, and a "liqueur glass". The designs extant in the company archives are mostly dated 1876–1880.

WD, vol. XI, pp. 27–29
Lit.: Neuwirth 1981c, pp. 153–231; Fillitz 1996, vol. 2, cat. no. 21.151

22a Flacon
Dsg.: 1876
B: painted on the bottom
H 18 cm
Sources: WD, vol. XI, pp. 27 ff.; CAP, series 2, "Aquamarine with gold and enamel decoration", papercut "8259-1876 MNA"
Inv. no. Gl 2572, from the former Arabian Room, inv. 1932

22b Pitcher
Dsg.: 1876
B: painted on the bottom
H 23.9 cm
Sources: WD, vol. XI, pp. 27 ff.; CAP, series 2, "Aquamarine with gold and enamel decoration", papercut "8254-1876 MNA"
Inv. no. Gl 2571, from the former Arabian Room, inv. 1932

23a

23 „Serie von gebuckelt eingeblasenen Krystall-Gegenständen. a) mit Gravirung, matt mit hellen Puncten. b) mit Vergoldung und Weissemail-Puncten", ab 1876

Bei der um 1850 erfundenen Technik der Irisierung wird das Glas mit Metalldämpfen beschlagen. Die Anregung dazu kam von den antiken Glasgefäßen, die durch die Verwitterung perlmuttartig schillerten. 1873 wurden auf der Weltausstellung in Wien erstmals irisierende Gegenstände präsentiert. Diese stammten aus der ungarischen Glasfabrik J. G. Zahn in Sladno (Zlatnó), wo der Chemiker Dr. L. V. Pántotsek tätig war. 1875 bot ein Helfer von Pántotsek Wilhelm Kralik an, das geheime Verfahren zu „verraten". Kralik ging darauf ein, sodass Lobmeyr schon 1876 auf der Münchner Kunst- und Kunstindustrie-Ausstellung irisierende Gegenstände ausstellen konnte (Neuwirth 1999, S. 354–355). Lobmeyr verwendete die Irisierung nicht nur auf farblosem, sondern auch auf farbigem Glas. „Nachdem er erst die bekannten Opalgläser in besonderer Vollkommenheit erzeugt, gelang es ihm, rein irisirende in den verschiedensten Nuancen von weiß, lila, grünlich, gelblich ec. in einer Schönheit darzustellen, von der man bis dahin kaum eine Ahnung hatte, die den ganzen Duft, das bezaubernd Leuchtende, magisch Spielende einer Seifenblase, fast noch überbietet" (Pecht 1876, S. 153).

Bald danach produzierten auch verschiedene andere europäische Manufakturen irisierendes Glas.

Die Entwürfe dieser gebuckelt eingeblasenen Serie wurden mit und ohne Irisierung und Dekor in Gravierung oder Bemalung in Gold und Weiß angeboten. Die Form war von Metallpokalen aus der Zeit um 1500 inspiriert. Die Serie umfasste Flaschen, Krüge, Vasen, Schalen, Aufsätze, Dosen, Becher und Stängelgläser.

Lobmeyr erzielte mit seinen irisierenden Gläsern große Erfolge: „The Austrian wares in that line cannot be surpassed" (Colné 1880, S. 292).

WZ, Bd. IX, S. 44–55

23 "Series of mold-blown knobbed crystal objects. a) with engraving, matte finish with light dots. b) with gilding and white enameled dots", from 1876

In iridescent technique, invented around 1850, the glass is exposed to metallic vapors. The inspiration was taken from ancient glass vessels which iridesced like mother-of-pearl due to weathering. Iridescent glass objects were first presented at the 1873 Vienna World's Fair. They came from the Hungarian glassworks of J. G. Zahn at Sladno (Zlatnó), where they had been produced under the supervision of the chemist Dr. L. V. Pántotsek, who had invented the process between 1848 and 1856, but kept it secret. In 1875, a collaborator of Pántotsek offered to divulge the secret to Wilhelm Kralik. Kralik agreed to the deal, so that Lobmeyr could already present iridescent objects at the 1876 Munich Art and Industrial Arts Exhibition (Neuwirth 1999, pp. 354–355). Lobmeyr used iridescence not only on colorless, but also on colored glass. "After he had first made the well-known opal glass in special perfection, he succeeded to produce purely iridescent glass in various different shades from white, purple to greenish, yellowish etc. in a beauty which was virtually unknown until then and almost surpassed the delicacy, the lovely shine, the magic playfulness of a soap bubble" (Pecht 1876, p. 153). Soon after that, other European manufactories also showed iridescent glass which became increasingly popular until the turn of the century.

The designs of this mold-blown knobbed series were offered with or without iridescence, and engraved decoration or gold and white painting. The shapes were inspired by metal goblets from around 1500. The series comprised bottles, pitchers, vases, bowls, centerpieces, boxes, beakers, and stem glasses. Lobmeyr scored great success with his iridescent glasses: "The Austrian wares in that line cannot be surpassed" (Colné 1880, S. 292).

WD, vol. IX, pp. 44–55

23a Becher mit Fuß

Entw.: 1876
Farbloses Glas mit Schliff
H 13,8 cm
Quellen: FAW, Serie 88, „gebuckelt irisirend mit Golddecor",
Zeichnung „8349-76 MNA Fußbecher", gleiche Form
Inv.-Nr. WI 48, Geschenk v. J. & L. Lobmeyr, inv. 26. Jan. 1901

Die Form des Fußbechers entspricht dem dieser Serie
von 1876, zeigt allerdings die undekorierte Form ohne
Irisierung.

23b Pokal mit Deckel

Entw.: 1877
Ausf.: Meyr's Neffen, Adolf, 1877
Farbloses Glas mit Irisierung (hellviolett) und Dekor in Gold
H 48,5 cm
Quellen: FAW, Bestellungsbuch MNA, 23. Febr. 1877, 3, „Pokale
mit Deckel kleinere mit hohlen Fuss gemodelt hellviolett
irisirend mit Golddecor und vergoldeten Emailpkt. wie Serie
Nr. 8342/52"; FAP, Karton 20, Serie 88, „Kristall gebuckelt
irisirend 1876", Pokal mit Deckel Schnitt „MNA 3. 1877 23/2"
Inv.-Nr. Gl 1431, angek. v. J. & L. Lobmeyr um 50 fl.,
inv. 25. Sept. 1879

24 „Gegenstände aus hellblauem Opalglase, gestreift eingeblasen, mit Gold- und weisser Emaildecoration. Nach eigenen Zeichnungen, Ornamente theils v. Arch. Rehlender", ab 1875

Hellblaues Opalglas mit Dekor in Weiß und Gold

Halbopakes Opalglas, das durchsichtiger als Milchglas
ist, wurde in verschiedenen Farbtönen erzeugt. Bei die-
ser Serie ist das blaue Opalglas, das je nach Dicke des
Glases mehr oder weniger durchsichtig erscheint, noch
mit weißem Opalglas für Henkel u. Ä. kombiniert. Die
Serie entstand ab 1875 und umfasste Aufsätze, Vasen,
Flaschen, Deckelgefäße, Pokal, Krug, Kännchen und
Becher mit Fuß.
Kurz danach entwarf Georg Rehlender (Biografie sie-
he Kat.-Nr. 11) den Dekor für eine Serie aus weißem,
gestreift eingeblasenem Opalglas (siehe Kat.-Nr. 25).
WZ, Bd. IX, S. 14–18

23a Beaker with Foot

Dsg.: 1876
Colorless cut glass
H 13.8 cm
Sources: CAV, Serie 88, "knobbed iridescent wit gold decora-
tion", drawing "8349-76 MNA footed beaker", same shape
Inv. no. WI 48, donation from J. & L. Lobmeyr, inv. 26 Jan. 1901

The shape of this footed beaker corresponds to the
series of 1876, though it is undecorated and without
iridescence.

23b Lidded Goblet

Dsg.: 1877
Mfr.: Meyr's Neffen, Adolf, 1877
Colorless iridescent glass (light purple) and gold decoration
H 48.5 cm
Sources: CAV, order book MNA, 23 Febr. 1877, 3, "Lidded
goblets, smaller ones molded with hollow foot, light-purple
iridescence, with gold decoration and gilded enameled dots.
As series no. 8342/52"; CAP, box 20, series 88, "crystal knobbed
iridescent 1876", lidded goblet papercut "MNA 3. 1877 23/2"
Inv. no. Gl 1431, purch. by J. & L. Lobmeyr for 50 Gulden,
inv. 25 Sept. 1879

24 "Objects of light-blue opal glass, mold-blown with stripes, with gold and white enamel decoration. After own drawings, ornamentation partly by Arch. Rehlender", from 1875

Light-blue opal glass with white and gold decoration

Semi-opaque opal glass, which is more translucent than
milk glass, was produced in different colors. In this
series, the blue opal glass, which appears more or less
transparent depending on the thickness of the glass, is
combined with white opal glass for handles etc. The
series was produced from 1875 and included centerpieces, vases, bottles, lidded boxes, a goblet, pitcher, jug,
and footed beaker.
Shortly after that, Georg Rehlender (biography see cat.
no. 11) the decoration for a series of white striped
mold-blown opal glass (see cat. no. 25).
WD, vol. IX, pp. 14–18

23b

24a   24b

24a Aufsatz

Entw.: 1875
Ausf.: Meyr's Neffen, Adolf, 1875
H 12 cm, L 36,3 cm, B 32,2 cm
Quellen: WZ, Bd. IX, S. 17; FAW, Serie „Blauopal mit
Weissemail und Golddekor", ab 1875, 6869-75, „Schale auf
Fuß"; FAP, Schnitt des Oberteiles „zu MNA 6868&69 1875"
Inv.-Nr. Gl 1272, Geschenk v. J. & L. Lobmeyr,
inv. 7. März 1876

24b Flakon („Liqueurflasche")

Entw.: 1875
FM: auf der Unterseite gemalt
H 20 cm
Quellen: WZ, Bd. IX, S. 17; FAW, 6880-1875, „Liqueurflasche";
FAP, Schnitt „MNA 6880 1875 blau opal"
Inv.-Nr. Gl 3250, 1964 angek.

24c Vase mit zwei Henkeln

Entw.: 1877
Ausf.: Meyr's Neffen, Adolf, 1877
FM: auf der Unterseite gemalt
H 28,5 cm
Quellen: WZ, Bd. IX, S. 17; FAW, „Adolf N. 176/4 Vasen Form
Nr. 168/blau opal gestreift eingeblasen 13/3 1877 J. & L. Lobmeyr"
Inv.-Nr. Gl 1435, angek. v. J. & L. Lobmeyr um 35 fl.,
inv. 25. Sept. 1879

24a Centerpiece

Dsg.: 1875
Mfr.: Meyr's Neffen, Adolf, 1875
H 12 cm, L 36.3 cm, B 32.2 cm
Sources: WD, vol. IX, p. 17; CAV, series "blue opal with white
enameling and gold decoration ", from 1875, 6869-75, "Fotted
bowl"; CAP, papercut of upper part "zu MNA 6868&69 1875"
Inv. no. Gl 1272, donation from J. & L. Lobmeyr,
inv. 7 March 1876

24b Flacon ("Liqueur Bottle")

Dsg.: 1875
B: painted on the bottom
H 20 cm
Sources: WD, vol. IX, p. 17; CAV, 6880-1875, "Liqueur
bottle"; CAP, papercut "MNA 6880 1875 blue opal"
Inv. no. Gl 3250, purch. 1964

24c Vase with Two Handles

Dsg.: 1877
Mfr.: Meyr's Neffen, Adolf, 1877
B: painted on the bottom
H 28.5 cm
Sources: WD, vol. IX, p. 17; CAV, "Adolf N. 176/4 Vases Form Nr.
168/blue opal striped mold blown 13/3 1877 J. & L. Lobmeyr"
Inv. no. Gl 1435, purch. by J. & L. Lobmeyr for 35 Gulden,
inv. 25 Sept. 1879

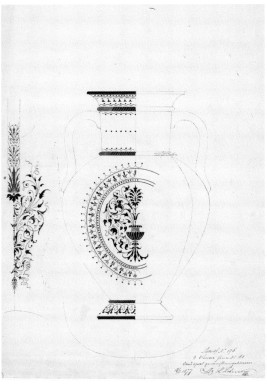

Vase (Werkzeichnung, FAW)
Vase (working drawing, CAV)

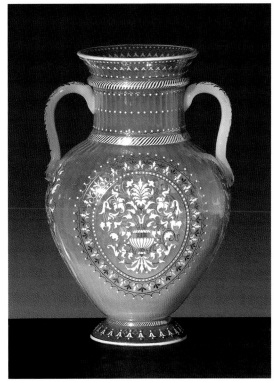

24c

25a

25 „Gegenstände aus weissem, irisiren-den Opalglase (Perlmutter opal) gestreift eingeblasen, mit Golddecoration u. färbigen Emailverzierungen auf matten Goldbändern. Nach eig. Zeichnungen, Ornamente theils v. Arch. Rehlender", ab 1876/77

Weißes Opalglas mit Irisierung, farbigem Dekor und Gold

Dieses Glas, das auch als „weiß opal metallisirt" (Firmenarchiv) bezeichnet wurde, zeigt Opalglas verbunden mit der neuen Technik der Irisierung.
WZ, Bd. IX, S. 10–13

25a Pokal mit Deckel

Entw.: 1876/77
Ausf.: Meyr's Neffen, Adolf, 1877
FM: auf der Unterseite gemalt
H 42,9 cm
Quellen: WZ, Bd. IX, S. 11; FAW, Bestellungsbuch MNA, 28. Febr. 1877, 41, „Pokale mit Deckel Perlmutteropal, innen gestreift gold und Emaildekor […]"; FAP, Serie 145, „Perlmutteropal optisch", Schnitt „MNA 7996-1876 richtige Form wie 41-1877"
Inv.-Nr. Gl 1432, angek. v. J. & L. Lobmeyr, inv. 25. Sept. 1879

25 "Objects of white iridescent opal glass (mother-of-pearl opalescent) mold-blown with stripes with gold decoration a. colored enameled ornamentation on matte gold bands. After own drawings, ornaments partly by Arch. Rehlender", from 1876/77

White iridescent opal glass, colored decoration and gilding

This glass, which was also called "white-opal metalized" (company archives), shows opal glass in combination with the new iridescent technique.
WD, vol. IX, pp. 10–13

25a Lidded Goblet

Dsg.: 1876/77
Mfr.: Meyr's Neffen, Adolf, 1877
B: painted on the bottom
H 42.9 cm
Sources: WD, vol. IX, p. 11; CAV, order book MNA, 28 Febr. 1877, 41, "Goblets with lid, mother-of-pearl opalescent, inside gild-stripes and enamel decoration […]"; CAP, series 145, "Mother-of-pearl opal, optical", Schnitt "MNA 7996-1876 richtige Form wie 41-1877"
Inv. no. Gl 1432, purch. by J. & L. Lobmeyr, inv. 25 Sept. 1879

Becher, Vase und Deckeldose dieser Serie, in: WZ, Bd. IX, S. 42
Beaker, Vase and Lidded Box of this series, in: WD, vol. IX, p. 42

Historisches Foto dieser Serie (FAW)
Historical photograph of this series (CAV)

26 „Gegenstände aus gelblichem Krystallglase mit Golddecoration u. Tritonen blau oder rosa lasirt auf weissem Email. Nach eigenen Zeichnungen. Figuren nach einem altfranzösischen Werke", ab 1876

Farbloses Glas mit farbigem Dekor und Gold

26 "Object of yellow crystal glass with gold decoration and tritons, blue or pink glazing on white enamel. After own drawings. Figures after an old-French piece", from 1876

Colorless glass with colored decoration and gilding

Für diese Serie dienten französische Kupferstiche aus dem 17. Jahrhundert als Vorbild, etwa Arbeiten von Raymond Lafage (1656–1690), der auf Werke von Raffael, Michelangelo und Annibale Carracci zurückgriff. Für einen Teller und einen Krug sind die verwendeten Vorlagen auf den Zeichnungen angegeben.

Die Malerei wurde wahrscheinlich in der Malerwerkstatt von Johann Friedrich Schürer (1823–1901) im südböhmischen Winterberg (Vimperk) ausgeführt. Auf den Vorlagen sind genaue Angaben zur malerischen Ausführung vermerkt.

In den Werkzeichnungen wurden Aufsatz, Krug, Becher mit Fuß, Vase, Deckeldose und Flasche abgebildet. 1878

For this series, 17th century French copperplate engravings served as models, such a works by Raymond Lafage (1656–1690), who in turn drew on works by Raphael, Michelangelo, and Annibale Carracci.
The models used for one plate and jug are indicated on the drawings.
The panting was presumably done in the workshop of Johann Friedrich Schürer (1823–1901) at Winterberg (Vimperk), South-Bohemia. The model drawings contain clear instructions for the painting work.
The working drawings include designs for a centerpiece, a jug, a footed beaker, a vase, a lidded box, and a bottle. In addition, a large bowl was produced in 1878.

wurde auch noch eine große Schale publiziert. Die Serie mit Figuren in zwei Farbvarianten (rosa und blau) wurde mit Erfolg auf der Pariser Weltausstellung 1878 gezeigt: „Die Anwendung feingetonter Emailmalerei und des Goldes auf Krystall bildet eine löbliche Bereicherung der farbigen Ziergefässe in der bereits hochentwickelten Glasindustrie" (Uhland 1880, S. 120).

WZ, Bd. IX, S. 41–43

Lit.: Uhland 1880, S. 120 (Schale dieser Serie); Klesse 1996, S. 11–16

26a Deckeldose

Entw.: 1876
FM: auf der Unterseite gemalt
H 12,8 cm, D 10 cm
Quellen: WZ, Bd. IX, S. 42; FAP, Serie 125, „Meeresgötter", Schnitt „MNA 7858.1876"
Inv.-Nr. Gl 3247, 1963 angek.

The series with figures in two color variants (pink and blue) was successfully presented at the 1878 Paris World's Fair. "The application of delicately shaded enamel painting and gilding on crystal is a praiseworthy enrichment for colored decorative vessels of the already highly developed glass industry." (Uhland 1880, p. 120)

WD, vol. IX, pp. 41–43

Lit.: Uhland 1880, p. 120 (bowl from this series); Klesse 1996, pp. 11–16

26a Lidded Box

Dsg.: 1876
B: painted on the bottom
H 12.8 cm, D 10 cm
Sources: WD, vol. IX, p. 42; CAP, series 125, "Sea Gods", papercut "MNA 7858.1876"
Inv. no. Gl 3247, purch. 1963

26a

27a

27 Serie „Neugelb gestreift irisierend mit Gold & Emaildekor", ab 1877

Gelbes transparentes irisierendes Glas mit Dekor in Weiß, Schwarz und Gold

Die Irisierung (siehe Kat.-Nr. 23) wurde nicht nur auf farblosem, sondern auch auf farbigem transparentem oder opakem Glas aufgebracht. Die Rippen im Glas entstanden durch das Einblasen der Glasmasse in eine Form. Diese Serie mit stilisierten renaissanceartigen Arabesken und Netzdekor passt stilistisch zu mehreren Serien, die zu dieser Zeit – teilweise ebenfalls mit der neuen Technik der Irisierung – produziert wurden (siehe Kat.-Nr. 25, Opalglas mit Irisierung, Kat.-Nr. 24, ohne Irisierung). Zu der 1877 entworfenen Serie, die auf der Pariser Weltausstellung von 1878 gezeigt wurde, gehörten auch: Vasen, Schalen, Bordeauxkrug, Fußbecher, „Liqueurkrügel" und „Liqueurglas", Flakon, Pokal mit Deckel und Aufsatz.

Lit.: Falke 1878, S. 185

27 Series "Chrome yellow, with iridescent stripes and gold & enamel decoration", from 1877

Yellow transparent iridescent glass with white, black, and gold decoration

Iridescence (see cat. no. 23) was not only used with colorless, but also with colored transparent or opaque glass. The ribs in the glass were produced by mold-blowing. This series with stylized Renaissance-style arabesques and network-pattern decoration stylistically fit in with several other series produced at that time, some of them also in iridescent technique. (see cat. no. 25, opal glass with iridescence, 24 without iridescence). The series after a design of 1877, which was exhibited at the 1878 Paris World's Fair, also included: Vases, bowls, a Bordeaux pitcher, footed beakers, a "liqueur mug," a "liqueur glass", a flacon, a lidded goblet, and a centerpiece.

Lit.: Falke 1878, p. 185

27a Schale

Entw.: 1877

Ausf.: Meyr's Neffen, Adolf, 1877

FM: im Zentrum der Oberseite gemalt

H 5,7 cm, D 49,1 cm

Quellen: FAW, Bestellungsbuch MNA, 20. Juni 1877; FAP,

Schnitt „MNA 725-1877"

Inv.-Nr. Gl 1433, angek. v. J. & L. Lobmeyr, inv. 25. Sept. 1879

27b Flakon

Entw.: 1877

Ausf.: Meyr's Neffen, Adolf, 1877

FM: auf der Unterseite gemalt

H 20,2 cm

Quellen: FAW, Bestellungsbuch MNA, 21. Juni 1877,

„Flacons mit Stöpsel"; FAP, Schnitt „MNA 727-1877"

Inv.-Nr. Gl 1436, angek. v. J. & L. Lobmeyr um 6,80 fl.,

inv. 25. Sept. 1879

27a Bowl

Dsg.: 1877

Mfr.: Meyr's Neffen, Adolf, 1877

B: painted in the top surface center

H 5.7 cm, D 49.1 cm

Sources: CAV, order book MNA, 20 June 1877;

CAP, papercut "MNA 725-1877"

Inv. no. Gl 1433, purch. by J. & L. Lobmeyr, inv. 25 Sept. 1879

27b Flacon

Dsg.: 1877

Mfr.: Meyr's Neffen, Adolf, 1877

B: painted on the bottom

H 20.2 cm

Sources: CAV, order book MNA, 21 Juni 1877, "Flacons with

stopper"; CAP, papercut "MNA 727-1877"

Inv. no. Gl 1436, purch. by J. & L. Lobmeyr for 6.80 Gulden,

inv. 25 Sept. 1879

27b

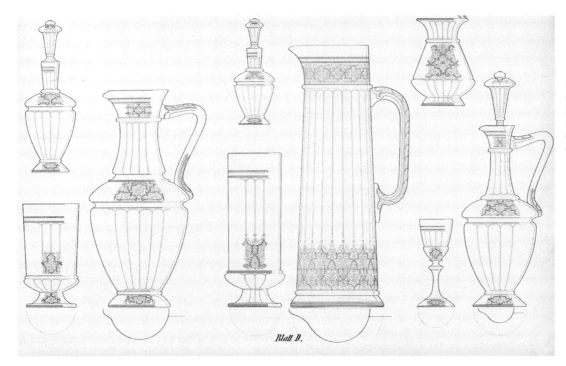

Glasgefäße „aus Krystallglas mit Gold-decoration, gelblich weissen u. hellblauen Emailornamenten", in: WZ, Bd. IX, S. 40
Glass vessels "of crystal glass with gold decoration, yellowish white and light blue enamel elements", in: WD, vol. IX, p. 40

28 Serie „Weiss u. hellblau Emailbänder mit Goldlinien", ab 1877

Farbloses Glas mit Dekor in Blau, Weiß und Gold

Die Serie wurde 1877 begonnen und bis in die achtziger Jahre ergänzt, wie die Deckeldose von 1887 mit etwas verändertem Dekor zeigt. Georg Rehlender, der in den Werkzeichnungen für den maurisch inspirierten Dekor genannt wurde, ist allerdings nur in den siebziger Jahren in Wien und als Entwerfer Lobmeyrs nachweisbar. Die im Firmenarchiv in der „Serie mit weiß und blau Email und Golddecor" erfassten dazu passenden Objekte sind zwischen 1877 und 1887 datiert und auch als „Kristall mit hellblau-weissem Emaildecor m. Gold umsäumt" bezeichnet.

In den Werkzeichnungen, die 1883 dem ÖMKI überlassen wurden, sind neben verschiedenen Bechern ein Stängelglas, Vasen, Schalen, Krüge, Flaschen und ein Aufsatz erfasst („Gegenstände aus Krystallglas mit Golddecoration, gelblich weissen u. hellblauen Email-ornamenten. Nach eigenen Zeichnungen. Ornamente v. Arch. Rehlender").

WZ, Bd. IX, S. 37–40

28 Series "White and light blue enamel bands with gold lining", from 1877

Colorless glass with blue, white and gold decoration

The series went into production in 1877 and was complemented until into the 1880s, as is shown by the lidded box of 1887 with a slightly changed decoration. Georg Rehlender, who was named in the working drawings as designer of the Moorish-style decoration, otherwise appears as a designer for Lobmeyr until the 1870s and in Vienna only. The objects included in the company archives as parts of the series "Series with white and blue enamel and gold decoration" are dated between 1877 and 1887 and are also referred to as "Crystal with light blue-white enamel decoration lined with gilding."

The working drawings handed over to the AMAI in 1883 included, aside from several beakers, a stem glass, vases, bowls, jugs, bottles, and a centerpiece ("Objects of crystal glass with gold decoration, yellowish white and light blue enamel ornamentation. After own drawings. Ornaments by Arch. Rehlender").

WD, vol. IX, pp. 37–40

28a   28b

28a Becher mit Fuß

Entw.: 1877

FM: auf der Unterseite gemalt

H 11,9 cm

Quellen: WZ, Bd. IX, S. 40; FAW, Bestellungsbuch MNA,
13. März 1877, 159, „Fussbecher Kristall glatt, mit weissen &
hellblauen Emailornamenten goldumsäumt", Zeichnungen mit
dieser Form in anderen Größen: Bierglas 166-77 mit
dazugehörigem Bierkrug, Champagnerbecher 697–86;
FAP, Schnitt „MNA 159.1877"

Inv.-Nr. Gl 2591, wohl Vermächtnis Ludwig Lobmeyr 1917,
nachträglich inv.

28b Deckeldose („Büchse mit Deckel")

Entw.: 1887

FM: auf der Unterseite gemalt

H 11,1 cm

Quellen: FAW, Bestellungsbuch MNA, 17. Sept. 1887, 2836,
„Büchsen mit Deckel II. Gr. Krystall glatt, m. weißen et.
hellblauen Emailornamenten et Golddecor […]"

Inv.-Nr. Gl 3248, 1964 angek.

28a Footed Beaker

Dsg.: 1877

B: painted on the bottom

H 11.9 cm

Sources: WD, vol. IX, p. 40; CAV, order book MNA, 13 March
1877, 159, "footed beaker, crystal, polished, with white an
light blue enamel ornamentation, gold lining", drawings
showing other sizes of the same form: beer glass 166-77 with
jug, champagne glass 697-86; CAP, papercut "MNA 159.1877"

Inv. no. Gl 2591, pres. bequest of Ludwig Lobmeyr 1917,
subs. inv.

28b Lidded Box ("Box with Lid")

Dsg.: 1887

B: painted on the bottom

H 11.1 cm

Sources: CAV, order book MNA, 17 Sept. 1887, 2836, "Boxes
with lids II. s. crystal polished with white and light-blue
enamel elements and gold decoration […]"

Inv. no. Gl 3248, purch. 1964

29 „Gefässe in arabischem Style", ab 1876

Entw.: Machytka & Schmoranz

Die in den Werkzeichnungen gesammelten „Gefässe in arabischem Style aus gelblichem Krystallglas mit bunter Email Malerei und Gold gezeichnet von den Architecten Machytka und Schmoranz" aus den Jahren 1876–1878 umfassen 34 Blätter mit fast 50 Objekten, vornehmlich Schalen, Vasen und Ampeln. In den arabischen Ornamenten waren oft auch arabische Inschriften eingefügt, deren Übersetzung auf der Unterseite der Objekte angebracht wurde. Die beiden Architekten Franz Schmoranz und Johann Machytka (siehe S. 37) hatten Reisen in den Orient unternommen und ausreichend Material mitgebracht. Für Formen und Dekore der arabischen Serie sind teilweise konkrete Vorbilder zu finden.

WZ, Bd. XV, S. 1–34 („Gefässe in arabischem Style aus gelblichem Krystallglas mit bunter Email Malerei und Gold gezeichnet von den Architecten Machytka und Schmoranz")

29 "Vessels in Arabian style", from 1876

Dsg.: Machytka & Schmoranz

The "vessels in Arabian style of yellowish crystal glass with colored enamel painting and gold, drawn by architects Machytka and Schmoranz" from 1876–1878 collected in the working drawings comprise 34 drawings of almost 50 objects, mainly bowls, vases, and hanging lamps. The Arabian ornaments also included Arabic inscription with the translations added on the bottom side of the objects. The two architects Franz Schmoranz and Johann Machytka (see p. 37) had travelled to the Orient and brought along sufficient material. For some of the forms and decorations of the Arabian series, specific models can be identified.

WD, vol. XV, p. 1–34 ("Vessels in Arabian style of yellowish crystal glass with colored enamel painting and gold, drawn by architects Machytka and Schmoranz")

29b

29a

29a Vase mit zwei Henkeln

Entw.: 1876

Inschrift (übers.): „Mohamed"

Farbloses Glas mit farbigem Dekor und Gold

FM: auf der Unterseite gemalt

H 26,1 cm

Quellen: WZ, Bd. XV, S. 9 verso (zeitgenössisches Foto);
FAW, Werkvorlage „7884-76"

Inv.-Nr. Gl 2574, aus dem ehem. Arabischen Zimmer,
1932 nachträglich inv.

Lit.: Neuwirth 1981c, S. 33; Neuwirth 1981a, S. 289;
Klesse 1996, S. 17–20

29b Becher

Entw.: 1877

Farbloses Glas mit farbigem Dekor und Gold

Inschrift (übers.): „Mein Trunk sei Dir Heilung u. Wohl-
bekommen."

FM: auf der Unterseite gemalt

H 11,2 bzw. 11,1 cm

Quellen: WZ, Bd. XV, S. 6, „Becher Nro 7892 Arabisch decor.
Der Grund ist überall durchsichtig. Die breiten Bänder, Schrift
u. Ornament sind rothbraun conturirt.1877"

Inv.-Nr. Gl 2578/1+2 (2 St.), aus dem ehem. Arabischen
Zimmer, 1932 nachträglich inv.

Lit.: Zeitschrift des bayerischen Kunst-Gewerbe-Vereins in
München, 1889, Taf. 7

29c Becher (siehe Abb. S. 39)

Entw.: 1878

Farbloses Glas mit Dekor in Blau und Gold

FM: auf der Unterseite gemalt

H 13,9 cm

Quellen: WZ, Bd. XV, S. 2, „Nro. 3870. – Becher, arabisch decorirt. – Der Grund ist überall durchsichtig. /1878"; FAW,
Bestellungsbuch MNA, 2. Nov. 1878, „Becher konisch Kristall
m. gelbbraunem Stich in arab. Decor I. Serie"; auf der
Werkvorlage dazu finden sich genaue Anweisungen zur
Ausführung: „Der Grund ist überall durchsichtig. – Die vergoldeten Ornamente und Ränder c-d sind zu poliren, ebenso die
großen Punkte um die Rosette f. – Alle anderen Conturen und
Linien sollen matt gelassen werden. – Das Email ist möglichst
dick aufzutragen [...]"

Inv.-Nr. Gl 2575, aus dem ehem. Arabischen Zimmer,
1932 nachträglich inv.

Lit.: Zeitschrift des bayerischen Kunst-Gewerbe-Vereins in
München, 1889, Taf. 7; Neuwirth 1981a, S. 292; Klesse 1996,
S. 20–21

29a Two-Handled Vase

Dsg.: 1876

Inscription (transl.): "Muhammad"

Colorless glass with colored decoration and gilding

B: painted on the bottom

H 26.1 cm

Sources: WD, vol. XV, p. 9 verso (contemporary photo);
CAV, working pattern "7884-76"

Inv. no. Gl 2574, from the former Arabian Room, inv. 1932

Lit.: Neuwirth 1981c, p. 33; Neuwirth 1981a, p. 289;
Klesse 1996, pp. 17–20

29b Beaker

Dsg.: 1877

Colorless glass with colored decoration and gilding

Inscription (transl.): "May my drink be curative and
wholesome to you."

B: painted on the bottom

H 11.2 or 11.1 cm

Sources: WD, vol. XV, p. 6, "Beaker no. 7892 Arabian decor.
Transparent ground all around. The broad bands, writing, and
ornamentation is red-brown contoured.1877"

Inv. no. Gl 2578/1+2 (2 p.), from the former Arabian Room,
inv. 1932

Lit.: Zeitschrift des bayerischen Kunst-Gewerbe-Vereins in
München, 1889, pl. 7

29c Beaker (see ill. p. 39)

Dsg.: 1878

Colorless glass with blue and gold decoration

B: painted on the bottom

H 18.8 cm

Sources: WD, vol. XV, p. 2, "No. 3870. – Beaker, Arabian
decoration. – Transparent ground all around. /1878"; CAV,
order book MNA, 2. Nov 1878, "Beaker, conical, crystal with
yellow-brown tinge in Arabian decoration 1st series "; the
working pattern includes detailed instructions: "The ground
is transparent everywhere. – The gilded ornaments and rims
c-d have to be polished, as well as the large dots around the
rosette. – All other contours and lines have matte finish. –
Apply enamel as thick as possible [...]"

Inv. no.: Gl 2575, from the former Arabian Room, inv. 1932

Lit.: Zeitschrift des bayerischen Kunst-Gewerbe-Vereins in
München, 1889, pl. 7; Neuwirth 1981a, p. 292; Klesse 1996,
pp. 20–21

29d Vase mit zwei Henkeln

Entw.: 1878

Ausf.: Meyr's Neffen, Adolf, 1878

Farbloses Glas mit Dekor in Blau, Grün, Weiß und Gold

FM: auf der Unterseite gemalt

H 20,5 bzw. 20,4 cm

Quellen: WZ, Bd. XV, S. 12, „Nro: 7882. Arabisch decorirte Vasenkörper" (laut Bestellungsbuch MNA ist es aber Nr. 2882/1878, „Vase mit Henkel rund gelblich Opalglas m. maurischem Decor in Lustrefarben II. Serie")

Inv.-Nr. Gl 1429, angek. v. J. & L. Lobmeyr um 34 fl., inv. 25. Sept. 1879

Inv.-Nr. Gl 2597, wohl Vermächtnis Ludwig Lobmeyr 1917, nachträglich inv.

Lit.: Neuwirth 1981c, S. 44; Fillitz 1996, Bd. 2, S. 609, Kat.-Nr. 21.142

Die Nelken waren ein beliebtes Motiv der türkischen Iznik-Keramiken, die damals fälschlich als „persisch-rhodische" Keramiken bezeichnet wurden (siehe Kat.-Nr. 31).

29e Zwei Flaschen („Vase")

Entw.: 1878

Farbloses Glas mit Dekor in Blau und Gold

FM: auf der Unterseite gemalt; Etikett: „42/1100/g C E L/7935"

H 30,6 cm

Quellen: WZ, Bd. XV, S. 8, „Vase Nro: 3869 arabisch decorirt (sechstheilig). 4/11/1878; Die Vase hat ganz durchsichtigen Grund. – Das Email ist überall mit Goldlinien eingesäumt und möglichst dick aufzutragen. Goldlinien n sind 3mal so breit als die Nebenlinien. – Weisses Email elfenbeinartig u. rothbraun cont."; FAW, Bestellungsbuch MNA, 2. Nov. 1878, „[…] in arab. Decor I. Serie"

Inv.-Nr. Gl 2576/1+2 (2 St.), aus dem ehem. Arabischen Zimmer, 1932 nachträglich inv.

Lit.: Neuwirth 1981a, S. 295; Fillitz 1996, Bd. 2, S. 608, Kat. Nr. 21.152

29f Becher

Entw.: 1878

Ausf.: Meyr's Neffen, Adolf, 1878

Farbloses Glas mit Dekor in Blau, Weiß und Gold

FM: auf der Unterseite gemalt

H 18,8 cm

Quellen: WZ, Bd. XV, S. 4, „Nro: 3871 – Becher arabisch dekorirt/ 1878"; FAW, Bestellungsbuch MNA, 2. Nov. 1878, „Becher hohe konisch Kristall m. gelbbraunen Stich in arabischen Decor I. Serie"

Inv.-Nr. Gl 1444, angek. v. J. & L. Lobmeyr um 28 fl., inv. 4. Nov. 1879

Lit.: Brožová 1975, Kat.-Nr. 321; Neuwirth 1981c, S. 41, Abb. 13; Neuwirth 1981a, S. 291

29d Two-Handled Vase

Dsg.: 1878

Mfr.: Meyr's Neffen, Adolf, 1878

Colorless glass with blue, green, white, and gold decoration

B: painted on the bottom

H 20.5 and 20.4 cm

Sources: WD, vol. XV, p. 12, "No: 7882. Arabian decorated vase bodies" (according to the MNA order book, this is no. 2882/1878, "Vase with round handle, yellowish opal glass w. Moorish decoration in lustre colors 2nd series")

Inv. no. Gl 1429, purch. by J. & L. Lobmeyr for 34 Gulden, inv. 25 Sept. 1879

Inv. no.: Gl 2597, pres. bequest of Ludwig Lobmeyr 1917, subs. inv.

Lit.: Neuwirth 1981c, p. 44; Fillitz 1996, vol. 2, p. 609, cat. no. 21.142

Carnations were a popular motif of Turkish ceramics from Iznik, which were then often wrongly referred to as "Persian-Rhodian" (see cat. no. 31).

29e Two Bottles ("Vase")

Dsg.: 1878

Colorless glass with blue and gold decoration

B: painted on the bottom; label: "42/1100/g C E L/7935"

H 30.6 cm

Sources: WD, vol. XV, p. 8, "Vase no: 3869 Arabian decoration (six parts). 4/11/1878; The Vase has a transparent ground. – The enamel is framed with gold lines and must be applied as thick as possible. Gold lines three times the width of the secondary lines. – White enamel, ivory-like and red-brown cont."; CAV, order book MNA, 2. Nov. 1878, "[…] in Arab. Decoration, 1st series"

Inv. no. Gl 2576/1+2 (2 St.), from the former Arabian Room, inv. 1932

Lit.: Neuwirth 1981a, p. 295; Fillitz 1996, vol. 2, p. 608, cat. no. 21.152

29f Beaker

Dsg.: 1878

Mfr.: Meyr's Neffen, Adolf, 1878

Colorless glass with blue, white, and gold decoration

B: painted on the bottom

H 18.8 cm

Sources: WD, vol. XV, p. 4, "No: 3871 – Beaker, Arabian decoration /1878"; CAV, order book MNA, 2 Nov. 1878, "Beakers, high, conical, crystal with yellow-brown tinge in Arabian decoration, 1st series"

Inv. no. Gl 1444, purch. by J. & L. Lobmeyr for 28 Gulden, inv. 4 Nov. 1879

Lit.: Brozová 1975, cat. no. 321; Neuwirth 1981c, p. 41, ill. 13; Neuwirth 1981a, p. 291

29f

Becher „in arabischem Style",
in: WZ, Bd. XV, S. 4 (Ausschnitt)

Beaker „in Arabian style",
in: WD, vol. XV, p. 4 (detail)

29d

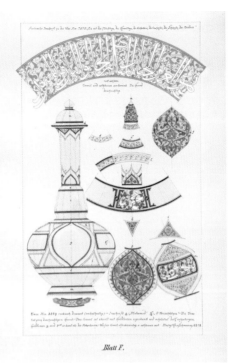

Flasche „in arabischem Style", in: WZ, Bd. XV, S. 8
Bottle „in Arabian style", in: WD, vol. XV, p. 8

29e

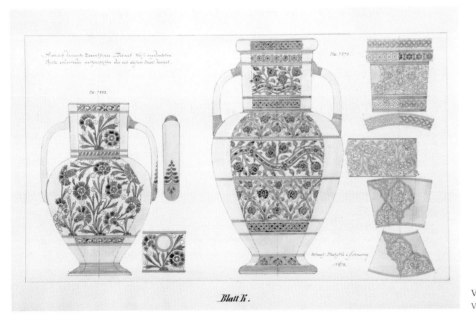

Vasen „in arabischem Style", in: WZ, Bd. XV, S. 12
Vases „in Arabian style", in: WD, vol. XV, p. 12

29g Flakon

Entw.: 1878

Farbloses Glas mit farbigem Dekor und Gold
Inschrift (übers.): „O Herr du bist der beste Helfer.",
„O Bewahrer.", „O Zuverlässlicher."
FM: auf der Unterseite gemalt; Etikett: „12,/80/760/MBIL/8III"
H 16,9 cm
Quellen: WZ, Bd. XV, S. 4, „Vase Nro: 7888 – Arabisch dekorirt"
Inv.-Nr. Gl 2577, aus dem ehem. Arabischen Zimmer,
1932 nachträglich inv.
Lit.: Uhland 1880, S. 69; Zeitschrift des bayerischen Kunst-
Gewerbe-Vereins in München, 1889, Taf. 7; Schlosser 1977,
Taf. XXIV; Neuwirth 1981a, S. 290

Als Ornamentvorlage diente hier eine „Amphora-
Flasche" aus dem Domschatz von St. Stephan in Wien
(Dom- und Diözesanmuseum), die auch von Gustav
Schmoranz in seine Publikation „Altorientalische Glas-
Gefässe" (Wien 1898) aufgenommen wurde. Damals
wurde die Flasche dem mesopotamischen Raum zuge-
schrieben und auf das 13. Jahrhundert datiert, heute wird
die Herkunft mit Syrien um 1300 angegeben.

29g Flacon

Dsg.: 1878

Colorless glass with colored decoration and gilding
Inscription (transl.): "Oh Lord, Thou art the best of helpers.",
"Oh Preserver.", "Oh Dependable You."
FM: painted on the bottom; label: "12, 80/760/MBIL/8III"
H 16.9 cm
Sources: WD, vol. XV, p. 4, "Vase no: 7888 – Arabian decoration"
Inv. no. Gl 2577, from the former Arabian Room, inv. 1932
Lit.: Uhland 1880, p. 69; Zeitschrift des bayerischen Kunst-
Gewerbe-Vereins in München, 1889, pl. 7; Schlosser 1977,
pl. XXIV; Neuwirth 1981a, p. 290

The model for the ornamentation was an "amphora
bottle" from the treasury of St. Stephen's (Cathedral
and Diocesan Museum) included by Gustav Schmoranz
in his publication on "Old-Oriental Glass Vessels"
(Vienna 1898). The bottle was then assigned to the
Mesopotamian region and dated 13th century; today
the origin is assumed to be Syria around 1300.

„Amphora Flasche", Domschatz zu St. Stephan,
Wien, in: Gustav Schmoranz: Altorientalische
Glas-Gefässe, Wien 1898, Taf. XIII (MAK,
Inv.-Nr. K.I. 11543)
"Amphora Bottle", Domschatz zu St. Stephan,
Wien, in: Gustav Schmoranz "Old-Oriental
Glass Vessels", Wien 1898, pl. XIII (MAK,
inv. no. K.I. 11543)

29h Flasche

Entw.: 1878

Farbloses Glas mit farbigem Dekor und Gold
Inschrift (übers.): „Das Reich gehört Gott, der Einzige und
Ewige, der Wahrhaftige.", „O du, der an diesem klaren Wasser
vorüber gehst, trinke."
FM: auf der Unterseite gemalt
H 30,5 cm
Quellen: WZ, Bd. XV, S. 7, „Flasche Nro. 3868 – Arabisch
decorirt (dreitheilig). Die Vase hat ganz durchsichtigen Grund. –
Das Email ist mit Goldlinien conturirt. – Die vergoldeten
Inschriften b.'b. sind allein mit braunen Emaillinien zu contu-
riren. – Alles Gold ist zu poliren. 1878"; FAW, Bestellungsbuch
MNA, 2. Nov. 1878, „[...] arab. Decor I. Serie"
Inv.-Nr. Gl 2573, aus dem ehem. Arabischen Zimmer,
1932 nachträglich inv.
Lit.: Zeitschrift des bayerischen Kunst-Gewerbe-Vereins in
München, 1889, Taf. 7; Neuwirth 1981a, S. 295

Stilistisch und auch formal dienten syrische emaillierte
Flaschen des 13. und 14. Jahrhunderts als Vorbild. Eine
solche Flasche mit vergleichbarer Form und ähnlichen
Motiven (nur die figuralen Motive wurden weggelas-

29h Bottle

Dsg.: 1878

Colorless glass with colored decoration and gilding
Inscription (transl.): "The realm belongs to God, the One and
Eternal, the Truthful.", "Oh thou, who passest this clear water,
drink."
B: painted on the bottom
H 30.5 cm
Sources: WD, vol. XV, S. 7, "Bottle no. 3868 – Arabian deco-
rated (three parts). The ground of the vase is all transparent. –
The enameling is contoured with gold lines. – The gilded
inscriptions b.'b. are to be outlined with brown enamel lines.
– Polished finish for all gilding. 1878"; CAV, order book
MNA, 2. Nov 1878, "[...] Arab. decoration, 1st series"
Inv. no. Gl 2573, from the former Arabian Room, inv. 1932
Lit.: Zeitschrift des bayerischen Kunst-Gewerbe-Vereins in
München, 1889, pl. 7; Neuwirth 1981a, p. 295

The models for style and form of this bottle were 13th
and 14th century Syrian enameled bottles. One such
bottle that is comparable in form and has similar decoration motifs (except for the figuration) was published by

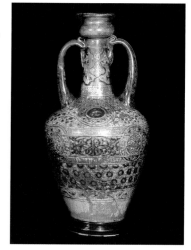

Amphora-Flasche, Syrien, um 1300
(Dom- und Diözesanmuseum, Wien,
Inv.-Nr. Prot. Nr. L-6)
Amphora Bottle, Syria, app. 1300 (Dom- und
Diözesanmuseum, Wien, inv. no. prot. no. L-6)

29g

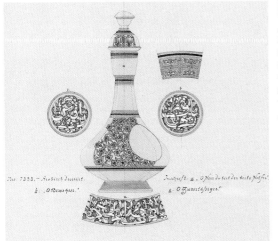

„Grosse Flasche", Collection Vapereau, Paris,
in: Gustav Schmoranz „Altorientalische
Glas–Gefässe, Wien 1898, Taf. XXIX
(MAK, Inv.-Nr. K.I. 11543)
"Grosse Flasche", Collection Vapereau, Paris,
in: Gustav Schmoranz "Old-Oriental Glass
Vessels", Wien 1898, pl. XXIX
(MAK, inv. no. K.I.11543)

29h

Flasche „in arabischem Style",
in: WZ, Bd. XV, S. 4 (Ausschnitt)
Vase „in Arabian style", in: WD, vol. XV,
p. 4 (detail)

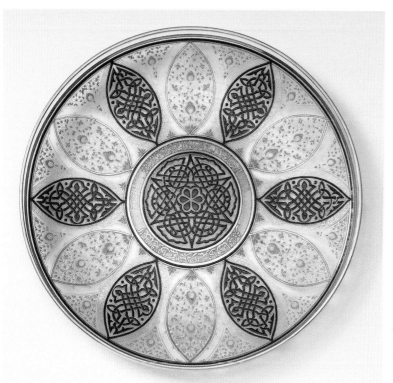

29i

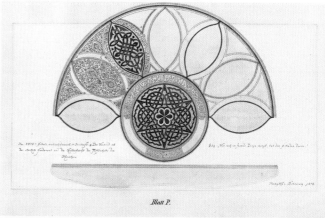

Schale „in arabischem Style", in: WZ, Bd. XV, S. 17
Bowl "in Arabian style", in: WD, vol. XV, p. 17

sen) publizierte Gustav Schmoranz („Altorientalische Glas-Gefässe", Wien 1898, Taf. XXIX, „Flasche aus französischem Besitz").

Gustav Schmoranz ("Old-Oriental Glass Vessels", Vienna 1898, pl. XXIX, "Bottle from French possession").

29i Schale

Entw.: 1878
Ausf.: Meyr's Neffen, Adolf, 1878
Farbloses Glas mit Dekor in Hell- und Dunkelblau und Gold
Inschrift (übers.): „Wer sich in fremde Dinge mengt, hat den Schaden davon.", „Die Klugheit ist die mächtigste Stütze des Menschen und die Rechtschaffenheit ist seine beste Eigenschaft." (Unterseite) bzw. „Der Verstand ist das stärkste Fundament und die Gottesfurcht das Trefflichste der Menschen. Wer sich in fremde Dinge mengt, hat den Schaden davon." (WZ)
FM: auf der Unterseite gemalt
D 38,7 bzw. 38,8 cm
Quellen: WZ, Bd. XV, S. 17, „Nro: 3873 – Schale, arabisch decorirt.–1878"; FAW, Bestellungsbuch MNA, 2. Nov. 1878, „Schalen 39 cm m. arabischen Decor I. Serie"
Inv.-Nr. Gl 1430, angek. v. J. & L. Lobmeyr um 75 fl., inv. 25. Sept. 1879
Inv.-Nr. Gl 2589, Vermächtnis Ludwig Lobmeyr 1917, nachträglich inv.
Lit.: Schmidt 1925, Taf. 13; Neuwirth 1981a, S. 294

29i Bowl

Dsg.: 1878
Mfr.: Meyr's Neffen, Adolf, 1878
Colorless glass with light and dark brown and gold decoration
Inscription (transl.): "He who mingles in foreign matters will come to harm.", "Prudence is man's mightiest support, and righteousness his best virtue." (Bottom side) "The mind is the strongest foundation, and fear of God is what best befits men. He who mingles in foreign matters will come to harm." (WD)
B: painted on the bottom
D 38.7 and 38.8 cm
Sources: WD, vol. XV, p. 17, "No: 3873 – Bowl, Arabian decoration.–1878"; CAV, order book MNA, 2 Nov. 1878, "Bowls 39 cm w. Arabian decoration, 1st series"
Inv. no. Gl 1430, purch. by J. & L. Lobmeyr for 75 Gulden, inv. 25 Sept. 1879
Inv. no. Gl 2589, bequest of Ludwig Lobmeyr 1917, subs. inv.
Lit.: Schmidt 1925, pl. 13; Neuwirth 1981a, p. 294

30 „Spanisch-maurische Serie aus gelblichem, halbopakem Glase mit Blau-Email u. Gold verziert. Die Ornamente nach Anleitung des Director F. Schmoranz ausgezeichnet von M. Knab", ab 1878

Gelbes opakes Glas mit Dekor in Blau und Gold

Für diese 1878 entworfene orientalisierende Serie dienten Keramiken als Anregung, die in transparentes Glas mit Malerei übertragen wurden. Die Vorbilder, spanisch-maurische Keramiken (auch als „hispano-maurisch" bezeichnet), waren durch die zeitgenössische Literatur und Objekte bekannt, wie sie sich in Privatsammlungen oder auch in den Sammlungen des ÖMKI befanden. Es handelte sich dabei um spanische Lüsterfayencen aus Valencia (15. und 16. Jahrhundert).

Die Serie, die vor allem verschiedene Vasen und Schalen, aber auch Flaschen, Becher und Kännchen umfasste, wurde schon auf der Weltausstellung 1878 in Paris erfolgreich präsentiert: „Endlich verstund er [Lobmeyr] durch eine überaus glückliche Anwendung besonders der maurischen Ornamentation einer Anzahl Service dieses Styls einen solchen feinen Farbenreiz zu geben, wie man ihn sonst fast in der ganzen Ausstellung vergeblich suchen wird" (Pecht 1878, S. 246).

Franz Schmoranz arbeitete zur gleichen Zeit auch an einer arabischen Serie (Kat.-Nr. 29). Der für die Zeichnungen der spanisch-maurischen Serie zuständige Moritz Knab absolvierte 1875 bis 1880 die Wiener Kunstgewerbeschule (1877–1880 Fachschule für Architektur bei Prof. Herdtle), danach war er in Herdtles Atelier tätig. Von 1882 bis 1886 war er bei Lobmeyr als Zeichner angestellt und entwarf mehrere stilistisch sehr unterschiedliche Serien. Gemeinsam mit Franz Schmoranz zeichnete er noch 1888 die Alhambra-Serie. Danach wurde er Leiter der Fachschule in Nixdorf (Mikulášovice), später jener im nordböhmischen Gablonz (Jablonec).

WZ, Bd. XVI, S. 8–14

Lit.: Schmidt 1889, S. 76; Neuwirth 1981c, S. 76–77

30 "Spanish-Moorish series of yellowish, semi-opaque glass, decorated with blue enamel and gilding. Ornaments drawn by M. Knab by instruction of Director F. Schmoranz", from 1878

Yellow opaque glass with blue and gold decoration

This oriental-style series of 1878 was inspired by ceramics which were translated onto painted transparent glass. The models, Spanish-Moorish ceramics (also called "Hispano-Moorish") were known from contemporary literature and from objects from private collections or the collections of the AMAI. These were Spanish lustre faiences from Valencia (15th and 16th century).

The series, which comprised different vases and bowls, but also bottles, beakers, and jugs, was successfully presented at the 1878 Paris World's Fair already: "Finally, he [Lobmeyr] knew, through a most felicitous application of, in particular, Moorish ornamentation, how to give to a number of services of this style such appealing coloring as can hardly be found anywhere else in this exhibition" (Pecht 1878, p. 246).

At the same time, Franz Schmoranz also worked on an Arabian series (cat. no. 29). Moritz Knab, who was responsible for the drawings of the Spanish-Moorish series, studied at the Vienna Industrial Arts School from 1875 to 1880 (1877–1880 School of Architecture with Prof. Herdtle); after that, he worked in Herdtle's studio. Between 1882 and 1886 he was employed by Lobmeyr as a draftsman and did designs for several series of widely different styles. 1888, he designed the Alhambra series together with Franz Schmoranz. Later, he became principal of the vocational schools of Nixdorf (Mikulášovice) and Gablonz (Jablonec) in North-Bohemia.

WD, vol. XVI, pp. 8–14

Lit.: Schmidt 1889, p. 76; Neuwirth 1981c, pp. 76–77

30a Vase mit zwei Henkeln

FM: auf der Unterseite gemalt
H 50,1 cm
Quellen: WZ, Bd. XVI, S. 9; FAW, Bestellungsbuch MNA,
2. Nov. 1878, „Vasen rund m. Henkeln 50/2 cm gelblich opal
maurische Decoration m. Lustrefarben" (3878-78 „Hyspanisch"
bezeichnet); FAP, Schnitt „3875 Adolf 4 Vasen gelblich opak gestreift eingebl. m. maurischem Decor 2/11 1878 J. & L. Lobmeyr"
Inv.-Nr. Gl 2583, Vermächtnis Ludwig Lobmeyr 1917,
nachträglich inv.

30b Vase mit zwei Henkeln (Abb. siehe S. 40)

FM: auf der Unterseite gemalt
H 36,6 cm
Quellen: WZ, Bd. XVI, S. 10; FAW, Bestellungsbuch MNA,
2. Nov. 1878, „Vasen rund m. Henkeln 37 cm gelblich opal
maurische Decoration m. Lustrefarben"; FAP, Schnitt „3876
Adolf 4 Vasen leicht gestreift gelblich opak m. maurischem
Decor 2/11 1878 J. & L. Lobmeyr"
Inv.-Nr. Gl 2584, Vermächtnis Ludwig Lobmeyr 1917,
nachträglich inv.

30c Vase

FM: auf der Unterseite gemalt
H 24,2 cm
Quellen: WZ, Bd. XVI, S. 12; FAW, Bestellungsbuch MNA,
2. Nov. 1878, „Vasen ohne Henkel rund 24 cm gelblich opal
maurische Decoration m. Lustrefarben 2. Serie"; FAP, Schnitt
„3886 Adolf 4/6 Vasen leicht gestreift gelblich opak. m.
maurischem Decor 2/11 1878 J. & L. Lobmeyr"
Inv.-Nr. Gl 2595, wohl Vermächtnis Ludwig Lobmeyr 1917,
nachträglich inv.

Die fächerförmigen Blütenmotive hatten ihr Vorbild auf
einer „Hispano-Maurischen Schüssel" aus der „Collection Fürst Johannes Liechtenstein", die runden Blüten
auf einer „Hispano-Maurischen Schüssel" aus der „Collection Baronin Th. Gödel-Lannoy" („Sammlung von
Abbildungen Keramischer Objecte aus dem nahen und
fernen Oriente", hrsg. v. Orientalischen Museum, Wien
1885, Taf. LI, LV).

30d Schale

FM: im Zentrum der Oberseite gemalt
D 41,1 cm
Quellen: WZ, Bd. XVI, S. 8; FAW, Bestellungsbuch MNA,
2. Nov. 1878, 3896, „Schalen gelblich Opalglas m. maurischem
Decor in Lustrefarben II. Serie"; FAP, Schnitt „3896 Adolf

30a Two-Handled Vase

B: painted on the bottom
H 50.1 cm
Sources: WD, vol. XVI, p. 9; CAV, order book MNA, 2 Nov.
1878, "Vases, round w. handles 50/2 cm, yellowish opal,
Moorish decoration with lustre colors" (3878-78 referred to
as "Hispanic"); CAP, papercut "3875 Adolf 4 vases yellowish
opaque, mold-blown with stripes, w. Moorish decoration
2/11 1878 J. & L. Lobmeyr"
Inv. no. Gl 2583, bequest of Ludwig Lobmeyr 1917, subs. inv.

30b Two-Handled Vase (see ill. p. 40)

B: painted on the bottom
H 36.6 cm
Sources: WD, vol. XVI, p. 10; CAV, order book MNA, 2 Nov.
1878, " Vases, round w. handles 37 cm yellowish opal, Moorish
decoration with lustre colors "; CAP, papercut "3876 Adolf 4
vases, light stripes, yellowish opaque with Moorish decoration
2/11 1878 J. & L. Lobmeyr"
Inv. no. Gl 2584, bequest of Ludwig Lobmeyr 1917, subs. inv.

30a

30c Vase

B: painted on the bottom
H 24.2 cm
Sources: WD, vol. XVI, p. 12; CAV, order book MNA, 2 Nov.
1878, "Vases without handles, round, 24 cm yellowish opal,
Moorish decoration w. lustre colors, 2nd series"; CAP, paper-
cut "3886 Adolf 4/6 vases, light stripes, yellowish opaque w.
Moorish decoration 2/11 1878 J. & L. Lobmeyr"
Inv. no. Gl 2595, pres. bequest of Ludwig Lobmeyr 1917,
subs. inv.

The fan-shaped floral motifs were modeled after a
"Hispano-Moorish Bowl" from the "Collection of
Prince Johannes Liechtenstein", the round blossoms
after a "Hispano-Moorish Bowl" from the "Collection
of Baroness Th. Gödel-Lannoy ("Collection of Representations of Ceramic Objects from the Near and Far
Orient", ed. by Oriental Museum, Vienna 1885,
pl. LII, LV).

30d Bowl

B: painted in the top-side center
D 41.1 cm
Sources: WD, vol. XVI, p. 8; CAV, order book MNA, 2 Nov.
1878, 3896, "Bowl yellowish opal glass w. Moorish decoration
in lustre colors 2nd series"; CAP, papercut "3896 Adolf bowls,

30c

„Hispano-Maurische Schüsseln", in: Sammlung von Abbildungen Keramischer Objecte aus dem nahen und fernen Oriente, hrsg. v. Orientalischen Museum, Wien 1885, Taf. LIII, LV (MAK, Inv.-Nr. K.I. 8142) "Hispano-Moorish Bowls", in: "Collection of Representations of Ceramic Objects from the Near and Far Orient", ed. by Oriental Museum, Vienna 1885, pl. LIII, LV (MAK, inv. no. K.I. 8142)

30d

Schalen leicht gestreift gelblich opak m. maurischem Decor 2/11 1878 J. & L. Lobmeyr" Inv.-Nr. Gl 2588, Vermächtnis Ludwig Lobmeyr 1917, nachträglich inv.

Das sechsteilige Blütenmotiv findet sich auf einer „Hispano-Maurischen Schüssel" aus der „Collection Fürst Johannes Liechtenstein", das ornamentale Band zwischen Zentrum und Randzone auf einer „Hispano-Maurischen Schüssel" aus der „Collection Baronin Th. Gödel-Lannoy („Sammlung von Abbildungen Kerami-scher Objecte aus dem nahen und fernen Oriente", hrsg. v. Orientalischen Museum, Wien 1885, Taf. LIII, LV).

light stripes, yellowish opaque w. Moorish decoration 2/11 1878 J. & L. Lobmeyr" Inv. no. Gl 2588, bequest of Ludwig Lobmeyr 1917, subs. inv.

The six-part floral motif is found on a "Hispano-Moorish Bowl" from the "Collection of Prince Johannes Liechtenstein," the ornamental band between the center and the rim on a "Hispano-Moorish Bowl" from the "Collection of Baroness Th. Gödel-Lannoy ("Collection of Representations of Ceramic Objects from the Near and Far Orient", ed. by Oriental Museum, Vienna 1885, pl. LIII, LV).

31 „Gefässe in persischem Style aus hellbraunem Glase mit bunter Emailmalerei und Gold. Die Formen nach eigener Zeichnung, die Ornamente vom Architecten Rehländer", ab 1878

Gelbes transparentes Glas mit farbigem Dekor und Gold

Persische Malerei als Dekor war bei Lobmeyr schon 1872 auf Gefäßen aus weißem Beinglas nach dem Entwurf von Valentin Teirich verwendet worden.

Die Vorbilder für diese orientalische Serie von 1878, die auch als „Serie mit Persischem Decor gezeichnet nach Rhodischen (Persischen) Fayencen" (Firmenarchiv) bezeichnet wurde, boten türkische Keramiken. Bei der im 19. Jahrhundert fälschlich als „rhodisch" bezeichneten Keramik nach Funden auf der Insel Rhodos handelte es sich um Iznik-Keramik aus der Türkei (16. und 17. Jahrhundert) in blauen, türkisen, grünen und roten Farben mit stilisiertem Blumendekor und schwarzen Konturen. Diese war einerseits aus zeitgenössischen Publikationen (Racinets „L'ornement polychrome", Paris 1872, Taf. „Art persan. Faiences"; „A Descriptive Catalogue of the Maiolica", London 1873), andererseits durch Museumsobjekte bekannt. So waren von Schmoranz für die Keramikabteilung „persische" Wandfliesen angekauft worden (Inv.-Nr. KE 2582-2657, inv. Sept. 1876). Auch persische Teller mit ähnlichem Dekor, bezeichnet als „persische o. rhodische Faiencen", befanden sich damals schon im Museum („Blätter für Kunstgewerbe", Bd. 4, 1875, S. 48).

Die Wirkung des Dekors war durch die Transparenz sicherlich eine andere als auf den Keramiken, gefiel aber sehr gut: die „[…] im maurischen und persischen […] Stil […] emaillierten Gefäße waren wunderbar" (Frauberger 1879, S. 49).

WZ, Bd. XVI, S. 1–7

Lit.: Gewerbehalle, Heft 3, 1886, Taf. 20; Neuwirth 1981c, S. 73, Abb. 29

31 "Vessels in Persian style of light brown glass with colored enamel painting and gilding. Forms after own drawings, ornaments by Architect Rehländer", from 1878

Yellow transparent glass with colored decoration and gilding

Persian painting had been used before by Lobmeyr for vessels of white bone glass to a design of Valentin Teirich in 1872.

The models for this oriental series of 1878 which was also referred to as "Series with Persian decoration designed after Rhodian (Persian) faiences" (company archives) were Turkish ceramics. These ceramics, which were often falsely called "Rhodian" after finds made on the island of Rhodos, in fact were 16th and 17th century Turkish Iznik ceramics in blue, turquoise, green, and red with stylized floral decorations and black contours.

These were known from contemporary publications (Racinet's "L'ornement polychrome", Paris 1872, pl. "Art persan. Faiences"; "A Descriptive Catalogue of the Maiolica", London 1873) and from museum objects. So, for example, Schmoranz had purchased "Persian wall tiles" for the ceramics department (inv. no. KE 2582-2657, inv. Sept. 1876). The museum holdings also included Persian plates with similar decoration, which were labeled "Persian or Rhodian faiences" ("Blätter für Kunstgewerbe", vol. 4, 1875, p. 48).

Due to the transparent glass, the effect of the decoration was certainly different from the originals, but met with much appreciation: the "[…] Moorish or Persian-style […] enameled vessels were wonderful" (Frauberger 1879, p. 49).

WD, vol. XVI, pp. 1–7

Lit.: Gewerbehalle, no. 3, 1886, pl. 20; Neuwirth 1981c, p. 73, ill. 29

„Persischer Teller" aus der Sammlung des ÖMKI, in: Blätter für Kunstgewerbe, Bd. 4, 1875, S. 48 (MAK, Inv.-Nr. K.I. 3251)
"Plate in Persian style", Collection of the ÖMKI, in: "Blätter für Kunstgewerbe", vol. IV, 1975, p. 48 (MAK, inv. no. K.I. 3251)

31a

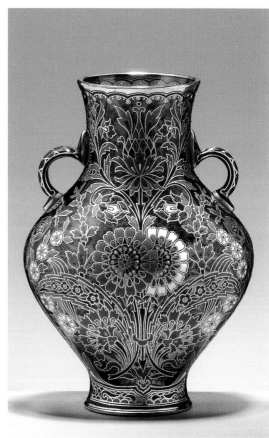

31b

31a Schale

Entw.: 1878

FM: im Zentrum der Unterseite gemalt

D 39 cm

Quellen: WZ, Bd. XVI, S. 1; FAW, Zeichnung der Schale
unsigniert, Bestellungsbuch MNA, 2. Febr. 1878, 3912,
„Schalen 40 cm“

Inv.-Nr. Gl 2585, Vermächtnis Ludwig Lobmeyr 1917,
nachträglich inv.

31b Vase mit zwei Henkeln

Entw.: 1878

FM: auf der Unterseite gemalt

H 20,8 cm

Quellen: WZ, Bd. XVI, S. 2; FAW, „Vasen oval m. persischem
Dekor 3900 b, 21.11.78“; FAP, Schnitt „MNA 3900–1878“

Inv.-Nr. Gl 2596, wohl Vermächtnis Ludwig Lobmeyr 1917,
nachträglich inv.

31a Bowl

Dsg.: 1878

B: painted in the bottom center

D 39 cm

Sources: WD, vol. XVI, p. 1; CAV, unsigned drawing of a
bowl, order book MNA, 2. Febr 1878, 3912, "Bowls 40 cm"

Inv. no. Gl 2585, bequest of Ludwig Lobmeyr 1917, subs. inv.

31b Two-Handled Vase

Dsg.: 1878

B: painted on the bottom

H 20.8 cm

Sources: WD, vol. XVI, p. 2; CAV, "Vases, oval w. Persian
decoration 3900 b, 21.11.78"; CAP, papercut "MNA 3900–1878"

Inv. no. Gl 2596, pres. bequest of Ludwig Lobmeyr 1917,
subs. inv.

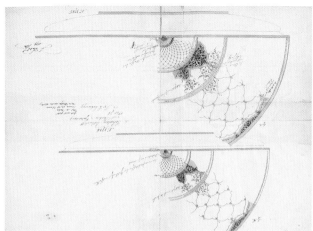

Schalen (Werkzeichnungen, FAW)
Bowls (working drawings, CAV)

32a

32 Serie „Violett mit Platin und Golddekor", ab 1878

Rotes transparentes Glas mit Dekor in Gold, Silber (Platin) und Schwarz

Die Ornamente greifen maurische Dekormotive, aber auch persische Niellodekorationen auf. Die Entwurfszeichnungen sind zum Teil von Josef Salb signiert, der schon Anfang der siebziger Jahre mehrere Serien mit orientalischem Dekor entworfen hatte.

Ähnlich wie bei den Serien mit Aluminium wurde hier Platin statt Silber verwendet, um die Verfärbung durch Oxidierung zu verhindern.

Josef Salb (1845–1904) war in Wien als „Kunstgewerbezeichner" tätig, bevor er 1876 Professor an der Staatsgewerbeschule in Salzburg wurde. Aber auch danach blieb er Lobmeyr als Entwerfer verbunden und lieferte stilistisch sehr unterschiedliche Entwürfe (siehe Kat.-Nr. 40).

32a Schale
Entw.: Josef Salb, 1879
FM: im Zentrum der Oberseite gemalt
D 40 cm

32 Series "Purple with platinum and gold decoration", from 1878

Red transparent glass with decoration in gold, silver (platinum) and black

The ornamentation draws on Moorish motifs, but also on Persian Niello decorations. Part of the design drawings are signed by Josef Salb, who had made several designs with Oriental decoration in the 1870s already. Similarly to the aluminum series, silver was substituted with platinum here to prevent tarnishing through oxidation.

Josef Salb (1845–1904) worked as an "industrial arts draftsmen" in Vienna, before he was appointed to a professorship at the Salzburg State Crafts School. Even after that he continued to work as a designer for Lobmeyr and supplied a number of designs in a variety of different styles (see cat. no. 40).

32a Bowl
Dsg.: Josef Salb, 1879
B: painted in the top-side center
D 40 cm

Quellen: FAW, Zeichnung der Schale „Nr. 3785/J. Salb 1879", Bestellungsbuch MNA, 19. Okt. 1878, 3785, „Schalen I 40 cm hell violett m. Platindecor schwarzen Ornament & weiß […]"; FAP, Schnitt „MNA 3785-1878"
Inv.-Nr. Gl 2579, aus dem ehem. Arabischen Zimmer, 1932 nachträglich inv.

Sources: CAV, drawing of the bowl "Nr. 3785/J. Salb 1879", order book MNA, 19. Oct. 1878, 3785, "Bowls I 40 cm light purple w. platinum decoration, black ornamentation & white […] "; CAP, papercut "MNA 3785-1878"
Inv. no. Gl 2579, from the former Arabian Room, inv. 1932

33 Glimmerglas

1878 entstanden mehrere Serien in farblosem bzw. gelblichem Glas oder weißem Opalglas mit eingeschmolzenem Silberflitter (Glimmerplättchen bzw. Glimmerbrocat, aus Glimmerpulver hergestellt). Durch gelbes Glas wirkte der Silberflitter golden. Diese Technik kam angeblich aus Venedig und wurde auch von der österreichischen Fabrik J. Schreiber und Neffen zu dieser Zeit angewendet (Falke 1879, S. 1).

Bei Lobmeyr wurden aus Glimmerglas verschiedenste Gefäße (Punschtopf, Punschbecher, Vasen, Flakons, Pokale, Schalen, Fußbecher u. a.) in diversen Varianten hergestellt. Die Formen waren schlicht gehalten, damit das spezielle Glas besser zur Wirkung kam. Die Objekte konnten zusätzlich mit Email und Gold bemalt oder mit aufgesetzten Glasperlen (in Blau oder Rot) dekoriert sein. Das ÖMKI kaufte von mehreren Varianten dieses Glases unmittelbar nach Herausgabe ein Anschauungsobjekt.

33a Schale
Serie „Glimmerglas gelb mit rubin Perlen"
Ausf.: Meyr's Neffen, Adolf, 1878
Gelbes transparentes Glas mit Glimmereinschlüssen, Dekor in Gold, aufgesetzte rote Glasperlen
FM: auf der Oberseite gemalt
D 23,5 cm
Quellen: FAW, Bestellungsbuch MNA, 22. Febr. 1878, 2122, „Schalen ohne Fuß gelb überfangen Glimmerglas und Golddecor m. rubin Perlen"
Inv.-Nr. Gl 1434, angek. v. J. & L. Lobmeyr um 50 fl., inv. 25. Sept. 1879

33b Flakon
Serie „Kristall, gelb und opal Glimmerglas m. Goldlinien u. emaillierten Bändern"
Ausf.: Meyr's Neffen, Adolf, 1878

33 Glimmer Glass (Mica Glass)

1878, a number of series of colorless or yellowish glass or white opal glass with fused-in silver spangle (mica scales or mica scraps, made from mica powder). The yellowish glass made the silver inclusions look golden. Allegedly, the technique came from Venice and was also used at that time by the Austrian glassworks of J. Schreiber und Neffen (Falke 1879, p. 1).

Lobmeyr produced a range of mica-glass vessels in a number of variants (punchbowl, punch cup, vases, flacons, goblets, bowls, footed beakers etc.) The forms were kept simple so as to accentuate the special quality of the glass. Sometimes the objects were also decorated with enameling or gilding or with stuck-on glass prunts (blue or red). The AMAI purchased specimens of different variants of this glass as soon as it was brought to the market.

33a Bowl
Series "Mica glass, yellow with ruby prunts "
Mfr.: Meyr's Neffen, Adolf, 1878
Yellow transparent glass with mica inclusions, gold decoration, red glass prunts
B: painted on the top side
D 23.5 cm
Sources: CAV, order book MNA, 22 Feb. 1878, 2122, "Bowls without foot, yellow casing, glimmer glass and gold decoration w. ruby pearls"
Inv. no. Gl 1434, purch. by J. & L. Lobmeyr for 50 Gulden, inv. 25 Sept. 1879

33b Flacon
Series "Crystal, yellow and opal mica glass with gold lining and enamel bands"
Mfr.: Meyr's Neffen, Adolf, 1878

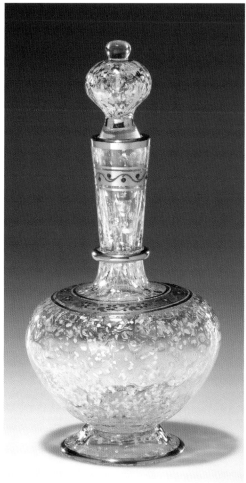

33a   33b

Farbloses Glas mit Glimmereinschlüssen, Dekor in Grün,
Rot und Gold
H 14,5 cm
Quellen: FAP, Serie 48, Schnitt „MNA 3964-78"
Inv.-Nr. Gl 1437, angek. v. J. & L. Lobmeyr um 2,40 fl.,
inv. 25. Sept. 1879

33c Krug (Abb. siehe S. 30)
Serie „Glimmerglas weissopal mit rubin Perlen"
Ausf.: Meyr's Neffen, Adolf, 1878
Weißes halbopakes Glas (Opalglas) mit Glimmereinschlüssen,
Dekor in Grün, Rot und Gold, aufgesetzte rote Glasperlen
FM: auf der Unterseite gemalt
H 31 cm
Quellen: FAW, Bestellungsbuch MNA, 20. Apr. 1878,
„Krüge m. eng. Hals ohne Stpsl. weiss opal Glimmerglas m.
Goldrändern u. Rubinperlen grün Emailblättern u. brau. Ern.
pkt."; FAP, Serie 49, „Glimmerglas weissopal", 1878, Schnitt
„MNA 2396-1878"
Inv.-Nr. Dep. 90, angek. v. J. & L. Lobmeyr, inv. 1879

Colorless glass with mica inclusions, red, green, and gold
decoration
H 14.5 cm
Sources: CAP, series 48, papercut "MNA 3964-78"
Inv. no. Gl 1437, purch. by J. & L. Lobmeyr fro 2.40 Gulden,
inv. 25 Sept. 1879

33c Jug (see ill. p. 30)
Series "Mica glass white opal with ruby prunts"
Mfr.: Meyr's Neffen, Adolf, 1878
White semi-opaque glass (opal glass) with mica inclusions,
green, red, and gold decoration, red glass prunts
B: painted on the bottom
H 31 cm
Sources: CAV, order book MNA, 20 Apr. 1878, "Jugs w. Engl.
Neck and without stopper, white opal mica glass, with gold
rims and ruby prunts green enameled leaves and brown dots";
CAP, series 49, "Mica glass, white opal", 1878, papercut
"MNA 2396-1878"
Inv. no. Dep. 90, purch. by J. & L. Lobmeyr, inv. 1879

34 Eis- bzw. Craqueléglas

Das Eisglas, auch als Craqueléglas bezeichnet, entstand dadurch, dass die Glasmasse kurz ins kalte Wasser gehalten wurde, wodurch sie an der Oberfläche sprang; dann wurde die Form wieder erwärmt und weiter geblasen. Um 1880 entstanden bei Lobmeyr verschiedene Varianten in dieser Technik, die als reizvolle neue Möglichkeit gesehen wurde: „[…] das craquelirte Glas, eine Spielerei, wenn man will, sicherlich kein eigentliches Kunstmotiv, hier aber verbindet sich diese Spielerei mit irisierenden Farben und zugleich mit so schönen Farben, dass man dieser wahrscheinlich vorübergehenden Novität ihre gefälligen Reize nicht absprechen kann" („Mittheilungen", Nr. 184, 1. Jan. 1881, S. 249, über die Weihnachtsausstellung 1880).

34a Vase
Entw.: 1880
Rosa transparentes Glas (Craqueléglas), gebuckelt mit weißen opaken Fadenauflagen
H 48,1 cm
Quellen: WZ, Bd. IX, S. 30 ff.; FAW, Bestellungsbuch MNA, 21. Dez. 1880, 8454-80 ff., „Vasen hell-rosa craquele geformt Ringe weiß"
Inv.-Nr. WI 41, Geschenk v. J. & L. Lobmeyr, inv. 26. Jan. 1902

Die 1880 entworfene Serie „Gegenstände aus bernsteinfärbigem Eisglase mit rosa Ringen, oder auch aus rosa Glase mit weiss opal Ringen. Nach eigenen Zeichnungen 1880/81" (WZ, Bd. XI, S. 30–36) konnte in verschiedenen Glasfarben ausgeführt werden und umfasste: Flaschen, Vasen, Krüge, Schalen, Trinkgläser, Schüssel, Pokal, Bowle, Kännchen und Deckeldose mit Teller.

34b Vase
Entw.: 1881
Gelbes transparentes Glas (Craqueléglas), gebuckelt mit Dekor in Blau und Gold
FM: auf der Unterseite gemalt
H 41,7 cm
Quellen: FAW, 29. Okt. 1881, Zeichnung „Vasen gelb craquelé mit blauen Emailbändern u. Golddecor", Bestellungsbuch MNA, 29. Okt. 1881, 318, „Vasen groß u. 4paß geformt

34 Ice or Crackle Glass

Ice glass, also called crackle glass, was made by dipping a partly inflated gather of white-hot glass into cold water to create fissures in the surface before the gather was re-heated and re-blown. Around 1880, Lobmeyr produced different variants of this technique, which was considered an attractive new possibility:: "[…] crackle glass, a playful trick, one might say, certainly not a genuine art motif, but here this trick combines with iridescent colors, and colors so beautiful that this novelty, transient as it presumably will be, cannot be said to have no pleasant charm to it" ("Mittheilungen", no. 184, 1 Jan. 1881, p. 249, about the Christmas exhibition of 1880).

34a Vase
Dsg.: 1880
Pink transparent glass (crackle glass), molded with white opaque trailing
H 48.1 cm
Sources: WD, vol. IX, p. 30 ff.; CAV, order book MNA, 21. Dec. 1880, 8454-80 ff., "Vases light pink crackled rings white" Inv. no. WI 41, donation from v. J. & L. Lobmeyr, inv. 26 Jan. 1902

The series of "Objects of ivory-color iceglass with pink rings or pink glass with white opal rings. After own drawings 1880/81" (WD, vol. XI, pp. 30–36) was available in different colors of glass and included bottles, vases, pitchers, bowls, drinking glasses, a bowl, a goblet, a punchbowl, a jug, and a lidded box with plate.

34b Vase
Dsg.: 1881
Yellow transparent glass (crackle glass), molded with blue and gold decoration
B: painted on the bottom
H 41.7 cm
Sources: CAV, 29. Oct. 1881, drawing "Vases yellow crackle with blue enamel bands and gold decoration", order book MNA, 29. Oct. 1881, 318, "Vases big and quatrefoil, light

34a

34b

Vasen dieser Serie (Werkzeichnungen, FAW)
Vases of this series (working drawings, CAV)

hell-gelb craquelé"; FAP, Schnitt „MNA 318-1881"
Inv.-Nr. Gl 2045, angek. v. J. & L. Lobmeyr um 37 fl.,
inv. 30. Okt. 1900

In der Serie „Craquelé gelb geätzt" wurden neben Vasen
auch „Liqueurflaschen" und „Liqueurgläser", Krüge,
Becher, Finger- und Mundschalen sowie „Caffeegläser"
hergestellt.

yellow crackle"; CAP, papercut "MNA 318-1881"
Inv. no. Gl 2045, purch. by J. & L. Lobmeyr for 37 Gulden,
inv. 30 Oct. 1900

The series "Crackle glass, yellow with etching"
included, aside from vases, "liqueur bottles" and "liqueur
glasses" jugs, beakers, finger and mouth bowls as well
as "coffee glasses".

35 „Trink-Service Krystall mit Rococoschliff No. 173. Nach eigener Zeichnung", ab 1882

Farbloses Glas mit Schliff und Schnitt

Die Formen finden sich schon beim Trink-Service Nr. 66 „mit Schälen und gravirter Borde" aus den fünfziger Jahren (1854), eine Werkvorlage von 1877 verwendet dieselben Formen, allerdings mit renaissanceartigem Dekor (Bestellungsbuch: „Becher und Wasserflasche Trinkservice 66 kristall geschl. als Muster gravirt"). Ab 1882 wurden diese Formen mit geschnittenem Rokokodekor als neues Trink-Service hergestellt. Anfang der achtziger Jahre kamen Rokokoornamente sowohl gemalt als auch geschnitten wieder in Mode.

Im 19. Jahrhundert waren nur Teile von Trink-Servicen erworben worden. Mit dem Trink-Service Nr. 173 konnte das Museum im 20. Jahrhundert wenigstens ein umfassendes Glasservice aus dem 19. Jahrhundert erwerben.

WZ, Bd. XIV, S. 1–2

35 "Drinking service crystal with Rococo cut no. 173. After own drawing", from 1882

Colorless glass, ground and cut

The forms can be found already in the drinking service no. 66 "with surface-grinding and engraved border" from the 1850s (1854), a working drawing of 1877 uses the same forms, but with Renaissance-style decoration (order book: "Tumbler and water bottle drinking service 66 crystal surface ground engraved pattern"). From 1882, these forms were produced as a new drinking service with a cut Rococo decoration. In the early 1880s, Rococo forms, painted or cut, came back into fashion again.

In the 19th century, only parts of drinking services were purchased. With the drinking service no. 173 bought in the 20th century, the museum eventually acquired a complete 19th century drinking service.

WD, vol. XIV, S. 1–2

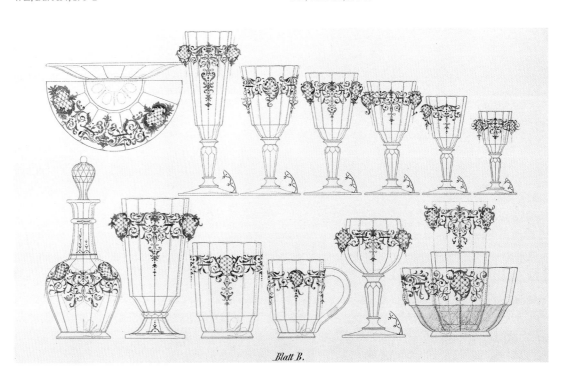

Teile des Trink-Services Nr. 173, in: WZ, Bd. XIV, S. 2
Parts of Drinking Service no. 173, in: WD, vol. XIV, p. 2

35g   35e   35d   35h   35a   35b   35f   35c

35a Flasche (Wasserflasche)

FM: am Bauch geschnitten

H 29 cm

Quellen: WZ, Bd. XIV, S. 1; FAP, Schnitt „MN & AJB
7329–1882 TS 66 TS 173 Wasserfl."

Inv.-Nr. Gl 3343a, Ankauf, inv. 1976 (6 St.)

35b Stängelglas (Rheinweinglas)

Grünes transparentes Glas mit Schliff und Schnitt

H 13 cm

Quellen: WZ, Bd. XIV, S. 2; FAP, Schnitt „MN & AJB […] 1882
TS 66 TS 173 Burgundergl. weis & Rheinweinglas grün"

Inv.-Nr. Gl 3343b, Ankauf, inv. 1976 (17 St.)

35c Stängelglas (Weinglas)

H 14,3 cm

Quellen: WZ, Bd. XIV, S. 2; FAP, Schnitt „7334–82"

Inv.-Nr. Gl 3343c, Ankauf, inv. 1976 (11 St.)

35a Bottle (Water Bottle)

B: cut into the body

H 29 cm

Sources: WD, vol. XIV, p. 1; CAP, papercut "MN & AJB
7329–1882 TS 66 TS 173 Water bottle."

Inv. no. Gl 3343a, purchase, inv. 1976 (6 pieces)

35b Stem Glass (Rhine Wine Glass)

Green transparent glass, ground and cut

H 13 cm

Sources: WD, vol. XIV, p. 2; CAP, papercut "MN & AJB […]
1882 TS 66 TS 173 Burgundy wine glass white and Rhine
wine glass green"

Inv. no. Gl 3343b, purchase, inv. 1976 (17 pieces)

35c Stem Glass (Wine Glass)

H 14.3 cm

Sources: WD, vol. XIV, p. 2; CAP, papercut "7334–82"

Inv. no. Gl 3343c, purchase, inv. 1976 (11 pieces)

35d Stängelglas (Weinglas)

H 10,9 cm

Quellen: WZ, Bd. XIV, S. 2

Inv.-Nr. Gl 3343d, Ankauf, inv. 1976 (10 St.)

35e Stängelglas (Champagnerglas)

H 17,9 cm

Quellen: WZ, Bd. XIV, S. 2; FAP, Schnitt „MN & AJB 7333-1882 TS 66 Chmp. h./TS 173/12 Ecken"

Inv.-Nr. Gl 3343e, Ankauf, inv. 1976 (15 St.)

35f Becher mit Fuß (Bierglas)

H 15,4 cm

Quellen: WZ, Bd. XIV, S. 2; FAP, Schnitt „MNA 966 1877/TS 66/TS 173/Biergl."

Inv.-Nr. Gl 3343f, Ankauf, inv. 1976 (18 St.)

35g Becher mit Fuß (Wasserbecher)

H 10,3 cm

Quellen: WZ, Bd. XIV, S. 2

Inv.-Nr. Gl 3343g, Ankauf, inv. 1976 (13 St.)

35h Stängelglas (Likörglas)

H 9,2 cm

Quellen: WZ, Bd. XIV, S. 2

Inv.-Nr. Gl 3343h, Ankauf, inv. 1976 (14 St.)

36 Serie „Weiss-Email-Spitzendecor", ab 1883

Farbloses, blaues oder rotes Glas mit Dekor in Weiß und Gold

Bei dieser Serie mit Spitzendekor handelt es sich um ein weiteres Beispiel mit der damals beliebten Rokokoornamentik: „[…] von Mustern des 18. Jahrhunderts angeregt. Da sehen wir Dosen und Vasen in hellen zarten Farben wie mit einem Goldregen besprengt, über den sich dann Spitzen mit Rococo-Mustern aus weißem Email gelegt haben" („Mittheilungen", Nr. 220, 1. Jan. 1884, S. 9).

Auf einer Ausstellung in München 1888 wurde die Herstellung beschrieben: „[…] eine Reihe rosarother, mit Gold gefärbter Geräte und Gefäße für den Toilettentisch mit feinem Spitzenmuster aus milchweißem Email ganz überdeckt und auf die hellrothen Flächen ist Goldstaub gestreut, im Muffelfeuer festgebacken" (Schmidt 1889,

---

35d Stem Glass (Wine Glass)

H 10.9 cm

Sources: WD, vol. XIV, p. 2

Inv. no. Gl 3343d, purchase, inv. 1976 (10 pieces)

35e Stem Glass (Champagne Glass)

H 17.9 cm

Sources: WD, vol. XIV, p. 2; CAP, papercut "MN & AJB 7333-1882 TS 66 Chmp. h./TS 173/12 corners"

Inv. no. Gl 3343e, purchase, inv. 1976 (15 pieces)

35f Fotted Beaker (Beer Glass)

H 15.4 cm

Sources: WD, vol. XIV, p. 2; CAP, papercut "MNA 966 1877/TS 66/TS 173/Beer gl."

Inv. no. Gl 3343f, purchase, inv. 1976 (18 pieces)

35g Footed Beaker (Water Beaker)

H 10.3 cm

Sources: WD, vol. XIV, p. 2

Inv. no. Gl 3343g, purchase, inv. 1976 (13 pieces)

35h Stem Glass (Liqueur Glass)

H 9.2 cm

Sources: WD, vol. XIV, p. 2

Inv. no. Gl 3343h, purchase, inv. 1976 (14 pieces)

36 Series "White enamel lace decoration", from 1883

Colorless blue or red glass with white and gold decoration

This series with lace decoration was another example of the Rococo ornamentation that was popular at the time: "[…] inspired by 18th century patterns. We see here boxes and vases light and tender colors as if sprayed by a rain of gold, superimposed with Rococo-pattern lace of white enamel" ("Mittheilungen", no. 220, 1. Jan 1884, p. 9).

At the 1888 exhibition in Munich, the making was described: "[…] a number of pink, gold-dyed utensils and vessels for the dressing table, all covered with delicate lace pattern of white enamel, with gold dust sprayed on the light red areas, fired in the muffle kiln" (Schmidt 1889, p. 76). This series was not only intended for the dressing table, for, apart from small bottles, lidded boxes,

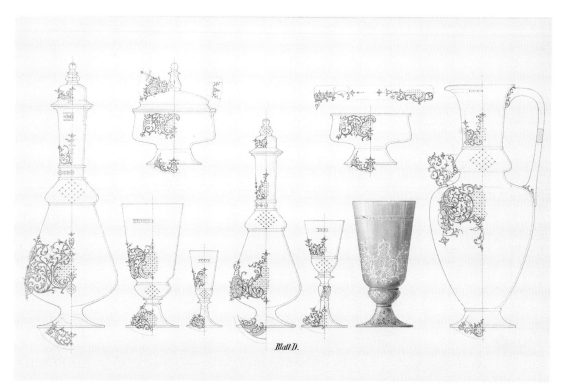

Glasgefäße „hellblau oder lichtrosa mit Email
Spitzenornamenten und Gold verziert",
in: WZ, Bd. XVII, S. 20
Vessels, "light blue or light pink decorated
with enamel lace ornaments and gold",
in: WD, vol. XVII, p. 20

S. 76). Diese Serie war allerdings nicht nur für den Toilettetisch gedacht, denn zu ihr gehörten neben kleinen Flaschen, Deckeldosen und Schalen auch ein Aufsatz, eine Flasche mit Becher und Teller („Liqueurflaschen, Liqueurgläser, Liqueurtassen"), Trinkgläser und ein Krug. In den Werkzeichnungen wurden die Gläser mit diesem Dekor als „Gefässe Krystall, hellblau oder lichtrosa mit Email Spitzenornamenten und Gold verziert nach eigenen Zeichnungen" erfasst. Die Gläser konnten in verschiedenen Farben ausgeführt werden. Die Serie wurde im Bestellungsbuch der Firma auch als „Serie mit gestaubtem Goldgrund und weiß Email Decor, ab 1883" bezeichnet. Die im Museum befindliche, erst 1887 entworfene Tasse wurde aus farblosem Glas mit dem Dekor der Serie ausgeführt. Die gleiche Form wurde zugleich auch für Serien in Rauchtopas oder weißem Opalglas mit anderem Dekor verwendet.

WZ, Bd. XVII, S. 17–20
Lit.: Mittheilungen, Nr. 220, 1. Jan. 1884, S. 9 (Weihnachtsausstellung 1883), Nr. 231, 1. Dez. 1884, S. 263 (Ausstellung des Wiener Kunstgewerbevereines); Schmidt 1889, S. 76

and bowls, it also included a centerpiece, a bottle with tumbler and tray, ("liqueur bottles, liqueur glasses, liqueur cups"), drinking glasses, and a pitcher.
In the working drawings the glasses were recorded as "vessels crystal, light blue or light pink decorated with enamel lace ornaments and gold after own drawings". The glasses could be produced in different colors. The series was included in the company's order book as "Series with sprayed gold ground and white enamel decoration, from 1883". The cup in the museum holdings, a design of 1887, was made of colorless glass with the series decoration. The same form was also used for series in smoky topaz and white opal glass with different decorations.

WD, vol. XVII, pp. 17–20
Lit.: Mittheilungen, Nr. 220, 1 Jan. 1884, p. 9 (1883 Christmas exhibition), no. 231, 1 Dec. 1884, p. 263 (Ausstellung des Wiener Kunstgewerbevereins); Schmidt 1889, p. 76

36a

36b

36a Schale mit Fuß („Schmuckschale")

Entw.: 1883

Ausf.: Meyr's Neffen, Adolf, 1883

Rotes transparentes Glas mit Dekor in Weiß und Gold

FM: auf der Unterseite gemalt

H 5,8 cm, D 9,2 cm

Quellen: WZ, Bd. XVII, S. 20; FAW, Bestellungsbuch MNA,
27. Juli 1883, 4408, „Schmuckschalen 3/4 Krystall, 2 hellblau,
2 blassrosa, Serie mit gestaubtem Goldgrund und weiß Email
Decor"; FAP, Karton 21, Serie 179, „Spitzendekor, kristall, rosa
oder hellblaues Glas mit weiß Email-Spitzendekor", Schnitt
„MNA Nr. 4408-83 Schmuckschalen 2 hellblau, 2 blassrosa,
weiß gestaubten Goldgrund u. weiss-Email Decor"

Inv.-Nr. Gl 1742, angek. auf der Weihnachtsausstellung 1884,
inv. 14. Jan. 1885

36b Tasse mit Untertasse
(„Sorbet"- oder „Punschkännchen")

Entw.: 1887

Farbloses Glas mit Dekor in Weiß und Gold

FM: auf der Unterseite gemalt

H 5,5 cm, D (Untertasse) 13 cm

Quellen: FAW, „Serie weiss-Email-Spitzendecor", ab 1883,
2566-87, „Sorbetkännchen", Bestellungsbuch MNA, 4. Aug.
1887, 2566, „Punschkännchen m. Teller Krystall glt. 1. Mstr. m.
Reliefgold (a), 1 Mstr. m. Weissemail u. Gold Krystall mit weiß
Emailspitzendekor (2567 Rauchtopas, 2568 weiß Opalglas)"

Inv.-Nr. Gl 2590, wohl Vermächtnis Ludwig Lobmeyr 1917,
nachträglich inv.

36a Footed Bowl ("Decorative Bowl")

Dsg.: 1883

Mfr.: Meyr's Neffen, Adolf, 1883

Red transparent glass with decoration in white and gold

B: painted on the bottom

H 5.8 cm, D 9.2 cm

Sources: WD, vol. XVII, p. 20; CAV, order book MNA, 27 July
1883, 4408, "Decorative bowls 3/4 crystal, 2 light blue, 2 pale
pink, series with sprayed gold ground and white enamel decoration"; CAP, box 21, series 179, "Lace decoration, crystal, pink
or light blue glass with white enamel lace decoration", papercut
"MNA Nr. 4408-83 Decorative bowls 2 light blue, 2 pale pink,
series with sprayed gold ground and white enamel decoration"

Inv. no. Gl 1742, purch. at the 1884 Christmas exhibition,
inv. 14 Jan. 1885

36b Cup with saucer
("sorbet" or "punch jug")

Dsg.: 1887

Colorless glass with white and gold decoration

B: painted on the bottom

H 5.5 cm, D (saucer) 13 cm

Sources: CAV, "Series white enamel lace decoration ", from
1883, 2566-87, "Sorbet jug", order book MNA, 4 Aug. 1887,
2566, "Punch jug with plate crystal, 1 sample with relief
gilding (a), 1 sample w. white enamel a. gold crystal with
white enamel lace decoration (2567 smoky topaz, 2568
white opal glass)"

Inv. no. Gl 2590, pres. bequest of Ludwig Lobmeyr 1917, subs. inv.

37 „Gefässe aus eisengrünem Glase, mit vergoldet u. versilberter Gravirung, in indischem Style theils nach indischen Eisengefässen gezeichnet von M. Knab", ab 1883

Braunes transparentes Glas mit Schnitt, versilbert (Aluminium) und vergoldet

Schon 1870 war im Museum ein „Glasservice, für Wasser, in indischem Stile" von Lobmeyr ausgestellt worden. 1872 wurde nach dem Entwurf von Josef Storck das „Dessert-Service No. 30, von dunkelgrünem Glase mit reicher Vergoldung in indischem Style" ausgeführt (WZ, Bd. V, S. 11–13). Schon bei dieser Serie wurden Ornamente von indischen Eisenarbeiten aus Racinets Vorlagenwerk „L'ornement polychrome" als Vorbild verwendet. 1874 wurden „Vasen aus tiefrotem opakem Glas mit bunten indischen Ornamenten" nach dem Entwurf von Josef Salb publiziert („Gewerbehalle", Heft 6, 1874, S. 93).

Bei der 1883 entstandenen indischen Serie diente der Dekor von Bidriarbeiten aus dem 18. Jahrhundert als Vorbild. Diese nach der indischen Stadt Bidar benannten Eisengefäße mit Silbertauschierungen waren in Europa seit der ersten Weltausstellung 1851 in London bekannt. Sie wurden in zeitgenössischen Publikationen abgebildet und im ÖMKI seit den sechziger Jahren angekauft. Wie auch bei anderen orientalischen Serien wurde von Moritz Knab (siehe Kat.-Nr. 30), der zu dieser Zeit als Zeichner bei Lobmeyr angestellt war, der Dekor eines anderen Materials in Glas umgesetzt. Ähnlich wie bei den Gläsern mit Filigrandekor wurde hier der Dekor eingraviert und mit Aluminium, das teilweise vergoldet war, gefüllt.

„Die Wirkung ist vornehm und gefällig, besonders bei den kleineren Gefäßen, an denen die indischen Gefäßformen beibehalten sind, während die größeren Vasen, als technische Leistungen höchst anerkennenswerth, durch ihre absonderliche Gestaltung, mit den groß-

37 "Vessels of iron-green glass, with gold and silver engraving, in Indian style partly after Indian iron vessels drawn by M. Knab", from 1883

Brown transparent glass, cut, silvered (aluminum) and gilded

In 1870 already, a "Glass service for water, in Indian style" had been exhibited by Lobmeyr. 1872, the "Dessert service no. 30 of dark-green glass with rich gilding in Indian style" was produced to a design by Josef Storck (WD, vol. V, pp. 11–13). In this series, ornaments of Indian metalwork from Racinet's model book "L'ornement polychrome" were used as models. 1874, "Vases of deep red opaque glass with colored Indian ornaments" to a design by Josef Salb were published ("Gewerbehalle", no. 6, 1874, p. 93).

The Indian series produced 1883 used 18th century Bidri ware decorations as models. These iron vessels with silver inlays were named after the Indian city of Bidar and had become known in Europe after the first World's Fair 1851 in London. They were published in contemporary publications and purchased by the AMAI from the 1860s.

As in the case of other oriental series, Josef Knab (see cat. no. 30), who was employed by Lobmeyr as a designer at that time, translated a decoration used in a different material into glass. Similarly to glasses with filigree decoration, the decoration was engraved and filled with partly gilded aluminum.

"The effect is noble and pleasant, notably so in the smaller vessels, where the Indian forms have been retained, while the bigger vases, quite laudable as technical achievements, with their strange designs, their large floral ornaments, produce a certainly unintended effect of polished wood." ("Mittheilungen", no. 220, 1 Jan. 1884, p. 9). Ludwig Lobmeyr also recalled that the vessels "[…] due to their sombre coloring did not catch on; not everything works out fine" (Neuwirth 1999,

Indische Schüsseln, in: Sammlung von Abbildungen türkischer, arabischer, persischer, zentralasiatischer und indischer Metallobjekte, Wien 1895, Taf. XL (MAK, Inv.-Nr. K.I. 11400)
Indian bowls, in: Sammlung von Abbildungen türkischer, arabischer, persischer, zentralasiatischer und indischer Metallobjekte, Vienna 1895, pl. XL (MAK, inv. no. K.I. 11400)

„Art indien. Nielles et métaux gravés", in: A. Racinet: L'ornement polychrome, Paris 1869–1872, Bd. II (MAK, Inv.-Nr. K.I. 19377)
"Art indien. Nielles et métaux gravés", in: A. Racinet: L'ornement polychrome, Paris 1869–1872, vol. II (MAK, inv. no. K.I. 19377)

37c

37a

blumigen Ornamenten, die gewiss nicht beabsichtigte Wirkung von polirtem Holz hervorbringen" („Mittheilungen", Nr. 220, 1. Jan. 1884, S. 9). Ludwig Lobmeyr erinnerte sich auch, dass die Gefäße „[…] der düstern Farbe wegen doch nicht ansprachen; es glückt eben nicht Alles" (Neuwirth 1999, S. 345). Die indische Serie umfasste: Flaschen, Deckeldose, Becher mit Fuß, Trinkglas, Krüge, Vasen, Schalen, Aufsatz, Pokal.

Fast gleichzeitig, Anfang der achtziger Jahre, stellte die Firma Fritz Heckert (1866 in Petersdorf [Piechowice] im Riesengebirge/Schlesien gegründet) Imitationen von indischen Bidriarbeiten aus bernsteinfarbenem Glas, geätzt und versilbert, mit ähnlichem Dekor her (Hagedorn 1995).

WZ, Bd. XV, S. 38–47

Lit.: Mittheilungen, Nr. 220, 1. Jan. 1884, S. 9; Schmidt 1889, S. 76; Neuwirth 1981b

p. 345). The Indian series comprised bottles, a lidded box, a footed beaker, a drinking glass, jugs, vases, bowls, a centerpiece, and a goblet.

Almost at the same time, in the early 1880s, the company of Fritz Heckert (established 1866 in Petersdorf im Riesengebirge [Piechowice], Silesia) produced imitations of Indian Bidri ware of amber-colored glass, etched and silvered, with a similar decoration (Hagedorn 1995).

WD, vol. XV, p. 38–47

Lit.: Mittheilungen, no. 220, 1 Jan. 1884, p. 9; Schmidt 1889, p. 76; Neuwirth 1981b

37a Schale mit Fuß („Schmuckschale")
Entw.: 1883
FM: im Zentrum der Oberseite geschnitten
H 7,3 cm, D 11,7 cm
Quellen: WZ, Bd. XV, S. 37 verso (Foto); FAW, „Schmuckschale 4793-83", Bestellungsbuch MNA, 22. Sept. 1883, „Schmuckschalen auf Fuß Serie Indisch eisengrün m. eingravirten Gold u. Silber (Aluminium) tauschirten Ornamenten";

37a Footed Bowl ("Decorative Bowl")
Dsg.: 1883
B: cut in the top-side center
H 7.3 cm, D 11.7 cm
Sources: WD, vol. XV, p. 37 verso (photo); CAV, "Decorative bowl 4793-83", order book MNA, 22 Sept. 1883, "Decorative bowls on foot series Indian iron-green w. engraved gold and silver (aluminum) inlaid ornaments ";

FAP, Karton 20, Serie 65, „Indische Serie", 1883, Schnitt „MNA Nr. 4793-83 Schmuckschale auf Fuß" Inv.-Nr. Gl 3253, 1964 angek.

CAP, box 20, series 65, "Indian series", 1883, papercut "MNA Nr. 4793-83 Decorative bowl on foot" Inv. no. Gl 3253, purch. 1964

37b Vase (Abb. siehe S. 43)
Entw.: 1883
FM: auf der Unterseite gemalt
H 17,6 cm
Quellen: WZ, Bd. XV, S. 37 verso (Foto); FAW, Bestellungsbuch MNA, 22. Sept. 1883, 4766, „Vasen 18 cm hoch"
Inv.-Nr. Gl 3252, 1964 angek.

37b Vase (Ill. see p. 43)
Dsg.: 1883
B: painted on the bottom
H 17.6 cm
Sources: WD, vol. XV, S. 37 verso (photo); CAV, order book MNA, 22 Sept. 1883, 4766, "Vases 18 cm high"
Inv. no. Gl 3252, purch. 1964

37c Schale
Entw.: 1883
Ausf.: Meyr's Neffen, Adolf, 1883
FM: im Zentrum der Oberseite geschnitten und versilbert
D 39,8 cm
Quellen: WZ, Bd. XV, S. 38 ff.; FAW, Bestellungsbuch MNA, 22. Sept. 1883, 4789, „Schalen tiefe Form dm 40 cm"
Inv.-Nr. Gl 1687, angek. v. J. & L. Lobmeyr, inv. 8. Jan. 1884

37c Bowl
Dsg.: 1883
Mfr.: Meyr's Neffen, Adolf, 1883
B: cut and silver-inlaid in the top-side center
D 39.8 cm
Sources: WD, vol. XV, p. 38 ff.; CAV, order book MNA, 22 Sept. 1883, 4789, "Bowls deep form diam 40 cm"
Inv. no. Gl 1687, purch. by J. & L. Lobmeyr, inv. 8 Jan. 1884

38 „Krystall mit Silberfiligran und türkisblauen Emailpunkten, 1884"

Farbloses Glas, geschnitten und versilbert (Aluminium), Dekor in Blau

Bei dieser von Lobmeyr eingeführten Technik des Silberfiligrans wurde eine feinlinige Zeichnung in das Glas geschnitten. Der Schnitt wurde mit Aluminium ausgestrichen, das gemeinsam mit den türkisen Emailtropfen in der Muffel eingebrannt wurde. Im Gegensatz zu Silber dunkelt Aluminium nicht nach. „[…] die feinen spielenden Lichter auf der hellen, nicht wie das Silber nachdunkelnden Metallfarbe des Aluminiums bringen eben den, an gewundene Filigrandrähtchen erinnernden, feinen Effect hervor" (Schmidt 1889, S. 76). Die Technik wurde nicht nur bei kleinformatigen Gefäßen wie Flakons, Fußschalen, Kännchen und Bechern angewendet, sondern auch bei Vasen, Krügen, Pokalen, Aufsätzen und Schalen. Die Serie wurde auf der Weihnachtsausstellung 1884 präsentiert und auch 1888 auf der Kunstgewerbe-Ausstellung in München gezeigt.

38 "Crystal with silver filigree and turquoise enamel dots, 1884"

Colorless glass, cut and silver-inlaid (aluminum), blue decoration

In the silver-filigree technique introduced by Lobmeyr, a fine-line drawing was cut into the glass. The cutting was painted with aluminum, which was then fired together with the enamel dots in the muffle kiln. Unlike silver, aluminum does not get darker with time. "[…] the subtly playing lights on the light metal color of the aluminum, which does not darken like silver, produce the fine effect reminiscent of wound filigree wiring" (Schmidt 1889, p. 76). The technique was not only used with smaller vessels such as flacons, foot bowls, jugs, and tumblers, but also with vases, pitchers, goblets, centerpieces and bowls. The series was presented at the 1884 Christmas exhibition as well as at the 1888 Arts and Craft Exhibition in Munich.

38a

Gefäße Krystall mit gravirtem und versilbertem Filigran u. Türkisperlen verziert,
nach eigenen Zeichnungen.
Blatt A.

Glasgefäße „mit gravirtem und versilbertem Filigran u. Türkisperlen verziert", in: WZ, Bd. XVII, S. 21
Vessels "with engraved and silver filigree and turquoise enamel dots", in: WD, vol. XVII, p. 21

WZ, Bd. XVII, S. 21–23 („Gefässe Krystall mit gravirtem und versilbertem Filigran u. Türkisperlen verziert, nach eigenen Zeichnungen")
Lit.: Mittheilungen, Nr. 232, 1. Jan. 1885, S. 287; Schmidt 1889, S. 76

38a Flakon
Entw.: 1884
Ausf.: Meyr's Neffen, Adolf, 1884
FM: auf der Unterseite geschnitten
H 18,7 cm
Quellen: FAW, Bestellungsbuch MNA, 19. Apr. 1884, 6060, „Flacons Krstll. Silberfiligran u. türkis Emailpunkten"; FAP, Schnitt „MNA 6060-84"
Inv.-Nr. Gl 1740, angek. auf der Weihnachtsausstellung 1884, inv. 14. Jan. 1885

WD, vol. XVII, pp. 21–23 ("Vessels crystal with engraved and silver-inlaid filigree and decorated with turquoise prunts, after own drawings")
Lit.: Mittheilungen, no. 232, 1 Jan. 1885, p. 287; Schmidt 1889, p. 76

38a Flacon
Dsg.: 1884
Mfr.: Meyr's Neffen, Adolf, 1884
B: cut into the bottom
H 18.7 cm
Sources: CAV, order book MNA, 19 Apr. 1884, 6060, "Flacons crystal. Silver filigree a. turqu. enamel dots"; CAP, papercut "MNA 6060-84"
Inv. no. Gl 1740, purch. at the 1884 Christmas exhibition, inv. 14 Jan. 1885

39 Flakon („mit türkischem Decor")

Entw.: 1884
Ausf.: Meyr's Neffen, Adolf, 1884
Farbloses Glas, geschnitten und vergoldet, mit farbigem Dekor
FM: auf der Unterseite gemalt; Etikett:
„14../900/MBLN/8412"
H 18,7 cm
Quellen: FAW, Bestellungsbuch MNA, 19. Apr. 1884; FAP,
Schnitt „N. 6059-84 Flacons mit türkischem Decor [...]"
Inv.-Nr. Gl 1739, angek. auf der Weihnachtsausstellung 1884,
inv. 14. Jan. 1885

In den Werkzeichnungen ist eine „Türkische Serie aus durchscheinendem schwarzbraunem Glase mit eingravirtem, vergoldetem Filigran und opakem Email verziert. Nach eigenen Zeichnungen. 1884" (Bd. XVI, S. 15–17) enthalten, die Gefäße aus braunviolettem Glas mit vergleichbarem Dekor aus Filigran und bunten Emailtropfen umfasst. Statt farbigem Glas wurde bei diesem Flakon allerdings farbloses Glas verwendet, Dekor und Technik entsprechen denen der Werkzeichnungen. Ähnlich wie bei der Serie mit Silberfiligran (Kat.-Nr. 38) wurde hier vergoldetes Filigran in den geschnittenen Dekor eingelegt und in der Muffel eingebrannt. Filigranarbeiten gehören zum traditionellen türkischen Kunsthandwerk. In Persien wurden auch Halbedelsteingefäße mit Goldbändern und Edelsteinen belegt. Eine solche – damals als „türkisch" bezeichnete – Schale aus Jade befindet sich in der Wiener Schatzkammer (Inv.-Nr. 1978).

Lit.: Mittheilungen, Nr. 232, 1. Jan. 1885, S. 287

39 Flacon ("with Turkish decoration ")

Dsg.: 1884
Mfr.: Meyr's Neffen, Adolf, 1884
Colorless glass, cut and gilded, with colored decoration
FM: painted on the bottom; label: "14../900/MBLN/8412"
H 18.7 cm
Sources: CAV, order book MNA, 19 Apr. 1884; CAP, papercut
"N. 6059-84 Flacons with Turkish decoration [...]"
Inv. no. Gl 1739, purch. at the 1884 Christmas exhibition,
inv. 14 Jan. 1885

The working drawings include a "Turkish series of transparent black-brown glass decorated with engraved gilded filigree and opaque enamel. After own drawings. 1884" (vol XVI, pp. 15–17), which comprises vessels of brown-purple glass with similar filigree decoration and colored enamel tears. Instead of colored glass, colorless glass was used for this flacon. The decoration and technique correspond to the working drawings. Similarly to the silver-filigree series (cat. no. 38), gilded filigree was inlaid in the cut decoration and fired in the muffle kiln.

Filigree work is part of traditional Turkish arts and crafts. In Persia, vessels of semi-precious stones were inlaid with gold bands and gems. One such bowl of jade – back then called "Turkish" – is in the Vienna Treasury (inv. no. 1978).

Lit.: Mittheilungen, no. 232, 1 Jan. 1885, p. 287

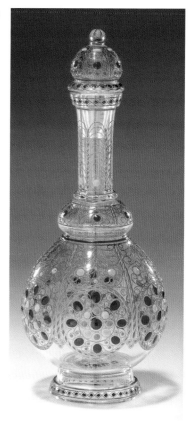

39

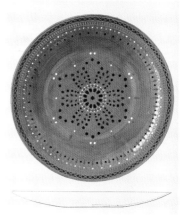

Schale „Türkische Serie", in: WZ,
Bd. XVI, S. 15
Bowl "Turkish series", in: WD, vol. 16, p. 15

40 „Gefässe aus Krystallglas, die Formen theils nach alten Mustern; die breiten Flächen entweder mit geglänzter Gravirung oder mit schwarzer goldumsäumter Malerei. Die Ornamente gezeichnet von Prof. Jos. Salb. 1884"

Diese Serie ist in Form und Dekor wohl von böhmischen Vorbildern inspiriert. In den Werkzeichnungen

40 "Vessels of crystal glass, forms partly after old models; broad surfaces either with polished engraving or black gold-framed painting. Ornaments drawn by Prof. Jos. Salb. 1884"

The series is presumable inspired by Bohemian models in decoration and form. In the working drawings, the forms with chamfered edges with decoration to the

wurden die Formen mit den hohlabgeschrägten Kanten mit Dekor nach dem Entwurf von Josef Salb entweder in schwarzer Malerei mit Gold oder in Gravierung dargestellt, was eine vollkommen unterschiedliche Wirkung ergab. Im Firmenarchiv sind zwei getrennte Serien für die verschiedenen Techniken des Dekors erhalten.

WZ, Bd. XII, S. 8–14

40a Pokal mit Deckel

Serie „Krystall mit hohlabgeschrägten Kanten reich graviert",
ab 1884
Entw.: Josef Salb, 1884 (Dekor)
Farbloses Glas mit Schnitt (poliert)
FM: geschnitten auf der Vorderseite
H 33,7 cm
Quellen: WZ, Bd. XII, S. 9; FAP, Schnitt „MNA Nr. 5963-84
Pokal auf niederem Fuße"
Inv.-Nr. Gl 2745, nachträglich inv.

40b „Champagnerschale", 1884

„Serie mit hohlabgeschrägten Kanten und schwarzer Malerei,
gez. nach J. Salb ab 1884"
Farbloses Glas mit Schliff, Dekor in Schwarz und Gold
FM: auf der Unterseite gemalt
H 12 cm
Quellen: WZ, Bd. XII, S. 12; FAW, Bestellungsbuch MNA,
31. März 1884, 5973, „Champagnerschalen mit 8eckigem Fuß
[…] Schälenschliff mit Gold und Schwarzdecor"
Inv.-Nr. Gl 1741, angek. auf der Weihnachtsausstellung 1884,
inv. 14. Jan. 1885

Der schwarze Dekor griff die Schwarzlotmalerei von Johann Schaper (1621–1670) auf. Der in Nürnberg tätige Scheibenglasmaler hatte Mitte des 17. Jahrhunderts das bis dahin nur bei der Glasmalerei für Kirchenfenster verwendete Schwarzlot auch für die Bemalung von Hohlgläsern herangezogen. In der von ihm entwickelten Technik, einer Malerei in zarten Sepiatönen bis hin zu Schwarz, malte er Landschaften, mythologische Motive, Bibelszenen u. a. m.

Schon auf der Wiener Weltausstellung 1873 wurde über Lobmeyr-Gefäße berichtet, die in dieser Art dekoriert waren. 1883 wurden von Lobmeyr auf der Weihnachtsausstellung des ÖMKI ähnliche Objekte gezeigt, die

design by Josef Salb are represented either in black painting with gold or with engraving, which resulted in entirely different effects. The company archives comprise two separate series for the different decoration techniques.

WD, vol. XII, p. 8–14

40a Lidded Goblet

Series "Crystal with chamfered edges, rich engraving",
from 1884
Dsg.: Josef Salb, 1884 (decoration)
Colorless cut glass (polished)
B: cut into the front side
H 33.7 cm
Sources: WD, vol. XII, p. 9; CAP, papercut "MNA Nr. 5963-84
Goblet on low foot "
Inv. no. Gl 2745, subs. inv.

40b "Champagne Glass", 1884

"Series with chamfered edges and black painting,
drawn after J. Salb from 1884"
Colorless cut glass, black and gold decoration
B: painted on the bottom
H 12 cm
Sources: WD, vol. XII, p. 12; CAV, order book MNA, 31
March 1884, 5973, "Champagne glass with octagonal foot
[…] surface grinding with gilding and black decoration"
Inv. no. Gl 1741, purch. at the 1884 Christmas exhibition,
inv. 14 Jan. 1885

The black decoration went back to the "Schwarzlot" painting technique of Johann Schaper (1621–1670). In the mid-17th century, the Nuremberg-based window glass painter had begun to apply "Schwarzlot" ("black lead", a mixture of copper and iron powder) which had hitherto been used in glass painting for church windows only to hollowware. In the technique he developed, a style of painting in soft shades from sepia to black, he painted landscapes, mythological motifs, biblical scenes etc. Lobmeyr vessels decorated in this style were reported at the 1873 Vienna World's Fair. 1883, similar objects which also were modeled after Schaper vessels were shown by Lobmeyr at the AMAI Christmas exhibition:

ebenfalls Schaper-Gefäße zum Vorbild hatten: „[…] hel-
le Gläser mit Landschaften und Figürchen in Schwarzloth
aufgemalt […]" („Mittheilungen", Nr. 220, 1. Jan. 1884,
S. 9). Stilistisch wurde dabei auch auf die Gefäße von
Schapers Nachfolgern Anfang des 18. Jahrhunderts,
Daniel Preissler und seinem Sohn Ignaz Preissler, zurückgegriffen.

In Berichten über die Münchener Kunstgewerbe-
Ausstellung von 1888 wurde auf die von Lobmeyr an-
gewendete Technik genau eingegangen: „[…] was
Lobmeyr brachte, waren keineswegs Nachahmungen der
alten Schapergläser, sondern durchweg neue reizvolle
Compositionen in der alten Technik, die gleichzeitig da-
hin erweitert wurde, dass auch die Radirnadel und die
Vergoldung beigezogen wurden" (Gmelin 1888, S. 304).

Lit.: Mittheilungen, Nr. 220, 1. Jan. 1884, S. 9; Gmelin 1888,
S. 304; Schmidt 1889, S. 76; Mundt 1981, Abb. 265

"[…] light glasses with landscapes and figurines painted
in black […]" ("Mittheilungen", no 220, 1. Jan 1884,
p. 9). In style, this glassware also drew on vessels by
Schaper's successors in the early 18th century, Daniel
Preissler and his son Ignaz.

Reports of the Munich Arts and Crafts Exhibition of
1888 described Lobmeyr's technique in detail: "[…]
what Lobmeyr presented was not imitations of the old
Schaper glasses, but mostly new attractive compositions
in the old technique, which at the same time was
expanded in such a way as to include engraving and
gilding." (Gmelin 1888, p. 304)

Lit.: Mittheilungen, no. 220, 1. Jan 1884, p. 9; Gmelin 1888,
p. 304, Schmidt 1889, p. 76; Mundt 1981, ill. 265

40a

40b

Pokal mit Deckel „mit schwarzer
goldumsäumter Malerei",
in: WZ, Bd. XII, S. 8
Lidded goblet "with black
gold-framed painting",
in: WD, vol. XII, p. 8

41

41 Schale mit Kopf der Aurora

Entw.: 1886
Ausf.: wohl Franz Ullmann, Steinschönau (Schnitt), 1886
Farbloses Glas mit Schnitt, Rand poliert
D 24,2 cm
Quellen: FAW, Allgemeines Bestellungsbuch, Franz Ullmann,
17. Dez. 1886, „Teller rund I. Gr. glt. m. Morgenstern u.
Randgravierung zu versehen 5946-75"
Inv.-Nr. Gl 1816, Geschenk der Fachschule Steinschönau, inv.
29. Febr. 1888

Laut Inventarbuch handelt es sich um eine Arbeit der
Fachschule Steinschönau (Kamenický Šenov), wo Franz
Ullmann zu dieser Zeit als Werkmeister für Gravierung
tätig war. Die Randgravierung bezieht sich offenbar auf
einen Entwurf von 1875. Ein vergleichbarer Teller mit
dem Kopf der Aurora ganz im Profil und anderem
Randdekor befindet sich im Museum für Angewandte
Kunst in Köln (Inv.-Nr. Ov 1065). Der Glasschnitt wird
nach einem ähnlichen Objekt im Kunstgewerbemuseum
Prag August Helzel zugeschrieben (um 1882–1885).
Lit.: Klesse 1996, S. 8

41 Bowl with head of Aurora

Dsg.: 1886
Mfr: pres. Franz Ullmann, Steinschönau (cutting), 1886
Colorless cut glass, polished rims
D 24.2 cm
Sources: CAV, general order book, Franz Ullmann,
17 Dec. 1886, "Plate round Teller, size 1, pol., engraved with
morning star and rim engraving 5946-75"
Inv. no. Gl 1816, donation from the Steinschönau Vocational
School, inv. 29 Febr. 1888

According to the inventory book, this was a piece made
at the vocational school of Steinschönau (Kamenický
Šenov), where Franz Ullmann worked as a work master
for engraving. The rim engraving obviously refers to a
design of 1875. A similar plate with the head of Aurora
in profile and different rim decoration is found in the
Cologne Museum of Applied Arts (inv. no. Ov 1065).
The cutting is ascribed to August Helzel on the basis of
a similar object at the Prague Arts and Crafts Museum
(around 1882–1885).
Lit.: Klesse 1996, p. 8

42

42 Schale mit Amoretto auf Panther

Ausf.: Meyr's Neffen, Adolf, um 1886; Franz Ullmann,
Steinschönau (Schnitt)
Farbloses Glas mit Schnitt (unvollendet)
D 24 cm
Quellen: FAW, Bestellungsbuch MNA, 23. Juni 1886, 538, „Teller
nach Zch. nur aus reinstem Krystall sehr sorgfältig thunlichst
bald auszuführen", Allgemeines Bestellungsbuch, Franz Ullmann,
22. Juli 1886, „Teller mit Amoretto auf Panther samt Rand-
gravirung zu graviren (5946-75)", 22. Nov. 1887, „Teller rund
23 1/2 cm dm mit Amor auf Panther zu gravieren (538-86)";
FAP, „Teller f. Figurengravirung", Schnitt (ohne Gravierung)
„MNA 538-86"
Inv.-Nr. Gl 1834, angek. v. J. & L. Lobmeyr um 24 fl.,
inv. 21. Nov. 1888

Schon Ende der siebziger Jahre wurden „Runde Teller
aus Krystallglas. Mit Renaissancegravirung. Nach eig.
Zeichnungen. Ornamente gezeichnet v. Regr. Prof.
Storck. Figuren nach franz. Reliefs" ausgeführt (WZ,
Bd. VII, S. 32). Auch bei diesem Teller stammt der Entwurf
der Randgravierung wohl aus den siebziger Jahren.
Warum er unvollendet angekauft wurde, ist nicht be-
kannt. Franz Ullmann (1846–1921) war seit 1881 als
Glasgraveur für Lobmeyr in Steinschönau (Kamenický
Šenov) tätig und von 1884 bis 1887 als Werkmeister für
Gravierung an der dortigen Fachschule angestellt. Er war
auch der Glasschneider verschiedener aufwendiger

42 Bowl with amoretto on panther

Mfr.: Meyr's Neffen, Adolf, around 1886; Franz Ullmann,
Steinschönau (cutting)
Colorless cut glass (uncompleted)
D 24 cm
Sources: CAV, order book MNA, 23 Juni 1886, 538, "Plate
after draw., make of purest crystal only, with great care and as
soon as possible", general order book, Franz Ullmann, 22 July
1886, "Plate with amoretto on panther plus rim engraving, to
be engraved (5946-75)", 22. Nov 1887, "Plate round 23 1/2
cm dm with Amor on panther to be engraved (538-86)";
CAP, "Plate f. figurative engraving", papercut (without
engraving) "MNA 538-86"
Inv. no. Gl 1834, purch. by J. & L. Lobmeyr for 24 Gulden,
inv. 21 Nov. 1888

"Round plate of crystal glass. With Renaissance engraving. After own drawings. Ornaments drawn by Regr.
Prof. Storck. Figures after French reliefs" were made in
the 1870s already (WD, vol. VII, p. 32). The design for
the rim engraving of this plate also dates back to the
1870s. Why the uncompleted plate was purchased is not
known. Franz Ullmann (1846–1921) had worked as a
glass engraver for Lobmeyr at Steinschönau since 1881,
and between 1884 and 1887 he was a work master for
engraving at the local vocational school. He also was the
glass cutter for a number of demanding pieces such as
the goblet and silver plate for the silver wedding of

Arbeiten wie des Pokals und des Tellers zur silbernen Hochzeit von August und Mathilde Rath (geb. Lobmeyr) im Jahr 1889 und der Schalen mit den drei Grazien (1894 und 1896) bzw. den vier Jahreszeiten (1894–1896).

Das Motiv des Amorettos auf Panther wurde bei mehreren Tellern in verschiedenen Größen verwendet, dabei findet sich auch einmal die Signatur des Glasschneiders Franz Fritsche (Glasmuseum Steinschönau).
Lit.: Pešatová 1968, Abb. 75; Großmann/Krutisch 1992, Kat.-Nr. 86 (Schale mit gleichem Mittelmotiv und ähnlichen Randmotiven)

August and Mathilde Rath (née Lobmeyr) in 1889 and of the bowls with the Three Graces (1894 and 1896) and Four Seasons (1894–1896).

The motif of the amoretto riding a panther was used in different sizes for different plates; in one case, the piece is marked with the signature of the glass cutter Franz Fritsche (Steinschönau Glass Museum).
Lit.: Pesatová 1968, ill. 75; Großmann/Krutisch 1992, cat. no. 86 (bowls with identical central motif and similar rim motifs)

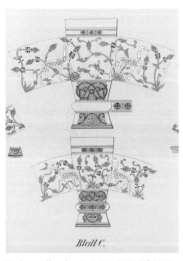

Becher „Alhambra Serie", in: WZ, Bd. XVI, S. 23 (Ausschnitt)
Beaker "Alhambra series", in: WD, vol. XVI, p. 23 (detail)

43 „Alhambra Serie aus Krystallglas mit eingravirten und vergoldeten Conturen; die Formen nach eigenen Zeichnungen, die Ornamente nach Anleitung des Director Schmoranz, ausgezeichnet von Moriz Knab. 1888"

Farbloses Glas mit Schnitt, vergoldet, farbiger Dekor und Gold

Franz Schmoranz, zu jener Zeit Direktor der Prager Kunstgewerbeschule, arbeitete für diese Serie mit Moritz Knab zusammen, der schon einige orientalische Serien entworfen hatte (siehe Kat.-Nr. 37 und „Serie im arabischen Styl aus Krystallglas mit transparenten Emailfarben u. eingravirten, vergoldeten Conturen" von 1885). Name und Inspiration für diese Serie leiteten sich von einer Vase aus der Alhambra ab. „La Jarra" gehörte zum Typus der hohen amphorenartigen Keramikvasen mit Flügenhenkeln, die in Nischen der Alhambra gestanden haben sollen. Schon in der ersten Hälfte des 19. Jahrhunderts wurde auf diesen Vasentypus zurückgegriffen. Durch Publikationen wie die von Jules Goury und Owen Jones („Plans, Elevations, Sections and Details of the Alhambra", London 1842–1845) war die Ausstattung der Alhambra umfassend dokumentiert und Schmoranz zweifellos bekannt.
Schon auf der Weltausstellung von 1873 wurden Gläser der Gebrüder Krause aus Steinschönau (Kamenický Šenov) mit Alhambra-Ornamenten gezeigt, „doch war

43 "Alhambra series of crystal glass with engraved and gilded contours; forms after own drawings, ornaments drawn by instruction of Director Schmoranz, drawn out by Moriz Knab. 1888"

Colorless cut glass, gilded, colored and gold decoration

For this series, Franz Schmoranz, at that time the director of the Prague Arts and Crafts School, worked together with Moritz Knab who had already designed a number of oriental series (see cat. no. 37 and "Series in Arabian style of crystal glass with transparent enamel coloring and engraved gilded contours" of 1885). The name and inspiration from this series were derived from a vase from the Alhambra. "La Jarra" belonged to the type of high amphora-like ceramic vases with wing-like handles which were supposed to have stood in the niches of the Alhambra. The type was taken up again in the first half of the 19th century already. Publications such as the one by Jules Goury and Owen Jones ("Plans, Elevations, Sections and Details of the Alhambra", London 1842–1845) contained detailed descriptions of the interior decoration of the Alhambra and were certainly known to Schmoranz.
At the 1873 World's Fair already, glassware with Alhambra ornaments by Bros. Krause from Steinschönau was exhibited, "though the effect of the vessels covered with

die Wirkung der damit in Blau, Roth und Gelb über-
zogenen Gefässe mit eine zu grelle" (Falke/Lobmeyr
1875, S. 22).

Im Wesentlichen erfolgte bei der Alhambra-Serie von
Lobmeyr wieder eine Umsetzung von Keramik in Glas,
sodass durch die Transparenz des Materials eine andere
Wirkung erzielt wurde. Neben den auf der Alhambra-
Vase vorkommenden gazellenartigen Tieren wurden für
die Glasgefäße Reiher, Kraniche, Pfaue, Schwäne, Strauße,
Enten, Adler, Pelikane, Giraffen und Pferde entworfen.
Im Stil des Dekors finden sich auch Bezüge zu Mam-
lukengefäßen des 13. und 14. Jahrhunderts aus Syrien.
Die Serie wurde 1888 auf der Kunstgewerbe-Ausstellung
in München gezeigt und umfasste Pokale, Krüge,
Flaschen, „Liqueurkrügel mit Stöpsel", „Liqueurgläser",
Becher mit Fuß, Schalen und Doppelhenkelvasen.
WZ, Bd. XVI, S. 21–25
Lit.: Schmidt 1889, S. 76; Bancroft 1893, Abb. S. 254; Neuwirth
1981c, S. 68, 69, Abb. 27; Fillitz 1996, Bd. 2, Kat.-Nr. 21.153

43a Krug

FM: auf der Unterseite gemalt
H 28,1 cm
Quellen: WZ, Bd. XVI, S. 22; FAW, Schnitt „4240-88",
Bestellungsbuch, 25. Febr. 1888, „Krüge I. Gr. Alhambra Serie,
Krystall glt. m. röthlich u. bräunlich grauem Stich oben und un-
ten aufgetrieben m. Emaildecor n. Vorlagen zu decorieren"
Inv.-Nr. Gl 2044, angek. v. J. & L. Lobmeyr um 38,50 fl.,
inv. 30. Okt. 1900

it in blue, red and yellow was too garish" (Falke/ Lobmeyr
1875, p. 22).

Basically, Lobmeyr's Alhambra series again was a translation from ceramics into glass, with a different effect
achieved through the transparency of the material. Apart
from gazelle-like animals appearing on the Alhambra
vase, herons, cranes, peacocks, ostriches, ducks, eagles,
pelicans, giraffes, and horses were designed for the
vessels. The decoration style also refers back to 13th
and 14th century Mameluke vessels from Syria.

The series was shown 1888 at the Munich Arts and
Crafts Exhibition and comprised goblets, pitchers,
bottles, a "liqueur mug with stopper", "liqueur glasses",
a footed beaker, bowls, and double-handled vases.
WD, vol. XVI, pp. 21–25
Lit.: Schmidt 1889, p. 76; Bancroft 1893, ill. p. 254; Neuwirth
1981c, pp. 68, 69, ill. 27; Fillitz 1996, vol. 2, cat. no. 21.153

43a Pitcher

B: painted on the bottom
H 28.1 cm
Sources: WD, vol. XVI, p. 22; CAV, papercut "4240-88", order
book, 25 Febr. 1888, "Pitchers I. size Alhambra series, crystal
polished w. reddish and brownish grey tint, top and bottom
reamed, to be decorated with enameling after patterns".
Inv. no. Gl 2044, purch. by J. & L. Lobmeyr for 38.50 Gulden,
inv. 30 Oct. 1900

43a

„La Jarra", in: Jules Goury, Owen Jones:
Plans, Elevations, Sections and Details of the
Alhambra, Bd. 1, London 1842, Taf. XLV
(MAK, Inv.-Nr. K.I. 563)
"La Jarra", in: Jules Goury and Owen Jones,
"Plans, Elevations, Sections and Details of the
Alhambra", vol. I, London 1842, pl. XLV (MAK,
inv. no. K.I. 563)

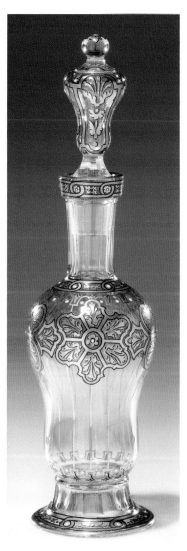

44a

44 Serie „Krystall mit Aluminium-bändern und Golddekor", ab 1888

Farbloses Glas mit Schliff und Dekor in Aluminium, Gold und Schwarz

Während Aluminium bei früheren Serien zum Ausfüllen von Gravierungen verwendet wurde (siehe Kat.-Nr. 37, 38), war es bei dieser Serie flächendeckend aufgebracht. Das Material hat gegenüber Silber den Vorteil, dass es nicht oxidiert.
Der Dekor weist Bezüge zu Metallarbeiten auf. 1888 wurden für diese Serie nur Vasen hergestellt, erst 1890 entstanden Krüge, Fußbecher, Flakons und weitere Vasen.

44a Flakon
Entw.: 1890
FM: im Ornament des Flaschenkörpers in Gold gemalt
H 18,1 cm
Quellen: FAW, Bestellungsbuch MNA, 15. März 1890, 9204, „Flacons oval, Krstl. glt. schmalgeschlt. und m. dunkelblauen gefaßten Aluminiumbändern Golddecor und weiß Emailpunkten nach Vorlage zu versehen"; FAP, Schnitt „MNA 9204-90"
Inv.-Nr. Gl 3251, 1964 angek.

45 Stängelglas („Copie eines Originals aus dem Jahre 1739 im k. k. österr. Museum")

Ausf.: Meyr's Neffen, Adolf, 1889
Farbloses Glas mit Schnitt, Dekor in Blau und Gold
FM: im Ornament des Kelches geschnitten
H 16,5 cm
Inschrift: „EbIbeDe toto qVos praebeo Vase LIqVores aC pretIosa stabIt paX aMor atqVe saLVs" (Trink ganz die Flüssigkeiten, die ich biete, aus dem Glas, und wertvoll wird bleiben der Friede, die Liebe und das Wohlergehen)
Quellen: FAW, Schnitt „7006-89" (siehe Abb. S. 6), Bestellungsbuch MNA, 20. Febr. 1889, 7006, „Stengelgläser Krystl. glt. ausgetrieben (für Sonnenuhrgravirung)"
WZ, Bd. XII, S. 32 („Gravirte Krystallgläser nach alten böhmischen Mustern")
Inv.-Nr. Gl 1947, angek. v. J. & L. Lobmeyr um 11,50 fl., inv. 20. Juni 1889

Im Firmenarchiv ist das Stängelglas als „Copie eines Originals aus dem Jahre 1739 im k. k. österr. Museum"

44 Series "Crystal with aluminum bands and gold decoration", from 1888

Colorless cut glass with aluminum, gold and black decoration

While in earlier series, aluminum was used to fill engravings (see cat. no. 37, 38), it was applied extensively in this series. Compared to silver, the material has the advantage of not oxidizing.
The decoration relates to metalwork. 1888, only vases were produced for this series; pitchers, footed beakers, flacons, and other vases followed in 1890 only.

44a Flacon
Dsg.: 1890
B: painted in gold in the body ornamentation
H 18.1 cm
Sources: CAV, order book MNA, 15 March 1890, 9204, "Flacons oval, crystal, polished, surface ground, to be made with dark blue aluminum bands, gold decoration, and white enamel dots after model"; CAP, papercut "MNA 9204-90"
Inv. no. Gl 3251, purch. 1964

45 Stem Glass ("Copy of an original from 1739 at the Imp. Roy. Austr. Museum")

Mfr.: Meyr's Neffen, Adolf, 1889
Colorless cut glass, blue and gold decoration
B: cut in the bowl ornamentation
H 16.5 cm
Inscription: "EbIbeDe toto qVos praebeo Vase LIqVores aC pretIosa stabIt paX aMor atqVe saLVs" (Drink the potions I offer from this glass, and peace, love, and welfare will be remain precious)
Sources: CAV, papercut "7006-89" (see ill. p. 6), order book MNA, 20 Febr. 1889, 7006, "Stem glasses crystal, pol. reamed (for sun dial engraving)"
WD, vol. XII, p. 32 ("Engraved crystal glasses after old Bohemian models ")
Inv. no. Gl 1947, purch. by J. & L. Lobmeyr for11.50 Gulden, inv. 20 June 1889

In the company archives, the stem glass is recorded as the "Copy of an original from 1739 at the Imp. Roy.

erfasst (siehe Abb. S. 13). Das böhmische Glas, das als Vorlage diente, wurde im ÖMKI erst um 1900 inventarisiert (Gl 1981), befand sich aber offensichtlich schon früher im Museum. Teile des geschnittenen Ornamentes wurden bei der „Copie" in blaue Malerei umgesetzt. Der Kunstwissenschaftler und Kurator Alois Riegl entschlüsselte die symbolhaften gravierten Linien und Zeichen: „Die Mittellinie mit dem Zeichen des Widders und der Wage und den Ziffern 6-6 bedeutet Tag- und Nachtgleiche, Frühling und Herbst, der äußere Kreis mit dem Krebs und 4-12-8 = Sommer, der innere mit dem Steinbock und 8-4 = Winter" (Firmenarchiv).

Ein weiteres Exemplar befindet sich im Museum der Firma Lobmeyr.

Lit.: Scholda 2000, S. 198

Austr. Museum" (see ill. p. 13). The Bohemian glass which served as a model here was inventoried at the AMIA around 1900 only (Gl 1981), but obviously was in the museum before that. Parts of the cut ornament were translated into blue painting in the "copy".

The art historian and curator Alois Riegl decoded the engraved symbolical lines and signs: "The middle line with the sign of Aries and Libra and the numbers 6-6 means the vernal and autumnal equinox, spring and fall, the outer circle with Cancer and 4-12-8 = summer, the inner one with Capricorn and 8-4 = winter" (company archives).

Another sample is in the Lobmeyr Company Museum.

Lit.: Scholda 2000, p. 198

45

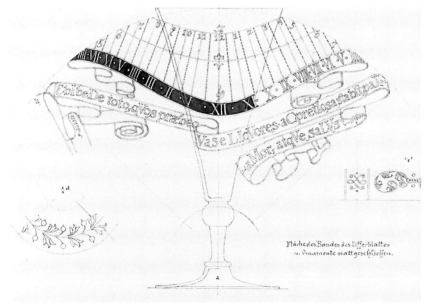

„Krystallgläser nach alten böhmischen Mustern", in: WZ, Bd. XII, S. 32 (Ausschnitt)
„Crystal glasses after old Bohemian models", in WD, vol XII, p. 32 (detail)

Stängelglas, 1739 (MAK, Inv.-Nr. Gl 1981)
Stem glass, 1739 (MAK, inv. no. GI 1981)

46a

46 Serie „Krystall mit vergoldeter oder versilberter Rococo-Gravirung, gezeichnet von M. Knab, 1889"

Farbloses Glas mit Schnitt, versilbert oder vergoldet,
und Dekor in Gold

Diese Serie wurde mit gleichem Dekor in zwei Varianten
ausgeführt: mit kaltvergoldeter oder versilberter (Alumi-
nium-)Gravierung. Aluminium zum Ausfüllen von
Glasgravierungen wurde von Lobmeyr erstmals 1883
verwendet (siehe Kat.-Nr. 37, 38). In dieser Serie, für
die Moritz Knab (siehe Kat.-Nr. 30) den Rokokodekor
entwarf, wurden Schmuckschalen, Pokale, Weinflaschen,
„Liqueurkrügel" und „Liqueurgläser", Henkelgläser,
Biergläser, Flakons und Bordeauxkrüge hergestellt.
Vergoldete Gravierungen waren als Dekor auch schon
im frühen 18. Jahrhundert verwendet worden.

46 Series "Crystal with gilded or silvered Rococo engraving, drawn by M. Knab, 1889"

Colorless glass with silvered or gilded cutting and
gold decoration

The series was produced in two variants with the same
decoration: with engraving with cold gilding or silver-
ing (aluminum). Aluminum to fill in glass engravings
was first used by Lobmeyr in 1883 (see cat. nos. 37, 38).
This series for which Moritz Knab (see cat. no. 30) designed the Rococo decoration, comprised decorative
bowls, goblets, wine bottles, "liqueur mugs" and
"liqueur glasses", handled glasses, beer glasses, flacons,
and Bordeaux pitchers. Gilded engraved decorations
had been used before in the 18th century.

46a Schale

Farbloses Glas mit Schnitt, vergoldet
FM: im Zentrum der Oberseite geschnitten
D 41,1 cm
Quellen: FAW, Bestellungsbuch MNA, 19. Nov. 1889, 8639,
„Prunkschalen krystl. glt. davon 1 Stk. m. versilberten polirten
Goldstreifen und 1 Stk. m. vergoldeter Gravierung wie Serie
7547–7706" (7547, „Fußbecher Krystl. glt. […] graviert u m.
versilbertem Aluminierung[…] zu versehen")
Inv.-Nr. Gl 2587, Vermächtnis Ludwig Lobmeyr 1917,
nachträglich inv.

46b Becher mit Fuß und Henkel („Henkelglas")

Farbloses Glas mit Schnitt, vergoldet
FM: am Henkel
H 17,6 cm
Quellen: FAW, „Henkelglas Nr. 7700/i-89/E. M. Knab 1889";
FAP, Serie 109, „Kristall mit kaltvergoldeter Rococogravierung
1889", Schnitt „MNA 7700-1889 m. Henkel"
Inv.-Nr. Gl 2593, wohl Vermächtnis Ludwig Lobmeyr 1917,
nachträglich inv.

46c Schale mit Fuß („Schmuckschale")

(Abb. siehe S. 42)
Farbloses Glas mit Schnitt, versilbert, und Dekor in Gold
FM: am Fuß geschnitten
H 11,4 cm, D 12 cm
Quellen: FAW, „Schmuckschale Nr. 7706-89 E. M. Knab
1889"; FAP, Serie 109, „Kristall mit kaltvergoldeter
Rococogravierung 1889", Schnitt „MNA 7706-1889"
Inv.-Nr. Gl 2598, wohl Vermächtnis Ludwig Lobmeyr 1917,
nachträglich inv.

47 Serie „Hochgoldornamente", ab 1891

Farbloses Glas mit Dekor in Gold, Weiß und Rot

Diese Serie wurde im Firmenarchiv auch als „Hochgold-
Serie, Krystl. glt. aufgetrieben, m. Goldrändern, Gold-
linien, Reliefgoldornamenten, blauen, rothen und weiß
Emailpunkten" bezeichnet. Dazu gehörten: Krüge,
Flakons, Aufsätze, Zuckerschalen, Eisteller, Büchsen mit
Deckel, Oberskännchen, Fußbecher, Stängelgläser,
Champagnerflöten und -becher, Pokal mit Deckel,
Fingerschalen.
Bei den Vorlagen zu den Rokokoornamenten handelte
es sich laut Entwurfszeichnungen um ein „franz. Muster".

46a Bowl

Colorless cut glass, gilded
B: cut into the top-side center
D 41.1 cm
Sources: CAV, order book MNA, 19 Nov. 1889, 8639, "Grand
bowls crystl. pol. 1 piece w. silvered polished gold strips and
1 p. w. gild. engraving as series 7547-7706" (7547, "footed
beaker crystl. pol. […] engr. a. w. silvered aluminum […]")
Inv. no. Gl 2587, bequest of Ludwig Lobmeyr 1917,
subs. inv.

46b Beaker with foot and handle ("Handle Glass")

Colorless cut glass, gilded
B: on the handle
H 17.6 cm
Sources: CAV, "Handled glass Nr. 7700/i-89/E. M. Knab
1889"; CAP, series 109, "Crystal with cold-gilded Rococo
engraving 1889", papercut "MNA 7700-1889 w. handle"
Inv. no. Gl 2593, pres. bequest of Ludwig Lobmeyr 1917,
subs. inv.

46c Fotted Bowl ("Decorative Bowl")

(see ill. p. 42)
Colorless cut glass, silvered and gold decoration
H 11.4 cm, D 12 cm
Sources: CAV, "Decorative bowl no. 7706-89 E. M. Knab
1889"; CAP, series 109, "Crystal with cold-gilded Rococo
engraving 1889", papercut "MNA 7706-1889"
Inv. no. Gl 2598, pres. bequest of Ludwig Lobmeyr 1917,
subs. inv.

47 Series "Raised gold ornaments", from 1891

Colorless glass with gold, white, and red decoration

The series was filed in the company archives as "Raised
gold, crystal pol. Molded, with gold rims, gold lines,
relief gold ornaments, blue, red, and white enamel
prunts". It included pitchers, flacons, centerpieces, sugar
bowls, ice-cream bowls, lidded boxes, creamers, footed
beakers, stem glasses, champagne flutes and saucers,
a lidded goblet, finger bowls.
According to the design drawings, the model of the
Rococo ornamentation was a "French pattern."

46b

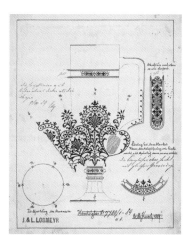

Becher mit Henkel (Werkzeichnung, FAW)
Handled beaker (working drawing, CAV)

47a

47a Teeschale mit Unterteller
FM: auf der Oberseite des Tellers gemalt
H 7,8 cm, D 12,6 cm
Quellen: FAW, „Teeschale mit Unterteller […] 1674-91/[…]",
Bestellungsbuch MNA, 1889–93, 8. Juli 1891, 1674,
„Theeschalen mit Unterteller rund Serie Krystl. glt. theils
geformt, wenn möglich mit verschmolzenen Rändern […],
Linien Reliefgoldornamenten, blauen rothen und weiß
Emailpunkten nach […] folgenden Vorlagen zu verfahren"
Inv.-Nr. Gl 2592, wohl Vermächtnis Ludwig Lobmeyr 1917,
nachträglich inv.

47a Tea cup with saucer
B: painted on the top-side of the saucer
H 7.8 cm, D 12.6 cm
Sources: CAV, "Tea cup with saucer […] 1674-91/[…]",
order book MNA, 1889–93, 8 July 1891, 1674, "Tea cups
with saucers, round, series crystl. pol. partly molded, if
possible with edge melting […], lines relief gold ornaments,
blue, red, and white enamel prunts, to be made after the
following models […]"
Inv. no. Gl 2592, pres. bequest of Ludwig Lobmeyr 1917,
subs. inv.

48 Serie „Hochgold mit Watteau-bildern", ab 1893
Entw.: wohl Moritz Knab (Dekor), 1889
Farbloses Glas mit farbigem Dekor und Gold

48 Series "Raised gold with Watteau pictures", from 1893
Dsg.: pres. Moritz Knab (decoration), 1889
Colorless glass with colored decoration and gold

48a

Um 1893 ging die Serie „Hochgold mit Watteaubildern"
mit Dekor in Email und Gold und Figuren nach dem
französischen Maler Antoine Watteau in Produktion. Sie
passte zu den Rokokoserien, die in den achtziger Jahren
beliebt geworden waren. Die Form des Gefäßes geht auf
1889 zurück und ist in den Werkzeichnungen in einer
anderen Serie erfasst: „Gefässe aus Krystallglas mit Figuren
und Ornamenten gravirt. Die Formen nach eigenen
Zeichnungen; die Ornamente von M. Knab nach Angabe
ausgeführt; Die Figuren von Fischer. 1889" (WZ, Bd.
XII, S. 27–30). Auch der gemalte ornamentale Dekor ist
eine Umsetzung der von Moritz Knab 1889 entworfenen Gravierungen derselben Serie.

Around 1893, the series "Raised gold with Watteau
pictures" with enamel and gold decoration and figurations after the French Painter Antoine Watteau went
into production. It suited in style to the Rococo series
which had become popular in the 1880s. The form of
the vessel dates back to 1889 and is recorded in the
working drawings under a different series: "Vessels of
crystal glass with engraved figures and ornamentation.
Forms after own drawings; ornamentation made by M.
Knab on instruction. Figures by Fischer. 1889" (WD,
vol. XII, pp. 27–30). The painted ornamental decoration
follows the engravings of the same series designed by
Moritz Knab 1889.

48a Deckelgefäß („Fußbecher mit Deckel")
FM: am Rand gemalt
H 17 cm
Quellen: FAW, Bestellungsbuch MNA, 6572, 3. Jan. 1889,
„Fußbecher m. Deckel rund Serie Krystl. m. schmalen Schälen,
Walzen, theils mit Hohlkehlenschliff m. geformten Füßen",
Bestellungsbuch MNA, 26. Apr. 1893, 4728, „Fußbecher Krystl.
glt. aus[f]getrieben, zunächst 2/3 Stücke […], an denen
2 schwache walzenartige schiefe Schnitte eingeschliffen sind";
FAP, Karton 20, Serie 60, „Hochgold mit Watteaubildern", 1893
Inv.-Nr. Gl 2594, wohl Vermächtnis Ludwig Lobmeyr 1917,
nachträglich inv.

48a Lidded Vessel ("Fotted beaker with lid ")
B: painted on the rim
H 17 cm
Sources: CAV, order book MNA, 6572, 3. Jan. 1889, "Footed
beaker, round, crystal, surface-ground, ribs, partly groove cut,
w. molded feet", order book MNA, 26. Apr. 1893, 4728,
"Footed beaker, crystal pol. reamed, 2/3 pieces at first […],
with 2 flat groove-like cuts engraved"; CAP, box 20, series 60,
"Raised gold with Watteau pictures", 1893
Inv. no. Gl 2594, pres. bequest of Ludwig Lobmeyr 1917,
subs. inv.

49 „Serie mit Purpurpalmetten", ab 1893

Farbloses Glas mit Dekor in Weiß, Rot und Gold

In der Serie mit flächendeckendem Palmettendekor in Emailfarben und Gold wurden Krüge, Flakons, Pokale, Fußbecher, Schalen, Büchsen mit Deckel, Schmuckschalen, Sorbetkännchen, Schäffchen mit Deckel und Teller, Oberskännchen, Punschtöpfe und Punschkännchen entworfen. Die Schale im Besitz des MAK gehört zu einem Punschtopf, wie er sich im Firmenmuseum befindet.

Das Motiv der Palmetten wurde zu dieser Zeit bei Serien in unterschiedlicher Technik verwendet, so 1887 bei Gefäßen „aus Krystallglas mit gravirten, polirten, goldumsäumten Palmetten und Weissemail-Punkten nach eigenen Zeichnungen" (WZ, Bd. XVII, S. 34) oder 1893 bei einer Serie mit vergoldeter oder versilberter „Rococo-Gravierung" (siehe etwa Kat.-Nr. 46).

Mit einer sehr ähnlichen netzartigen Struktur wurde 1893 eine weitere Serie überzogen: „Serie Krystall glatt mit Purpur Kleeblättern in weiß Email-Netz-Decor".

49a Schale

Entw.: 1893
FM: im Zentrum der Oberseite gemalt
H 4,8 cm, D 37,5 cm
Quellen: FAW, „Serie mit Purpurpalmetten", 1893, Schale 4998-93, Bestellungsbuch MNA, 14. Juni 1893, 4998, „Schalen groß"; FAP, Schnitt „4998-93 MNA"
Inv.-Nr. Gl 2586, Vermächtnis Ludwig Lobmeyr 1917, nachträglich inv.

50 Spiegel

Entw. u. Ausf.: vor 1874
Holz, Glasplatten (z. T. diamantiert), Spiegelglas mit Schnitt, halbkugelige Glasknöpfe
H 70 cm, B 46 cm
Inv.-Nr. Gl 1254, Geschenk des Kaisers, inv. 30. März 1875

Der Spiegel befand sich 1873 im Kaiserpavillon der Wiener Weltausstellung im „Zimmer der Herrn Erzherzoge". Als der Pavillon 1875 abgetragen wurde, wur-

49 "Series with purple palmettes", from 1893

Colorless glass with white, red, and gold decoration

For the series with surface-covering palmette decoration in enamel colors and gold, jugs, flacons, goblets, footed beakers, bowls, lidded boxes, decorative bowls, sorbet jugs, little tubs with lids and saucers, creamers, punch-bowls, and punch jugs were designed. The bowl in the MAK holdings belongs to a punch bowl in the company museum.

The palmette motif was used in different techniques for several series at that time, as, for example, in vessels "of crystal glass with engraved. Polished, gold-lined palmettes and white enamel dots after own drawings" (WD, vol. XVII, p. 34) or in the 1893 series with gilded or silvered "Rococo engraving" (see e. g. cat. no. 46). 1893, another series was produced which had a very similar network-like decoration: "Series crystal pol. With purple cloverleaves in white enamel decoration."

49a Bowl

Dsg.: 1893
B: painted in the top-side center
H 4.8 cm, D 37.5 cm
Sources: CAV, "Series with purple palmettes", 1893, bowel 4998-93, order book MNA, 14 June 1893, 4998, "Bowls, large"; CAP, papercut "4998-93 MNA"
Inv. no. Gl 2586, bequest of Ludwig Lobmeyr 1917, subs. inv.

50 Mirror

Dsg. a. mfr.: before 1874
Wood, glass sheets (partly diamond-point engraved), mirror glass with cutting, hemispherical glass buttons
H 70 cm, B 46 cm
Inv. no. Gl 1254, donation from the Emperor, inv. 30 March 1875

The mirror was part of the furniture of the "Archdukes' Room" in the Imperial Pavilion at the 1873 Vienna World's Fair. When the pavilion was dismantled 1875,

49a

den Teile der Einrichtung, vor allem Möbel und Stoffe, dem Museum überlassen (MAK-Archiv, 126/1875, 316/1875, 518/1875; Haus-, Hof- und Staatsarchiv, OMeA, Rubrik 133/6, 1875).

Die Spiegelproduktion bei Lobmeyr ist als eigener wichtiger Bereich zu sehen. Das MAK ist nur im Besitz dieses schlichten, traditionell wirkenden Spiegels mit geschnitztem Holzrahmen (renaissanceartige Festons). Daneben produzierte Lobmeyr aber sehr aufwendige Spiegel mit gravierten Spiegelteilen, mit und ohne Goldumrahmung, in der Tradition der barocken Spiegelrahmen, aber unter Verwendung von Stilelementen des Orients oder der Renaissance. Die Rahmen aus geschlif-

parts of the interior decoration, in particular furniture and textiles, were handed over to the museum (MAK Archives, 126/1875, 316/1875, 518/1875; Haus-, Hof-und Staatsarchiv, OMeA, section 133/6, 1875).

Mirrors were an important production segment of Lobmeyr. The MAK only holds this plain, traditional-looking mirror with a carved wooden frame (Renaissance-style festoons). Apart from this, Lobmeyr also produced very lavish mirrors with engraved mirror parts, with or without gold framing, in the tradition of Baroque mirror frames but with the use of oriental or Renaissance style elements. The frames of cut, engraved, and foiled glass could have sizes of up to two by four

TAF. XXX.

Von der Wiener Weltausstellung 1873.

ORIENTALISCHER SPIEGEL, entworfen von Professor JOSEF STORCK,
ausgeführt von J. & L. Lobmeyer und Hanusch & Dziedinsky in Wien.

50

„Orientalischer Spiegel, entworfen von Professor Josef Storck, ausgeführt von J. & L. Lobmeyr und Hanusch & Dziedinsky in Wien", gezeigt auf der Wiener Weltausstellung 1873, in: Blätter für Kunstgewerbe, Bd. 2, 1873, Taf. 30 (MAK, Inv.-Nr. K.I. 3251)

"Oriental mirror, designed by Professor Josef Storck, produced by J.& L. Lobmeyr and Hanusch & Dziedinsky in Wien", presented at the Vienna World's Fair 1873, in: „Blätter für Kunstgewerbe", vol. 2, 1873, pl. 30 (MAK, inv. no. K.I. 3251)

fenem, graviertem und belegtem Glas konnten bis zu vier mal zwei Meter groß sein. Außerdem führte Lobmeyr die Malerei auf der Spiegelfläche ein und präsentierte schon 1871 erfolgreich Spiegel mit gemalten Blumengirlanden und Amoretten aus dem Atelier August Eisenmengers u. a.

meters. In addition, Lobmeyr introduced painted decorations on the mirror surface and in 1871 already successfully presented mirrors with painted flower garlands and amorettos to designs by the studio of August Eisenmenger a. o.

51   Armleuchter für vier Kerzen, 18. Jh. (mit späteren Ergänzungen von J. & L. Lobmeyr)

Stahl, Bergkristall, Glas
H 65 cm
Quellen: MAK-Archiv, 596/1881, „aus geschnittenem Stahl alter Erzeugung und neuerer Ergänzung, ferner Bergkristalltheile und Christalglasergänzungen"
Inv.-Nr. Gl 1606, Geschenk v. Ludwig Lobmeyr 1881, inv. 27. Nov. 1887

51   Four Candle Candelabra, 18th century (with later additions by J. & L. Lobmeyr)

Steel, rock crystal, glass
H 65 cm
Sources: MAK Archives, 596/1881, "of cut steel of old making and newer additions, furthermore rock-crystal parts and crystal glass additions"
Inv. no. Gl 1606, donation from Ludwig Lobmeyr 1881, inv. 27 Nov. 1887

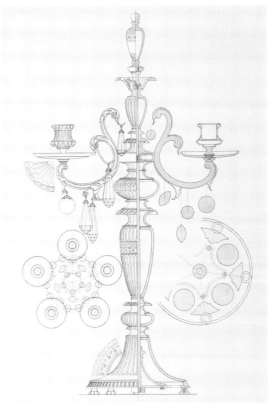

Kerzenleuchter, Dessert-Service Nr. 168, in: WZ, Bd. VI, S. 48
„Candle Candelabra", Dessert Service no. 168, in: WD, vol. VI, p. 48

51

Bei diesem Objekt handelt es sich um einen Armleuchter aus dem 18. Jahrhundert, der von Lobmeyr offensichtlich restauriert wurde. Diesen Leuchtertypus griff Ludwig Lobmeyr bei seinem persönlichen Trink- und Dessert-Service Nr. 168, das er 1877 entwarf, für ein „Girandol für 6 Kerzen" mit Silbermontierung von J. C. Klinkosch auf (siehe Abb. oben).

This object is an 18th century candelabra which obviously was restored by Lobmeyr. For his personal drinking and dessert service no. 168, a design of 1877, Lobmeyr fell back on this style for a "6 Candle Girandole" with silver mounting by J. C. Klinkosch (see ill. top left).

Namen- und Ortsregister

Register of Personal and Place Names

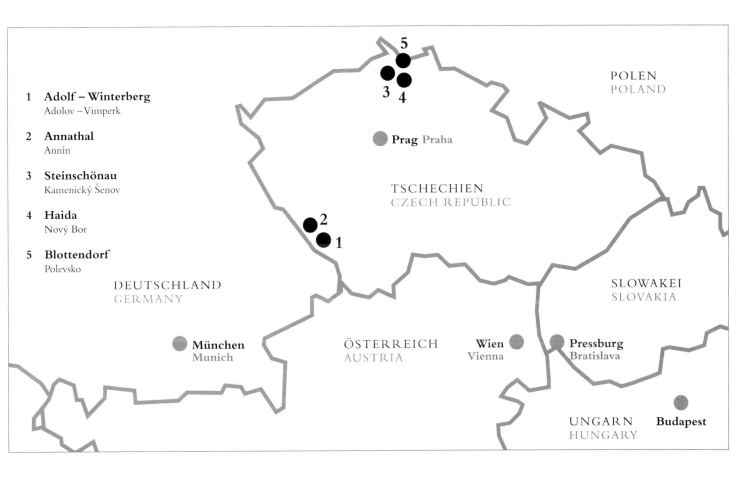

1 **Adolf – Winterberg**
Adolov –Vimperk

2 **Annathal**
Annín

3 **Steinschönau**
Kamenický Šenov

4 **Haida**
Nový Bor

5 **Blottendorf**
Polevsko

POLEN
POLAND

Prag Praha

TSCHECHIEN
CZECH REPUBLIC

SLOWAKEI
SLOVAKIA

DEUTSCHLAND
GERMANY

München
Munich

ÖSTERREICH
AUSTRIA

Wien
Vienna

Pressburg
Bratislava

UNGARN
HUNGARY

Budapest

Glossar

Adolf	Standort der Adolfshütte bei Winterberg in Südböhmen, die Meyr's Neffen gehörte, dem Hauptlieferanten von Lobmeyr (heute Adolov)
Aluminiumdekoration	Mit Aluminium gefüllte Gravierungen oder bedeckte Flächen, die im Gegensatz zur Silberdekoration nicht oxidieren
Annathal	Standort der Glashütte Josef Eduard Schmid in Südböhmen (heute Annín)
Ätzen	Siehe Glasätzung
Aurora	Römische Göttin der Morgenröte
Bestellungsbuch	Enthält Aufträge der Firma Lobmeyr an Glasfabriken und Glasraffineure. Für einige Firmen, etwa MNA, wurden eigene Bücher angelegt, weitere Bestellungen wurden in so genannten Allgemeinen Bestellungsbüchern erfasst.
Blottendorf	Ort in der Region um Haida in Nordböhmen, die auf Glasveredelung spezialisiert war (heute Polevsko)
Craqueléglas	Glas mit beabsichtigter Rissbildung in der Oberfläche oder einer bestimmten Schicht. Entsteht dadurch, dass die Glasmasse kurz ins kalte Wasser gehalten wird, wodurch sie an der Oberfläche springt; dann wird die Form wieder erwärmt und weiter geblasen.
Eisglas	Siehe Craqueléglas
Emailmalerei	Technik der Glasmalerei mit Schmelzfarben (Emailfarben), die sich durch Einbrennen mit der Glasoberfläche verbinden; es gibt deckende und transparente Farben.
Fachschule	Der Unterricht der an das ÖMKI angeschlossenen Kunstgewerbeschule erfolgte in verschiedenen Klassen, die als Fachschulen bezeichnet wurden. Außerdem gab es in der ganzen Monarchie weitere Fachschulen, die einzelne kunsthandwerkliche Zweige unterrichten und fördern sollten und in enger Verbindung mit dem ÖMKI standen.
Fadendekor	Entsteht, indem Glasfäden in die Masse eingeschmolzen oder auf die Oberfläche aufgeschmolzen werden.
Farbenglas (Farbglas)	In der Glasmasse gefärbtes Glas; entsteht durch die Beimischung verschiedenster chemischer Substanzen zur Glasschmelze.
Firmenmarke	Signatur der Herstellerfirma
Flachglas	Im Gegensatz zu Hohlglas flach gewalztes Glas für Fensterglas, Spiegel, Glasbilder usw.
Glasätzung	Durch Ätzung wird ein Teil der Glasoberfläche abgetragen; je nach Konzentration und Einwirkungsdauer der verwendeten Säure spricht man von Blankätzen, Mattätzen oder Tiefätzung.
Glasraffinerie	Eigene Werkstätte zur Glasveredelung in Kalttechnik, wie Schliff, Schnitt und Kaltmalerei
Glasschliff	Bearbeitung der Glasoberfläche mit Metallrädchen unter Einsatz von Schleifmitteln
Glasschnitt	Feinbearbeitung der Glasoberfläche mit kleinen rotierenden Kupferrädchen; der dadurch entstehende Dekor erscheint matt (Mattschnitt), kann aber zusätzlich auspoliert werden (geblänkter Schnitt). Man unterscheidet Tiefschnitt und Hoch- oder Reliefschnitt.
Glasveredelung	Dekorationsformen am kalten Glas (Schliff, Schnitt, Malerei)
Glasverleger	Glasproduzent ohne eigene Glashütte, der Glasgegenstände nach seinen Angaben in verschiedenen Hütten anfertigen und von Manufakturen und Raffinerien veredeln lässt; die Erzeugnisse vertreibt er unter seinem eigenen Namen.
Glimmerglas	Glas mit eingeschmolzenem Silberflitter (Glimmerplättchen bzw. Glimmerbrocat, hergestellt aus Glimmerpulver)
Gravierung (Gravur)	Glasschnitt
Haida	Zentrum einer Region in Nordböhmen, die auf Glasveredelung spezialisiert war (heute Nový Bor)
Hohlglas	Sammelbegriff für Glasgefäße, also hohle (nicht flächige) Glaserzeugnisse
Irisierung	Metallische Beschichtung der Glasoberfläche durch Aufdampfen von Metallsalzen; führt zu einem Schillern der Oberfläche (Irisieren).
Kentaurin (Kentaurotritonin)	Fabelwesen: Oberkörper weibliche Menschengestalt, Unterleib Pferd; wenn der Pferdeleib in einen Fischschwanz übergeht, auch als Kentaurotritonin bezeichnet.
Kristallglas	Besonders klares Glas von hoher Qualität mit hoher Lichtbrechung; traditionelles böhmisches Glas, das in seinen Eigenschaften dem Bergkristall nahe kommen sollte. Es ist härter und elastischer, aber leichter als Bleikristall, das durch einen besonders hohen Bleianteil weicher und dadurch einfacher zu bearbeiten wird.
Montierung (Silbermontierung)	Metallfassung von Glasgefäßen
Muffel (Muffelofen)	Geschlossener Ofen mit einer Brennkammer aus Schamotte (Muffel genannt) zum Einbrennen von Emailmalereidekor
Nereide	Meeresnymphe in der griechischen Mythologie
Opakes Glas	Undurchsichtiges Glas
Opalglas	Halbopakes, wie ein Opal in Farben schillerndes (opalisierendes) Glas in verschiedenen Tönungen
Optisches Glas	Beim Herstellen der Glasform wird die Glasblase in einer Metallform vorgeformt und dann frei ausgeblasen, wodurch eine gewisse Reliefform entsteht.
Papierschnitt	Zeigt die Form eines Gefäßes, das nach dieser Vorlage in der Glashütte hergestellt wird.
Raffinerie	Siehe Glasraffinerie
Rohglas	Hohlglas, das zur Weiterverarbeitung in meist von Hütten oder Händlern betriebenen Manufakturen oder Raffinerien bestimmt ist
Rubinglas	Mit Kupfer, Gold oder Selen gefärbtes rotes Glas
Schliff	Siehe Glasschliff
Schnitt	Siehe Glasschnitt
Steinschönau	Ort in jener nordböhmischen Region, die auf Glasveredelung spezialisiert war; außerdem Standort einer 1856 gegründeten Glasfachschule (heute Kamenický Šenov)
Tafelglas	Siehe Flachglas
Tauschierung	Edelmetalle (Gold, Silber) werden zur Verzierung in unedle Metalle (z. B. Bronze) eingehämmert oder eingelegt.
Triton	Mythologisches Wasserwesen: bärtiger Mann, dessen Unterleib in einen Fischleib übergeht, oft kombiniert mit einem Pferdevorderleib
Überfang	Zwei oder mehr übereinander liegende verschiedenfarbige Glasschichten
Winterberg	Ort in Südböhmen; war ein bedeutender Standort einer Glashütte und von Glasmalern (heute Vimperk).

Glossary

Adolf	Location of the Adolf glassworks near Winterberg (Vimperk), South-Bohemia, which belonged to Meyr's Neffen, Lobmeyr's main supplier (today Adolov).
Aluminum decoration	Aluminum-filled engraving or aluminum-covered surfaces, which, unlike silver, were not subject to oxidation.
Annathal	Location of the glassworks of Josef Eduard Schmid in South-Bohemia (today Annín)
Aurora	Roman goddess of the dawn
Blottendorf	Village in the region around Haida, North-Bohemia, specialized on glass refining (today Polevsko)
Brand	Manufacturer's mark or signature
Casing	Application of two or more glass layers of different color
Colored glass	Glass colored in the batch (mixture of raw materials such as silica, soda, potash etc.), produced by adding different chemical substances, mostly metallic oxides
Crackle glass	Glass with intended fissures in the surface or a specific layer of the glass, produced by dipping hot glass into cold water, which makes the surface crackle. The form is then reheated and re-blown.
Crystal glass	Particularly clear glass of high quality and refractivity; traditional Bohemian glass with qualities supposedly similar to natural rock crystal. Harder and more elastic, but lighter than lead crystal, which is softer and easier to work due to a high share of lead.
Cutting see	Glass cutting
Enamel painting	Glass painting technique using meltable paints (enamel paints) that are fused into the glass surface by firing; there are opaque and transparent paints.
Engraving	Glass cutting
Etching	see Glass etching
Female Centaur (Centauro-Triton)	Fabulous creature: human upper body, horse-like lower body; also called Centauro-Triton, if the horse body ends with a fish fin.
Glass cutting	Detail work on the glass surface with small rotating copper wheels; the decoration thus produced appears matte (matte finish), but may be polished (polished cutting). Techniques distinguished are intaglio, and raised or relief cutting.
Glass refining	Application of decorations on cold glass (cutting, engraving, painting)
Glass etching	By etching, part of the surface of the glass is removed; depending on the concentration of, and exposure to, the acid, blank etching (acid polishing), matte etching and deep etching are distinguished.
Glass grinding	Working of the glass surface with rotating metal wheels and an abrasive.
Glass refinery	Specialized workshop for cold-worked glass refining such as cutting, grinding, and painting
Glimmer glass (mica glass)	Glass with fused-in silver scraps (mica scales made of mica powder)
Grinding	see Glass grinding
Haida	Center of a North-Bohemian region specialized on glass refining (today Nový Bor)
Holloware	Generic name for glass vessels, i.e. hollow, not flat glass products
Ice glass	see Crackle glass
Inlaying	Precious metals are inlaid or hammered into non-precious metals (e.g. bronze) for decoration.
Iridescence	Thin transparent layering of the glass surface by spraying on metallic salts; creates a rainbow-like color effect (iridescence).
Mounting (silver mounting)	Metal setting for glass vessels
Muffle (muffle kiln)	Closed kiln with a fire-clay box (the muffle) for low-temperature firing of enamel decorations
Nereid	Sea nymph in Greek mythology
Opaque glass	Non-transparent glass
Opal glass	Semi-opaque glass producing an opal-like (opalescent) color effect in different shades
Optical glass	In produced the glass form, the gather is shaped in a metal mold and then pipe-blown, which produces a certain relief effect.
Order book	Contains job orders by Lobmeyr to glassworks or refineries. For some companies, such as MNA, special order books were kept; other suppliers are recorded in the so-called General Order Books.
Outsourcing manufacturer	Glass producer who does not operate his own glassworks, but has glass objects produced by other glass factories and refineries, which he sells under his own label.
Papercut	Cut-out rendering of the shape of a vessel, which is then produced in the glassworks after this pattern.
Plate glass	see Sheet glass
Refinery	see Glass refinery
Raw glass	Hollow glass for further processing by manufactories or refineries operated by glassworks or merchants
Ruby glass	Red glass, colored with copper, gold, or selenium
Sheet glass	Glass that is rolled out flat for window panes, mirrors, glass paintings etc. in contrast to hollow glass.
Steinschönau	City in the North-Bohemian glass-refining region; location of a glassworking school established 1856 (today Kamenický Šenov)
Trailing	Application of glass threads (trails), which are fused into the glass or onto the surface.
Triton	Mythological sea creature: bearded man whose lower body ends in a fish body, often with a horse-like front part.
Vocational schools	Education in the Industrial Arts School associated with the AMAI was organized in classes, which were called vocational schools. In addition, vocational schools that were in close contact with the AMAI existed throughout the monarchy to teach and promote the arts and crafts.
Winterberg	Place in South-Bohemia; formerly an important glassworks location and glass painting center (today Vimperk)

Ausgewählte Literatur Selected Literature

Angaben in eckigen Klammern dienen der Zuordnung von im Katalogteil verwendeten Kurztiteln. Specifications in square brackets are for the assignment of the titles in the catalogue.

Alcouffe, Daniel/Bascou, Marc: 1851–1900. Le Arti decorative alle grandi esposizioni universale, Mailand 1988

Bancroft, Hubert Howe: The Book of the Fair, Chicago 1893

Brožová, Jarmila: Historismus. Umělecké řemeslo 1860–1900, Prag 1975

Brožová, Jarmila: České sklo 19. století, Brünn 1979

Bucher, Bruno: Die Glassammlung des K. K. Oesterreich. Museums, Wien 1888

Bük, Julius von: Glas- und Thonwaaren auf der Weltausstellung in Barcelona, in: Sprechsaal, Coburg, Nr. no. 5, 1889, S. p. 77

Cohausen, Oberst von/Poschinger, G. von: IX. Gruppe group: Industrie der Stein-, Thon- und Glaswaaren, in: Amtlicher Bericht über die Wiener Weltausstellung im Jahre 1873. Erstattet von der Centralcommission des Deutschen Reiches für die Wiener Weltausstellung, Braunschweig 1874

Colné, Charles/Blake, Comm.: Glass and Glassware, in: Reports of the US Commissioner to the Paris Universal Exhibition of 1878, Washington 1880, S. p. 290–293, Taf. pl. XVII

Falke, Jacob: Die Kunstindustrie der Gegenwart. Studien auf der Pariser Weltausstellung im Jahre 1867, Leipzig 1868

Falke, Jacob: Die Kunstindustrie auf der Wiener Weltausstellung 1873, Wien 1873 [= Falke 1873]

Falke, Jacob: Die Wiener Weltausstellung und die Kunstindustrie. IV. Das Glas, in: Gewerbehalle, Stuttgart, 1873, S. p. 161–163

Falke, J.: Exposition Universelle de 1878. La Verre de Bohême et sa transformation par Louis Lobmeyr, in: L'Art. Revue Hebdomadaire Illustrée, Paris, Bd. vol. II, 1878, S. p. 183–191

Falke, Jakob von: Glasausstellung im österreichischen Museum I., in: Beilage zur Wiener Abendpost, Wien, 2. Mai 1879

Falke, Jakob von: Glasausstellung im österreichischen Museum II., in: Beilage zur Wiener Abendpost, Wien, 3. Mai 1879 [= Falke 1879]

Falke, Jacob von: J. & L. Lobmeyr's Ausstellung im Oesterr. Museum, in: Mittheilungen des k. k. Oesterreich. Museums für Kunst und Industrie, Wien, N. F. Bd. vol. 2, Nr. no. 39, März 1889, S. p. 313–317

Falke, Jakob/Lobmeyr, Ludwig: Die Glasindustrie, Gruppe group IX, Section 3, Heft issue 89, in: Officieller Ausstellungs-Bericht, herausgegeben durch die General-Direction der Weltausstellung 1873, Wien 1875

Fillitz, Hermann (Hrsg.): Der Traum vom Glück. Die Kunst des Historismus in Europa, Wien 1996

Frauberger, Heinrich: Die Kunst-Industrie auf der Pariser Weltausstellung 1878, Leipzig 1879

Glas aus Wien. J & L Lobmeyr. Vom Biedermeier bis zur Gegenwart, Ausstellungskatalog, Zürich u.a. et al. 1979

Glass by J. & L. Lobmeyr of Vienna, in: The Art Journal. The Paris Exhibition 1900, London 1901, S. p. 252–253

Gmelin, Leop.: Die Arbeiten aus Thon und Glas, in: Chronik der deutsch-nationalen Kunstgewerbe-Ausstellung in München 1888. Im Auftrage des Directoriums herausgegeben von Dr. Paul v. Salvisberg, München 1888

Großmann, G. Ulrich/Krutisch, Petra: Renaissance der Renaissance. Sonderausstellung des Weserrenaissance-Museums Schloß Brake, Ausstellungskatalog, München–Berlin 1992

Hagedorn, Anette: Die orientalisierenden Gläser der Firma Fritz Heckert im europäischen Kontext, in: Böhmisches Glas. Phänomen der mitteleuropäischen Kultur des 19. und frühen 20. Jahrhunderts, Schriften des Passauer Glasmuseums, Bd. vol. 1, Passau 1995, S. p. 84–89

Höltl, Georg (Hrsg.): Das böhmische Glas. 1700–1950, Bd. vol. 3: Historismus, Passau 1995

Huldigung der Oesterreichischen Handels- und Gewerbekammern zur Feier der Vermälung seiner K. und K. Hoheit des Kronprinzen Herrn Erzherzogs Rudolfs mit Ihrer K. Hoheit der Frau Prinzessin Stefanie von Belgien. Wien, den 10. Mai 1881, Wien 1881

100 Jahre Österreichisches Museum für Angewandte Kunst. Kunstgewerbe des Historismus, Ausstellungskatalog, Wien 1964

150 Jahre österreichische Glaskunst. Lobmeyr 1823–1973, Ausstellungskatalog, Wien 1973

Jedding, Hermann: Hohe Kunst zwischen Biedermeier und Jugendstil. Historismus in Hamburg und Norddeutschland, Hamburg 1977

Jöbstl, Elke: Die Trinkservice der Firma „J. & L. Lobmeyr" von 1823–1894, Diplomarbeit, Salzburg 1987

J. & L. Lobmeyr. 150 Jahre, Wien 1973

Klesse, Brigitte: Gläser des Historismus aus Wien in Köln, in: Kölner Museums-Bulletin, Köln, Heft issue 4, 1996, S. p. 4–23

Leisching, Eduard: Ludwig Lobmeyr, in: Neue österreichische Biographie, Bd. vol. 1, Wien 1923, S. p. 132–145

Lobmeyr, Ludwig/Ilg, Albert/Boeheim, Wendelin (Hrsg.): Die Glasindustrie, ihre Geschichte, gegenwärtige Entwicklung und Statistik, Stuttgart 1874

Lobmeyr's Glas-Ausstellung im Museum, in: Die Presse, Wien, 6. April 1879, S. p. 8–9

Lützow, Carl von (Hrsg.): Kunst und Kunstgewerbe auf der Wiener Weltausstellung 1873, Leipzig 1875

Mondron, Léon: Exposition Universelle de Vienne. Documents & Rapports des Jurés & Délégués Belges. Industrie de la Verrerie, Brüssel 1874

Mundt, Barbara: Historismus. Kunsthandwerk und Industrie im Zeitalter der Weltausstellungen, Kataloge des Kunstgewerbemuseums Berlin, Bd. vol. VII, Berlin 1973

Mundt, Barbara: Historismus. Kunstgewerbe zwischen Biedermeier und Jugendstil, München 1981

Netzer, Susanne: Ein fürstliches Geschenk. Glasteller der Firma Lobmeyr aus dem Jahre 1885, in: Kunst und Antiquitäten, München, II. Heft issue, 1988, S. p. 84–87

Neuwirth, Waltraud: J. & L. Lobmeyr – arabische Dekore. Die Künstler und ihre Arbeiten, in: Antiquitäten-Zeitung, München, Nr. no. 10, 1981, S. p. 282–296 [= Neuwirth 1981a]

Neuwirth, Waltraud: J. & L. Lobmeyr – die indischen Dekore. Orientierung, in: Antiquitäten-Zeitung, München, Nr. no. 9, 1981, S. p. 241–246 [= Neuwirth 1981b]

Neuwirth, Waltraud: Orientalisierende Gläser. J. & L. Lobmeyr, Wien 1981 [= Neuwirth 1981c]

Neuwirth, Waltraud: Theophil von Hansen. Glas. Entwürfe für Lobmeyr, in: Antiquitäten-Zeitung, München, Nr. no. 4, 1981, S. p. 101–111, Nr. no. 5, S. p. 135–140 [= Neuwirth 1981d]

Neuwirth, Waltraud: Kostbarkeiten des Historismus, in: Antiquitäten-Zeitung, München, Nr. no. 7, 1987, S. p. 160–162

Neuwirth, Waltraud: Schöner als Bergkristall. Ludwig Lobmeyr. Glas Legende, Wien 1999

Pecht, Friedrich: Kunst und Kunstindustrie auf der Wiener Weltausstellung, Stuttgart 1873

Pecht, Friedrich: Aus dem Münchner Glaspalast. Studien zur Orientierung in und außer demselben während der Kunst- und Kunstindustrie-Ausstellung des Jahres 1876, Stuttgart 1876

Pecht, Friedrich: Kunst und Kunstindustrie auf der Pariser Weltausstellung 1878, Stuttgart 1878

Pecht, Friedrich: Aus meiner Zeit. Lebenserinnerungen, München 1894

Pešatová, Zuzana: Böhmische Glasgravuren, Prag 1968

Rath, Stefan: Lobmeyr. Vom Adel des Handwerks, Wien 1962

Revival Styles in the 19th Century. An Exhibition from the Collection of the Budapest Museum of Applied Arts, Ausstellungskatalog, Budapest 1992

Schack von Wittenau, Clementine: Ergänzendes zum „Geschenk an den König von Belgien", eine Auftragsarbeit der Firma Lobmeyr aus den Jahren 1884/85, in: Festschrift für Brigitte Klesse, Berlin 1994, S. p. 117–132

Schlosser, Ignaz: Das Alte Glas, 3. Aufl., Braunschweig 1977

Schmidt, Alex.: Von der Kunstgewerbe-Ausstellung in München 1888, in: Sprechsaal, Coburg, Jg. year XXII, Nr. no. 5, 1889, S. p. 75–77

Schmidt, Robert: 100 Jahre österreichische Glaskunst. Lobmeyr 1823–1923, Wien 1925

Scholda, Ulrike: Theorie und Praxis im Wiener Kunstgewerbe des Historismus am Beispiel von Josef Ritter von Storck (1830–1902), phil. Diss., Salzburg 1991

Scholda, Ulrike: „Man suchte die Kunstgewerbetreibenden heranzuziehen, ich sank von selber hin …". Ludwig Lobmeyr und das k. k. Österreichische Museum für Kunst und Industrie, in: Kunst und Industrie. Die Anfänge des Museums für angewandte Kunst in Wien, Ausstellungskatalog, Ostfildern-Ruit 2000, S. p. 193–202

Smith, Walter: The Masterpieces of the Centennial International Exhibition, Bd. vol. II: Industrial Art, Philadelphia 1876

Spiegl, Walter: Glas des Historismus, Braunschweig 1980

Teirich, Valentin: Die Glasarbeiten auf der Wiener Weltausstellung, in: Blätter für Kunstgewerbe, Wien, Bd. vol. 3, 1874, S. p. 81–88

Trink- und Dessert-Service aus Krystallglas im Auftrage S. M. des Kaisers Franz Josef I. nach Entwürfen des Professor Josef Storck ausgeführt von J. & L. Lobmeyr. Acht Blatt Photographien, Wien 1873

Uhland, Wilhelm Heinrich (Hg.): Illustrirter Katalog der Pariser Welt-Ausstellung von 1878, Leipzig 1880

Urbancová, Jana: Neo-Renaissance and Neo-Baroque Ornament on North-Bohemian Engraved Glass, in: Journal of Glass Studies. The Corning Museum of Glass, Corning, Bd. vol. 23, 1981, S. p. 74–81

Wesenberg, Angelika/Hennig, Wolfgang: Glas. Historismus und die Historismen um 1900, Ausstellungskatalog, Berlin 1977

Historische Ausstellungskataloge (allgemein)
Historical Exhibition Catalogues (general)

Amtlicher Bericht über die Industrie- und Kunst-Ausstellung zu London im Jahre 1862, Berlin 1863

The Art Journal. The Illustrated Catalogue of the Paris International Exhibition 1878, London 1878

Bericht über die zweite allgemeine österreichische Gewerbs-Produkten-Ausstellung im Jahre 1839, Wien 1840

Catalog der Ausstellungen von J. & L. Lobmeyr K. K. Hofglaswaaren-Lieferanten und Glasraffineure in Wien und von Wilhelm Kralik, Firma: Meyr's Neffe Glasfabrikant in Adolf bei Winterberg in Böhmen in Verbindung mit J. & L. Lobmeyr, Wien 1873

Catalog der vom k. k. Oesterr. Museum für Kunst und Industrie in Wien veranlassten Ausstellung in Reichenberg, Reichenberg 1868

Fachmännische Berichte. Die Ausstellung oesterreichischer Kunstgewerbe. 4. November 1871–4. Februar 1872. K. k. Österr. Museum für Kunst und Industrie, Wien 1872

Illustrirter Katalog der Londoner Industrie-Ausstellung von 1862, Leipzig 1863

Illustrirter Katalog der Pariser Industrie-Ausstellung von 1867, Leipzig 1868

Katalog der kunstgewerblichen Ausstellung in Brünn, veranstaltet von dem mährischen Gewerbe-Vereine, Brünn 1869

Katalog der kunstgewerblichen Ausstellung in Prag veranstaltet von dem k. k. österreichischen Museum für Kunst und Industrie in Wien und von der Handels- und Gewerbekammer in Prag 1868, Prag 1868

Katalog der österreichischen Kunstgewerbe-Ausstellung im neuen Museumsgebäude Stubenring 5. K. k. österr. Museum für Kunst und Industrie, Wien 1871

Katalog der vom steiermärkischen Vereine zur Förderung der Kunstindustrie veranstalteten dritten Ausstellung kunstgewerblicher Erzeugnisse älterer und neuerer Zeit, Graz 1867

Österreichisch-ungarische industrielle und landwirthschaftliche Ausstellung in Triest 1882. Ausstellung des K. K. Österreichischen Museums für Kunst und Industrie, Wien 1882

Welt-Ausstellung 1873 in Wien. Amtlicher Catalog der Ausstellung der im Reichsrathe vertretenen Koenigreiche und Laender Oesterreichs, Wien 1873

Zeitschriften (allgemein)
Newspapers (general)

Blätter für Kunstgewerbe, herausgegeben von edited by Valentin Teirich, Josef Storck und Bruno Bucher, Wien 1872–1898

Gewerbehalle. Organ für den Fortschritt in allen Zweigen der Kunst-Industrie, Stuttgart 1863–1893

Mittheilungen des k. k. österr. [ab 1872: Oesterreich.] Museums für Kunst und Industrie. Monatschrift für Kunst und Kunstgewerbe, Wien 1864–1897

Konkordanz der Inventar- und Katalognummern
Concordance of Inventory and Catalogue Numbers

Inv.-Nr. Inv. No.	Kat.-Nr. Cat. No.	Inv.-Nr. Inv. No.	Kat.-Nr. Cat. No.
Dep. 90	33c	Gl 2572	22a
Dep. 94	1d	Gl 2573	29h
Gl 929	3	Gl 2574	29a
Gl 1090	13a	Gl 2575	29c
Gl 1091	13b	Gl 2576	29e
Gl 1118	6a	Gl 2577	29g
Gl 1119	6b	Gl 2578	29b
Gl 1121	6c	Gl 2579	32a
Gl 1122	12	Gl 2580	17a
Gl 1129	10	Gl 2581	9b
Gl 1238	15	Gl 2582	9a
Gl 1239	14	Gl 2583	30a
Gl 1240	16a	Gl 2584	30b
Gl 1254	50	Gl 2585	31a
Gl 1256	8a	Gl 2586	49a
Gl 1270	18	Gl 2587	46a
Gl 1272	24a	Gl 2588	30d
Gl 1273	21a	Gl 2589	29i
Gl 1274	11a	Gl 2590	36b
Gl 1299	21b	Gl 2591	28a
Gl 1402	20	Gl 2592	47a
Gl 1429	29	Gl 2593	46b
Gl 1430	29	Gl 2594	48a
Gl 1431	23b	Gl 2595	30c
Gl 1432	25a	Gl 2596	31b
Gl 1433	27a	Gl 2597	29d
Gl 1434	33a	Gl 2598	46c
Gl 1435	24c	Gl 2740	19a
Gl 1436	27b	Gl 2741	19b
Gl 1437	33b	Gl 2742	19c
Gl 1444	29f	Gl 2743	19b
Gl 1446	7a	Gl 2745	40a
Gl 1463	4a	Gl 2746	19d
Gl 1464	5a	Gl 2747	18c
Gl 1465	1a	Gl 3247	26a
Gl 1466	1b	Gl 3248	28b
Gl 1467	1c	Gl 3250	24b
Gl 1468	2	Gl 3251	44a
Gl 1517	18b	Gl 3252	37b
Gl 1606	51	Gl 3253	37a
Gl 1687	37c	Gl 3343a	35a
Gl 1739	39	Gl 3343b	35b
Gl 1740	38a	Gl 3343c	35c
Gl 1741	40b	Gl 3343d	35d
Gl 1742	36a	Gl 3343e	35e
Gl 1816	41	Gl 3343f	35f
Gl 1834	42	Gl 3343g	35g
Gl 1947	45	Gl 3343h	35h
Gl 2044	43a	WI 41	34
Gl 2045	34b	WI 48	23
Gl 2571	22b		

MAK Wien / Vienna
Österreichisches Museum für angewandte Kunst /
Gegenwartskunst
Austrian Museum of Applied Arts / Contemporary Art
Stubenring 5, A-1010 Wien / Vienna, Austria
Tel. (+43-1) 711 36-0, Fax (+43-1) 713 10 26
E-Mail: office@MAK.at, www.MAK.at

C.E.O. and Artistic Director
Peter Noever

SUPERVISORY BOARD
Andreas Treichl Vorsitzender / Chairman, C.E.O. Erste Bank, Wien / Vienna
Nathalie Hoyos Stellvertretende Vorsitzende /
Vice Chairman, Bundeskanzleramt / Federal Chancellery Austria
Cornelius Grupp C.E.O. CAG Holding Marktl Lilienfeld
Roman Koller Landesschulrat für die Steiermark / Styrian Schoolboard
Georg Mayer MAK
Claudia Oetker Kunstsammlerin Frankfurt – Wien /
Art Collector, Frankfurt – Vienna
Wolfgang Polzhuber Bundesministerium für Wirtschaft und Arbeit /
Federal Ministry of Economic Affairs
August Ruhs Universität Wien / University of Vienna
Silvia Zendron Bundesministerium für Finanzen /
Federal Ministry of Finance

MAK CENTER FOR ART AND ARCHITECTURE,
Los Angeles
Schindler House
835 North Kings Road
West Hollywood, CA 90069, USA
Tel. (+1-323) 651 1510
Fax (+1-323) 651 2340
E-Mail: office@MAKcenter.org
www.MAKcenter.org

Mackey Apartments
1137 South Cochran Avenue
Los Angeles, CA 90019, USA
Tel. (+1-323) 651 1510

MAK GOVERNING COMMITTEE
Brigitte Böck
Harriett F. Gold
Peter Noever
Barbara Redl
Joseph Secky
Robert L. Sweeney
Martin Weiss ex officio

DIRECTOR
Kimberli Meyer

MAK ART SOCIETY Wien / Vienna
Zur Förderung des MAK / Established to promote
and support the MAK
Stubenring 5, A-1010 Wien / Vienna, Austria
Tel. (+43-1) 711 36-207
Fax (+43-1) 711 36-213
E-Mail: MAKartsociety@MAK.at

VORSTAND / BOARD OF DIRECTORS
Eva Schlegel Präsidentin / President
Cornelius Grupp Präsident / President
Peter Noever Stellvertretender Präsident / Vice-President
Gregor Eichinger Schriftführer / Keeper of the Minutes
Manfred Wakolbinger Kassier / Cashier
Ingrid Gazzari
Michael Hochenegg

GENERALSEKRETARIAT / EXECUTIVE OFFICE
Michaela Hartig

RECHNUNGSPRÜFER / AUDITORS
Johannes Strohmayer
Arno Hirschvogl

INTERNATIONAL MAK ADVISORY BOARD
Gerti Gürtler Präsidentin / President, Wien / Vienna
Marylea van Daalen Moskau / Moscow – Berlin
James Dyson London
Rolf Fehlbaum Basel
Ernfried Fuchs Wien / Vienna
Francesca Habsburg Wien / Vienna
Heinz F. Hofer-Wittmann Etsdorf/Kamp
Eva-Maria von Höfer Wien / Vienna
Stella Kay Moskau / Moscow
Ursula Kwizda Wien / Vienna
Ronald S. Lauder New York
Franz-Hesso zu Leiningen Tegernsee
Veronika Piech Wien / Vienna
Leonid Rath-Lobmeyr Wien / Vienna
Thaddaeus Ropac Salzburg
Frederick & Laurie Samitaur Smith Los Angeles
W. Michael Satke Wien / Vienna
Penelope Seidler Sydney
Thomas Streimelweger Wien / Vienna
Lorenzo Targetti Florenz / Florence
Iwan Wirth Zürich / Zurich

MAK ARTIST BOARD
Vito Acconci New York
Coop Himmelb(l)au Wien / Vienna
Bruno Gironcoli Wien / Vienna
Zaha M. Hadid London
Jenny Holzer New York
Dennis Hopper Los Angeles
Rebecca Horn Bad König
Magdalena Jetelová Bergheim Thorr
Ilya & Emilia Kabakov New York
Jannis Kounellis Rom / Rome
Maria Lassnig Wien / Vienna
Thom Mayne Los Angeles
Oswald Oberhuber Wien / Vienna
Roland Rainer † Wien / Vienna
Kiki Smith New York
Franz West Wien / Vienna
Lebbeus Woods New York
Heimo Zobernig Wien / Vienna

CAT GROUP
Zur Förderung der Entwicklung und Realisierung
des CAT / Established to promote the
development and realization of CAT –
Contemporary Art Tower

Johannes Strohmayer Präsident / President
Karl Newole Vizepräsident / Vice-President

CAT INTERNATIONAL ADVISORY BOARD
Catherine David
Boris Groys
Cornelius Grupp
Andreas Treichl
Paul Virilio

MAK Studies 1
Joseph Binder
Wien – New York
MAK Wien Vienna 2001
ISBN 3-900688-49-4

MAK Studies 2
Ernst Deutsch-Dryden
En Vogue!
MAK Wien Vienna 2002
ISBN 3-900688-51-6

MAK Studies 3
Carlo Scarpa
Das Handwerk der Architektur
The craft of architecture
MAK Wien Vienna / Hatje Cantz Ostfildern-Ruit 2003
ISBN 3-7757-1403-0
Verlagsausgabe vergriffen Trade edition sold out

MAK Studies 4
Hermann Kosel
The Holy Every Day
MAK Wien Vienna 2003
ISBN 3-900688-55-9

MAK Studies 5
Verletzliche Beute Fragile Remnants
Spätantike und frühislamische Textilien aus Ägypten
Egyptian Textiles of Late Antiquity and Early Islam
MAK Wien Vienna / Hatje Cantz Ostfildern-Ruit 2005
ISBN 3-7757-1699-8

Abb. S. 151: „Art indien. Nielles et métaux gravés", in: A. Racinet:
L'ornement polychrome, Paris 1869–1872, Bd. II (MAK, Inv.-Nr. K.I. 19377)
Ill. p. 151: "Art indien. Nielles et métaux gravés", in: A. Racinet:
L'ornement polychrome, Paris 1869–1872, Vol. II (MAK, inv. no. K.I.19377)